KING ARTHUR AND HIS KNIGHTS

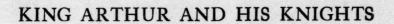

GARDEN CITY PUBLISHING COMPANY, GARDEN CITY, NEW YORK

CL
ALL RIGHTS RESERVED
PRINTED IN UNITED STATES AT
COUNTRY LIFE PRESS
GARDEN CITY, NEW YORK

KING

Illustrated in Color by
Frank E. Schoonover

THEN SIR BLEOBERIS BRAKE HIS SPEAR UPON SIR GARETH. *Page 211*

ARTHUR
AND HIS KNIGHTS

By
HENRY FRITH

CONTENTS

BOOK THE FIRST

BOOK THE SECOND

CONTENTS

BOOK THE THIRD

BOOK THE FOURTH

CONTENTS

BOOK THE SIXTH

CONTENTS

BOOK THE SEVENTH

CONTENTS

BOOK THE ELEVENTH

ILLUSTRATIONS

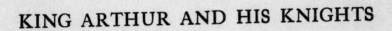

KING ARTHUR AND HIS KNIGHTS

BOOK THE FIRST

CHAPTER I

OF THE BIRTH OF ARTHUR, AND HOW HE WAS CARRIED BY MER-
LIN TO SIR ECTOR, AND OF THE TRIAL OF THE SWORD IN THE
CHURCHYARD OF ST. PAUL'S

IT CAME to pass in the days of Uther Pendragon, that
Merlin the Magician foretold the coming of King Arthur,
who would be the son of the King Uther called "Pendragon."
So Uther, when he became King, recalled the words of Merlin, and caused two dragons to be made in the likeness of the
fiery clouds which had appeared when Aurelius was buried
in the Giants' Dance, called Stonehenge, on Salisbury Plain.

The two golden dragons having been fashioned according
to the King's order, one was placed in Winchester Cathedral,
and the other was borne before him whenever he went into
battle; whereupon he was called Pendragon, or Dragon's
Head. He went out to battle and subdued the Scots and others,
and then returned to London, where he administered justice,
being all the time unmarried.

But it befell that at a grand banquet and high feast at
Easter, there a very numerous company assembled, and
amongst this worshipful and gracious company appeared Gorlöis, Duke of Cornwall, who lived at Tintagel, and had aforetime been at war with Uther of the Dragon's Head. With
Gorlöis came his spouse Igraine, the most beautiful woman in
all Britain, and with her was King Uther much pleased;
indeed, his heart was sore because of her, and when afterwards
the Duke Gorlöis was slain in battle, King Uther journeyed
to the castle of Tintagel and besought the fair Igraine to be
his chosen wife.

But at first the Pendragon could not succeed in his desires,
and he therefore sent for Merlin the Magician, and asked his
assistance and advice whereby he could obtain the lovely lady

for his Queen. Merlin promised him his aid on one condition: viz., that the first-born son should be given to him, for the subtle Merlin knew that the child would be the great King Arthur.

And the King, nothing doubting, agreed to the condition as Merlin had required. Thus the King's wooing ended happily, and the fair Igraine became Queen, according to the desire of Uther Pendragon.

Then came Merlin to the King, and said, "When your child is born, let one of the lords of the land have the nourishing of him. Sir Ector is a man both good and true; into his hands shall the child be delivered. Let him be handed to me at the postern-gate unchristened, and I will carry him to Sir Ector."

All this the King agreed to do. So when the child was born he bade his servants, two knights and two ladies, to carry the child to the postern-gate, where they would find an old man, to whom they should hand the babe bound as he was in cloth of gold. The child was delivered thus to Merlin, who had disguised himself as a poor mendicant, and he bare it to a priest and had it named Arthur. He then was taken to Sir Ector's house, and nursed by the knight's wife herself. In that house he remained for many years, and no man save Merlin and the King knew that he was Arthur, the son of King Uther Pendragon.

Now it came to pass that after two years had elapsed Uther fell sick, and lay very ill, and his enemies usurped his territory. But Merlin aroused the monarch, and he was carried to battle in a horse-litter against the Saxons, who disdained to contend against a sick general. So in scorn, and partly in shame to engage an ailing enemy, they returned into their city, leaving the gate thereof open in scorn of Pendragon and his litter.

This haughty careless pride of the Saxons cost them dear, for Uther commanded his men to lose no time, but to assault the town, which they did. The Saxons found when too late that they were overreached, and rushed out of the fight, but it was no use. Nevertheless, the conflict raged till night, and was renewed the next day, until the Saxon leaders, Eosa and Octa, were slain; then their adherents turned and fled, leaving the Britons a full triumph.

King Uther Pendragon was mightily pleased at the turn events had taken. He was so rejoiced that he raised himself up in his litter, and cried out,—

"They called me half dead, and so indeed I was; but victory to me half dead is better than defeat and the best health, for to die with honour is far better than to live disgraced."

Howbeit, the Saxons were not defeated, and were ready to continue the contest. But the King had become so ill that his friends prevented him from warring any more, so the enemy then devastated the land, and as they could not reach the King by fair means they employed the meanest treachery to kill him.

To this end they, while he lay sore sick at Verulam, sent and poisoned the water in the well whereof the King drank; and so the pains of death attacked the King and all who had drunk of the well before the treachery was discovered. The hole was filled in with clay, but the King died, and many hundreds with him, of the poison.

Full of sorrow and weeping, the brave knights and gentlemen took counsel with Merlin as to the succession, and having assembled round the King's bed as he lay gasping out his life, they inquired of him,—

"Lord, shall thy son Arthur be King of all this realm in the after days?"

Then Uther turned himself round, and said, "I give him God's blessing and mine, and bid him pray for my soul, and righteously and worshipfully that he claims the crown upon forfeiture of my blessing." And therewith he yielded up the ghost.

The Queen was very sorrowful. And the King was buried, amidst much lamentation of all classes, close by his brother, within the circle of the Giants' Dance.

As soon as the King was interred, all the great men of the kingdom began to look upon themselves as fit rulers for the land. But Merlin, bearing the King's words in mind, besought the Archbishop of Canterbury, and advised him to call together the knights and great men in London upon Christmas Day, so that, by some miracle or trial, the true King might be discovered and the realm at peace.

To this the Archbishop agreed, and the knights were summoned to London, to the greatest church there, for the purpose of choosing a king by a certain sign to be given at St. Paul's Church, where the Archbishop had prayed that a miraculous act should decide the question of the kingly succession. There was remarked in the churchyard a certain square stone, and the attention of all the company was curiously directed to it, as the Archbishop offered up his prayer.

Arthur had all this time been at the house of Sir Ector, and had, during the fifteen years which he had passed as the knight's son, grown up a tall and comely lad, gentle in his manners, and greatly accomplished in all the exercises pertaining to chivalry and the training of a knight. He had passed as the son of Sir Ector and his lady wife, knowing nothing of his true parentage; so when King Uther Pendragon had named Arthur his successor, the barons and knights had been indignant, considering him as less than one of themselves. Therefore they sought their own advantage, as aforesaid; but, nevertheless, under pain of cursing by the Archbishop, they assembled at the great church of the apostle in London, as Brice had directed them.

The great marble stone in the churchyard was observed by all the people, and, behold! a naked sword was stuck in the middle of it in an anvil of steel, and about the sword was written the following words, that all could read:

Whoso Pulleth Out The Sword From This Stone Is Born The Rightful King Of England

But the Archbishop would permit no one to touch the sword until the Mass had been performed; and then the knights and barons made attempt, and tried many times to move the weapon, but none could accomplish the task.

When all had in vain tried to move the sword, the Archbishop decided that the man whom Heaven had selected was not present, and therefore no king could be chosen. Meanwhile ten knights were selected to guard the sword and the stone, and during the time, until New Year's Day, the Archbishop endeavoured to keep the people and knights together in London by tournaments and jousting, until the proper person should appear.

So it happened that upon the New Year's Day, Sir Ector, who loved joust and tourney, rode in, accompanied by Sir Kay his son, and Arthur his adopted brother; but Sir Kay was without his sword, having left it in his lodging by mistake. When, therefore, he came to the jousting, he begged his brother Arthur to ride back for his weapon, and he did so. Arthur hastened back with a good will; and when he came to the lodging he found that he could not obtain admittance, for all the inmates had gone out to see the tournament. The lad was very angry at his disappointment, and did not know how to bring his brother a weapon—for he said, "My brother shall not go without a sword."

In this temper he bethought him of the sword he had perceived sticking from the great stone in the churchyard, and he determined to possess it if possible, not knowing the legend, nor the attempt of those who had failed to draw it forth.

Arthur therefore hastened back to the churchyard, and, tying his horse up at the gate, entered under the canopy beneath which the stone was, and where the knights had been on guard. At that time, however, they had proceeded to the jousting, and without reflection Arthur advanced, and hastily, with fierceness, pulled the sword, which came out of the stone easily in his hand.

Meantime the legend concerning the stone and the sword had been related by the assembled knights to Sir Ector and Sir Kay, and they determined to strive for it. But when

Arthur, in his ignorance, appeared, carrying the particular sword, and handed it to Sir Kay, the young knight was delighted, and carried it joyfully to his father, saying,—

"Lo! here, sir, is the sword of the stone, whereof it is I who shall be king of this land."

Sir Ector was much surprised, and immediately returned with his son and Arthur, accompanied by many knights, to the churchyard, where the stone remained. But first they entered the church, and Sir Ector upon the Holy Book demanded of his son how he became possessed of the sword.

"Sir," replied Sir Kay, "by my brother Arthur, for he brought it to me."

"How gat ye the sword?" said Sir Ector to Arthur, who was standing by.

"Sir," replied the youth, "I will tell you. I returned home for my brother's sword, and found no one at home, and thinking that my brother should not be without a sword, I came hither eagerly, and pulled this out of the stone without any pain."

"Did ye not find the knights guarding the sword?" asked Sir Ector.

Arthur replied, "Nay."

And then said the old knight to him, "Arthur, I understand by this that thou shalt be king of this land."

"Wherefore I?" inquired Arthur, "and for what cause?"

"Sir," said Ector, "for God will have it so. For there should never man have drawn out that sword but he that shall be rightwise king of this land. But let me see thee put back the sword, and draw it forth again."

"That is no mastery," replied Arthur. And straightway he passed into the churchyard, and put it into the stone again.

"Now," said Sir Ector to his son, "do thou assay."

Sir Kay clutched the pommel, and endeavoured with all his might to extract the weapon; but he could not move it.

"Now shall ye assay," said the knight to Arthur.

"I will well," replied the young man. And he grasped the sword, and with ease pulled it out from the anvil and the stone.

Therewithal Sir Ector and his son fell upon their knees and did him homage.

CHAPTER II

HOW ARTHUR OBTAINED THE SWORD, AND HOW HE BECAME
KING. OF THE ALLIANCE WITH KINGS BORS AND BAN, AND HOW
A GREAT BATTLE WAS FOUGHT

WHEN Arthur perceived that Sir Ector and his son
kneeled down before him, he was much distressed in
his noble nature, and said,—

"Alas! mine own dear father and brother, why kneel ye
thus to me?"

"Nay, my Lord Arthur," replied Sir Ector, "we are of no
blood kinship, and though little thought we how high thy
kin might be, thou wast never more than foster-child of
mine."

Then Sir Ector told him all as it had happened, as we have
already read, concerning the stranger who had brought him
to be nourished, and how the man had disappeared.

Arthur listened to the relation, and when it had finished
he fell upon Sir Ector's breast, and lamented that "in one
day he had lost his father, his mother, and his brother."

Sir Ector perceived his trouble, and after a while he was
emboldened to say, "Sir, when thou shalt be made King, I
pray thee be gracious to me and mine."

"If not," replied Arthur, "I were no true man's son at all,
for thou art he in all the world to whom I owe the most, and
my good lady and mother, thy wife, hath ever kept and fostered me as though I were her own. So if it be God's will that
I be King hereafter, desire of me whatever thing thou wilt
and I will do it."

"I will but pray that thou wilt make my son Sir Kay, thy
foster-brother, Seneschal of thy lands," replied the knight.

To this Arthur at once agreed gladly, and promised that
no other should hold the office while he and his brother lived.

8

When these things had been accomplished, the knights and Arthur went to the Archbishop and informed him what had happened, and how the miracle of the sword had been achieved. When the prelate perceived the weapon in Arthur's hand he at once summoned all the princes, knights, and barons to meet at St. Paul's Church, and witness the withdrawing of the sword according to the will of Heaven.

An immense concourse of people attended, and the sword was then put back again into the stone, when none who assayed could move it except Arthur, who pulled it easily.

Then the tumult waxed warm, for many hailed Arthur as their king, while many others disputed it in wrath, declaring that it was not fitting such a state should be conferred upon a boy whom no one knew. So the barons managed to delay the matter until Candlemas, and then again till the following Easter, upon one pretence or other, although no one but Arthur appeared to claim the kingdom who could also pull out the sword.

But at Pentecost the Archbishop, acting upon Merlin's counsel, got together a band of knights, who recognized Arthur as King, and they threatened to kill any one who dared to dispute his sovereignty. And when Arthur alone once again pulled out the sword, the people cried, "Long live King Arthur!" and the knights who best had served King Uther Pendragon—viz., Sir Baudwin of Britain, Sir Ulfius, and Sir Brastias, with Sir Kay, remained with Arthur day and night until the Feast of Pentecost. Then the coronation was achieved, and Arthur was crowned King, after he had been knighted, with great pomp. He received homage, and made Sir Kay High Steward, as he had promised, Sir Bedawaine (or Baudwin) was Constable, and Sir Ulfius Chamberlain. Afterwards the King, with his Court and retinue, journeyed into Wales, and he was again crowned King in the old city of Caerleon-upon-Usk.

But although the barons had accompanied the King to Caerleon, they did not acknowledge him as their lord. They went up as if to do him homage; but after the grand banquet, when Arthur rose up to bestow upon his followers his royal bounty, the rebellious kings and chiefs stood up and disclaimed him, declaring they would have none of the gifts of a "beardless boy," the unknown son of an unknown father.

Upon this a terrible tumult arose in the banqueting-hall, and the men drew their swords right willingly. Arthur was very indignant, and threw himself upon the rebels, followed by his adherents. They rushed upon the discontented chiefs, and a sore battle ensued, in which the King's side was victorious, and drove the rebels helter-skelter from the hall into the streets, and through Caerleon to the gates, and thrust them out, closing the gates behind them. King Arthur in his eagerness broke his sword.

But the chiefs who had thus been driven out had amongst them six famous kings, viz., King Lot, King Nantess, King Urien, King Carados, King Yder, and King Anquisant. These would have none of his presents, and when Arthur sent messages to them they returned disdainful replies; whereupon King Arthur, with the advice of his adherents—fearing an attack—shut himself up in a fortified tower, with a chosen five hundred men and supplies.

It was well he did this, for the kings laid siege against him in Caerleon; but after a while Merlin came into the camp, and inquired why they had thus uprisen against the King. They inquired in return why the boy Arthur had been so raised to the kingdom.

"Sirs," replied Merlin, "I will tell you the cause; for he is King Uther Pendragon's son, born in wedlock of Igraine the duke's wife, of Tintagel; and he shall overcome all his enemies, and have under his obeisance Wales, Ireland, and Scotland."

The kings, when they heard Merlin, were astonished, and laughed at him; but some believed him. But it was by all of them agreed that they would parley with Arthur; and Merlin proceeded to the city to induce him to come out. To this Arthur consented, and Merlin answered,—

"Speak with them and spare them not, but answer them,

for ye shall overcome them all whether they will or will not."

Arthur accordingly did as Merlin enjoined, but no good came of the interview, for an engagement ensued, in the course of which three hundred men deserted and went over to King Arthur, which rejoiced him greatly. In the end the kings were defeated and pursued, until Merlin came and counselled Arthur to follow the kings no farther.

After these events Arthur returned to London, and there took counsel of his barons, who feared the incursion of his kingly enemies, who were mighty and greater in numbers than the adherents of the Prince. When the parley had continued some time, Merlin gave it as his opinion that Arthur had better seek assistance in his need.

"There are," said he, "two brethren beyond the sea, kings both, and marvellous good men, one knight called Ban of Bennick, and the other King Bors of Gaul. On these warreth the King Claudas, who being mighty of goods putteth the kings to the worst. Wherefore it is my counsel that our King and sovereign lord send unto the Kings Ban and Bors by two trusty knights, with letters well devised, that if they will come and see King Arthur and his Court, and so help him in his wars, he will be sworn to help them in their wars against King Claudas."

This was Merlin's advice, and it was acted on. Ulfias and Brastias were made messengers, and, well armed, they crossed the sea, and rode toward the city of Bennick. But their adventures were only beginning. In the same place where they lodged were eight knights, who wished them to render themselves prisoners.

"We be on duty," replied the knights, "as messengers to Kings Ban and Bors from Arthur of Britain, and must not be stayed."

"Therefore," replied the eight knights, "ye shall die or be our prisoners, for we be knights of King Claudas."

Therewith two of them put their spears in rest to attack the knights, and Ulfius and Brastias dressed their spears to meet them. They advanced against each other with a great

shock. In this encounter the messenger-knights were victorious, for the enemies' spears brake, while the others firmly
held bore the Frenchmen clear out of their saddles to the
ground, whereon the British knights left them groaning to
death, and rode away.

But the other six knights had no intention of permitting the
messengers to proceed on their journey, and again they
separated, two detaching themselves from the party, and
charging upon the British. But Ulfius and Brastias awaited
the worst, and urging their horses at the moment, struck these
men down also, and left them for dead upon the road, receiv-
ing no injury themselves.

Still they had four other enemies to vanquish, which feat
they accomplished, thus leaving all the eight foreign knights
on the field either badly bruised or wounded, if not dead.
And when the King's messengers at length arrived at the
town of Bennick, it was fortunate that they found there both
the kings of whom they had come in search.

Ban and Bors received them kindly; and having been informed of their mission, they took them in their arms, and
made great joy of them, and welcomed them very warmly.
When the letters were read the kings were more overjoyed
even than before, and accepted the terms which the British
King had proposed, telling the knights to tarry as long as they
wished, and they should have such cheer as could be procured
in those marches.

The adventures of the knights were then related, and the
Kings laughed, wishing they could have also encountered
their "good friends," and they should not have escaped so
easily. After these things, presents were heaped upon them,
and they came away with the assurance that Kings Ban and
Bors would come to Arthur in all the haste that they might.

Then the knights returned, and crossing the sea, came and
told Arthur the answer, their adventures, and how they had
sped.

"What time think ye the Kings will arrive?" asked Arthur.

"About All-hallowmas," said the knights.

And preparations were made accordingly for the reception of the Kings and their retainers.

Ban and Bors arrived at the time specified, accompanied by three hundred knights, accoutred for peace or war. King Arthur rode ten miles out from London to meet them, and great rejoicings were held. These pleasant days included a tourney. The knights were divided into two parties, and attacked each other in friendly contest. Griflet and Ladinas met in the lists, and fought until their shields fell to pieces; and both the French and English knights lay so long on the ground that all spectators thought them dead. Sir Kay, with five companions, came bursting out, and smote six others down all in fair play; but Sir Kay fell, which his companions seeing, they rushed in fury at the opponents; and had not King Arthur and his kindly guests leaped upon hackneys, which were near by, there would have been much bloodshed, for the companions of Sir Kay were exceeding wroth. But Arthur and the other kings gave orders, crying out, as they rode amongst the knights, that all were to depart unto their lodgings. So the strife was put an end to, and the knights went home, unarmed them, and so to even-song and supper.

After that the prizes were distributed, and Sir Kay, Sir Lucas, and Griflet each received a reward. Subsequently they raised their forces, and collected ten thousand men from France, who came with Merlin into Britain, landing at Dover. The Enchanter led them by a series of devious paths to the forest of Bedegraine, and in a valley kept them secretly.

Then Merlin rode unto Arthur and the Kings, and told them how he had sped, at which they were astonished and pleased. So all the knights, with King Arthur and the Kings Bors and Ban, came to the castle of Bedegraine, and found their allies in fair fellowship, with no want of victual.

CHAPTER III

HOW THE ELEVEN KINGS ENCOUNTERED ARTHUR, AND OF THE FIGHTING THAT ENSUED AMONGST WORSHIPFUL KNIGHTS

MEANTIME the six Kings who had opposed King Arthur at Caerleon had made an alliance with five other Kings, and having collected their adherents, they declared war against Arthur and swore to destroy him. This oath was taken by all.

The King of Camberut brought with him five thousand men, the King of Northumberland had three thousand, King Brandegoris of Strangore brought five thousand, and the Prince of the Hundred Knights—a passing good man and a young—had four thousand on horseback. The other Kings, Lot, Urience, Idres of Cornwall, Cradduras, Agerisance of Ireland, Nentus, and Caradoc, all brought their thousands in support. So the eleven Kings had an army of fifty thousand horsemen and ten thousand foot to engage King Arthur.

On their way they laid siege to the castle of Bedegraine, and encamped against it. But Arthur with his men made a sally, with his trusty allies Ban and Bors, and a desperate encounter ensued. Ten thousand men were left upon the field when morning dawned, for the eleven Kings had made a fair fight of it.

Ere daybreak, however, Merlin came and counselled the Kings with Arthur to form an ambuscade with a portion of his army, while the remainder continued the combat when morning dawned. This was agreed to, and to Ulfius and Brastias were delivered three thousand horsemen, who set upon the army of the eleven Kings.

When these perceived the small number of their enemies, and the havoc they occasioned, they were both angry and ashamed. Then an attack was made, and Sir Ulfius had his horse slain under him; but he fought, says the chronicle, "marvellous well on foot," notwithstanding that Eustace of Camberut and the King Clariance of Northumberland pressed him sorely. To his rescue came quickly Brastias, who smote Eustace with a spear, and in return for this attention Clariance made at Brastias, and they met with such a terrible shock that both knights and their steeds rolled upon the ground, and their horses' knees were sorely injured withal, "brast to the bone."

The battle raged fiercely. Sir Kay arrived upon the scene, and with his immediate followers engaged the eleven Kings, and Griflet with Lucas was set upon by Kings Brandegoris, Agerisance, and Idres of Cornwall. Horse and man were put to the earth by this onset, which Sir Kay perceiving, he rode at King Nentus and overturned him. He then led the King's steed to Griflet, who was fighting on foot, and so horsed him; and then Sir Kay passed on furiously, and smote King Lot.

The attack by Sir Kay was noticed by the Prince of the Hundred Knights, who, nothing daunted, made at the Seneschal and smote him in turn, taking his horse to King Lot, who was sorely hurt. Similar feats were also performed by others, until all the eleven Kings were horsed again, and then they swore vengeance. Sir Ector also came upon the field, and King Arthur, perceiving the strait in which Ulfius was, made at King Cradduras and smote him through the left side, and unhorsed him.

The King, restraining the steed, took him by the bridle, and making his way to Ulfius, said to him,—

"Mine old friend, take thou this horse, for great need is thine."

"Gramercy," said Ulfius, "for the steed." And Arthur surprised all men that day in his valour. But the King of Wales smote Sir Ector and gained his steed, which Arthur perceiving, clave the King by one terrible blow through the helm and to the horse's neck, so that man and horse came to the ground together.

And thus the battle waxed and waned. The three Kings,

Bors, Ban, and Arthur, outdid themselves that day, and Arthur by his own hand slew twenty knights, steering his horse within and out, striking right and left. Meantime the ambushment was broken, and King Idres was sorely pressed, with great slaying of men and horses, and great muddle in the breaking of spears.

The fight continued, and neither side would give way. King Ban, attired in green and gold, came rushing to the fray, and his mighty blows resounded from the wood and water. And now comes a terrific combat of Ban and the Prince of the Hundred Knights, who had beheld his prowess and spurred forward to encounter him.

The Prince made at King Ban, and smote him a terrible blow high upon the helm, which "astonished him sore," and King Ban was very wroth. He followed him closely, and the opponent perceiving the attack, held up his shield and spurred his horse. But the blow of the terrible Ban descended and carved a cantel off the shield, and the sword slid down behind the Prince's back, cut through the steel trappings and the horse into two pieces.

The Prince nimbly disengaged himself from his steed, now dead in two halves, and made at Ban, who dealt him so fierce a blow that he fell headlong to the earth, and Ban turned upon King Morganne. But King Ban, fighting on foot, kept his foes at bay as far as he might reach with his sword, and no one came within the circle of his arm but received a grievous buffet. To him King Arthur, having slain a man-at-arms and clove him to the teeth, brought a horse.

"Fair brother," said he to the valiant Ban, "have this horse, for ye have need thereof, and me repenteth sore of your great damage."

"It shall be soon revenged," replied King Ban; "for I trust mine use is not such but some of them may sore repent this."

"I will well," said Arthur; "for I see your deeds full actual; nevertheless I might not come to you at that time."

But always the eleven Kings and their adherents never turned back, and Arthur was very wroth at the resistance.

"By my faith," said King Ban, "they are the best fighting men, and knights of most prowess, that ever I saw or heard speak of; and those eleven Kings are men of great worship, and if they were belonging unto you there were no king under heaven who had such eleven knights, and of such worship."

The eleven Kings on their side drew together, and King Lot said to them,—

"Lords, ye must other ways, or else the great loss is behind. We wait upon the footmen, and ye see what we have already lost. Let us put our footmen from us, and when the horsemen be together, let none break upon pain of death."

"It is well said," replied King Nentus; and they all sware they would never fail each other. Then they mended their harness, and took new spears, and stood as still as if it had been a clump of wood.

Then forty knights came forward to break the battle, and the eleven Kings rushed upon them, and great slaughter ensued, until Merlin arrived upon a great black horse, and stayed King Arthur's hand, saying,—

"Hast thou not done enough? Of threescore thousand thou hast this day left on live but fifteen thousand, and it is time to say 'ho!' For God is wroth with thee, and those eleven Kings shall not be overthrown; but an thou tarry longer thy fortune shall turn."

So Merlin with other words persuaded King Arthur, and he withdrew his men, for he answered that for three years the Kings should not trouble Arthur. Then Merlin took leave and went unto his master, Bleize—that dwelt in Northumberland —and Bleize wrote the battle word by word as Merlin told him.

After this Merlin came again to King Arthur, who was at Bedegraine in Sherwood, and he was disguised so that King Arthur knew him not. It was on the morn after the Candlemas Day, and Merlin, in his disguise, carrying wild geese in his hand, came to the King and said,—

"Sir, will ye give me a gift?"

"Wherefore, churl, should I give thee a gift?" replied the King haughtily.

"Sir," said Merlin, "ye were better to give me a gift that is not in your hand, than to lose great riches; for here in the place where the great battle was is great treasure hid in the earth."

"Who told thee so, churl?" inquired the King.

"Merlin," replied the man, "told me so."

Then Brastias recognized the person of Merlin, and said unto the King, "Sir, it is Merlin who speaks with you."

And then was King Arthur much astonished and abashed, and had marvel of Merlin, as had they all.

After a time King Arthur, with Kings Bors and Ban, departed, and came into the country of Cameliard, and rescued King Liodgrance, and slew King Rience's people. The King thanked them, and there first had Arthur sight of Guenever, the daughter of the King of Cameliard, and ever after he loved her; and they were wedded, as it will be told in this book. Kings Bors and Ban took their leave to go into their own country, for King Claudas did great destruction on their lands; and they parted with Arthur for a time.

But the eleven Kings retired to the city of Sortrante, to dress their wounds and refresh themselves. And while they tarried came a messenger to tell them the Saracens had invaded their lands, and had burnt and slain all the people they came by, and had laid siege to Wandesboro' Castle.

"Alas! here is sorrow on sorrow," said the Kings.

And they consented to remain, to keep all the Marches of Wales, Cornwall, and the North. King Idres was placed in the city of Nauntes in Britain, with four thousand men-at-arms. King Nentus of Garlot took possession in Windesaw, and put knights in all the Marches. So they kept together for the space of three years, and all this while they furnished themselves with arms and supplies, and all manner of habiliment, to avenge the Battle of Bedegraine.

CHAPTER IV

KING ARTHUR'S DREAM OF THE QUESTING BEAST, AND HOW
GRIFLET WAS MADE A KNIGHT, AND FOUGHT WITH THE
KNIGHT OF THE FOUNTAIN

AFTER the Kings had departed into their own lands,
King Arthur rode to Caerleon, and his sister—on the
mother side, the wife of King Lot of Orkney—came to his
Court. At this time Arthur dreamed a marvellous dream, and
it afflicted him so that he made a great hunting party to put
it out of his head, for his vision told him of fiery dragons and
serpents which would devour all his land, though after he
vanquished them.

So the hunting party was called, and the King pressed
forward into the forest. No sooner was he there, however,
than he perceived a hart.

"This hart will I chase," said the King. And he hurried
onward for a long time after the beast, and was more than
once close upon it. But at last the King's horse was spent, and
he fell down dead. Then came a churl, and offered the King
another horse, which he went to fetch.

During the time while the hart was in the brake and the
horse dead, the King sat down by a fountain, and fell into
great thoughts, until he was aroused by the noise of hounds.
And then he saw advancing towards him the most curious
beast that ever was heard of. This strange animal went to the
spring and drank, and then sped away again with a great
noise.

The King after this fell on sleep, and, behold! there came
unto him a knight on foot, and inquired whether he had seen
the strange beast.

"Such a one I saw," replied the King.

"Sir," said the stranger, "I have followed that beast until

I have killed my horse; so would I had another to follow my quest."

The King's horse at that time coming up with the yeoman, the hunter prayed him to let him have it. This was King Pellinore, who followed the questing beast.

"Sir," said Arthur, "leave me the quest, and I will follow it for another twelvemonth."

"Ah, fool!" said the knight unto Arthur, "vain is thy desire. It shall never be achieved except by me or my nearest of kin." So saying, he spurred away upon the King's horse, saying, "Gramercy, this horse is mine now."

"Well," said the King, "thou mayest take my horse by force; but an I might prove thee whether thou art a better man on horseback or I."

"Well," replied the knight, "seek me here, and nigh this well shalt thou find me."

So he passed on his way. And while they were fetching the King a horse, Merlin, in the semblance of a child, came unto him, and also in the guise of an old man. The King was astonished when the child told him concerning his father, Uther Pendragon, and announced to him that he was the son of that King.

"I will not believe thee, child," said King Arthur; and he was angry.

So Merlin as the child departed, and came again unto him as an old man, whereat the King was glad, for the old man looked wise. Then Merlin declared himself when Arthur demanded who he was.

"I am Merlin," he said, "and I was he in the child's likeness."

"Ah!" said King Arthur, "ye are a marvellous man, but I marvel much at thy words that I must die in battle."

"Marvel not," replied Merlin, "for it is God's will that ye be punished for your foul deeds. But I may well be sorry, for I shall die a shameful death, to be put in the earth quick, but ye shall die a merciful death."

Then the King's horse came up, and Arthur rode into Caer-

leon, where he inquired of Ulfius and Brastias concerning his
birth as revealed to him by Merlin. The which they confirmed, and told him that Uther Pendragon was his father,
and Igraine his mother. Then sent he for the Queen, who
came; and Ulfius accused her of treachery in not proclaiming
Arthur her son, and so sparing him so much war and fighting.

Igraine, therefore, told all the circumstances, and when
they had been explained, King Arthur took the Queen in his
arms and kissed her. And the King made a great feast, which
lasted eight days.

Then on a day there came into the court a squire on horseback, leading a knight wounded to the death, and told how
"a knight in the forest had raised up a pavilion by a well, and
hath slain my master, a good knight, whose name is Miles.
Wherefore I beseech you that my master may be buried, and
that some knight may revenge my master's death."

Then came Griflet that was but a squire, and he was but
young—of the age of King Arthur. So he besought the King,
for all his service that he had done him, to give him the order
of knighthood.

"Thou art full young and tender of years," said Arthur,
"for to take so high an order on thee."

"Sir," said Griflet, "I beseech you make me a knight."

"Sir," said Merlin, "it were a pity to lose Griflet, for he
will be a passing good man when he cometh to age, abiding
with you the term of his life. And if he adventure his body
with yonder Knight of the Fountain, it is in great peril if
ever he come again, for he is one of the best knights in the
world, and the strongest man-at-arms."

"Well," said King Arthur.

So, at the desire of Griflet, he was knighted.

"Now," said King Arthur unto Sir Griflet, "since I have
made thee knight thou must grant me a gift."

"What ye will, my lord," replied Sir Griflet.

"Thou shalt promise me, by the faith of thy body, that
when thou hast jousted with the Knight of the Fountain,

whether it fall that ye be on foot or horseback, that in the same manner ye shall come again to me without any question or making any more debate."

"I will promise you," said Griflet, "as you desire."

Then took Griflet his horse in haste, and dressed his shield, and took his spear in his hand, and rode till he came to the fountain, where he saw a rich pavilion, and thereby, under a cloth, stood a fair horse, saddled and bridled, and on a tree a shield of divers colours, and a great spear.

Then Griflet smote on the shield with the butt of his spear, and the shield fell to the ground.

With that the knight came out of the pavilion, and said,—

"Fair knight, why smote ye down my shield?"

"For I will joust with you," said Griflet.

"It is better ye do not," said the knight; "for ye are but young, and late made knight; and your might is nothing to mine."

"As for that," said Griflet, "I will joust with you."

"That is me loth," replied the knight; "but sith I must needs I will dress me thereto. But whence be ye?"

"Sir, I am of Arthur's Court," said Griflet.

So they ran at each other, that Sir Griflet's spear all shivered, and therewithal he smote Griflet through the shield and the left side, that the truncheon stuck in his body, so horse and knight fell down.

When the Knight of the Fountain saw Sir Griflet lie so upon the ground, he alighted, and was passing heavy, for he wist he had killed him. And then he unlaced his helm and got him air, and with the truncheon he set him on his horse, and so betook him to God, saying he had a mighty heart, and, if he might live, he would prove a passing good knight.

And so Sir Griflet rode to the Court, where great dole was made for him. But through good leeches he was healed and saved.

CHAPTER V

HOW MESSENGERS CAME FROM THE EMPEROR OF ROME, AND HOW ARTHUR FOUGHT WITH A KNIGHT, AND WAS SAVED BY MERLIN

ABOUT this time came messengers from the Emperor of Rome to ask of Arthur truage for the realm, else would the Emperor destroy him and his land. But Arthur refused to give him truage.

"I owe the Emperor no truage, and none will I hold him; but on a fair field I shall give him my truage, that shall be with a sharp spear, and that shall not be long, by my father's soul, Uther Pendragon."

For King Arthur was very wroth, because of the hurt of Sir Griflet. And so he told a man of his chamber to have his horse and armour without the city on the morrow; and he met the man and his horse accordingly, and mounted up and dressed his shield. Then he took his spear, and bade the Chamberlain tarry there until he came again.

He then rode on quickly until daybreak, and, when it was light, he became aware of three churls who were chasing Merlin. But when the King appeared, and cried out to them, they fled, and left Merlin unharmed.

"Oh, Merlin," cried King Arthur, "thou hadst been slain for all thy craft had I not been here."

"Not so," replied Merlin. "I could save myself, an I would; and thou art nearer to death than am I, an God be not thy friend; thou goest to the death-ward."

They continued thus talking as they proceeded to the fountain, and there was the pavilion beside it. A knight sat in it, full armed, in a chair.

"Sir Knight," said Arthur, "why and for what cause

abidest thou here? Be it so that no knight may ride hitherward unless he joust with thee? I rede thee leave that custom."

"This custom," said the armed knight, "have I used, and I will use, maugre any who say nay. An any be grieved at my customs, let him amend it."

"I will amend it," said King Arthur.

"I will thus defend it," replied the knight.

Anon, therefore, he took his horse, and dressed his shield, and took a spear; and they met so hard upon each other's shields, that they shivered their spears to pieces. Thereupon King Arthur snatched his sword; but the knight said,—

"Nay, it is fairer that we twain run more together with sharp spears."

"I will well," said Arthur, "an I had any more."

"I have enow," replied the knight.

And there came out a squire bringing two spears; and King Arthur took one, and the knight another. Then they spurred their horses and came together with all their might, and brake their spears in their hands.

Then again did Arthur set hand on his sword; but the knight said,—

"Nay; ye shall do better: ye are a passing good jouster as ever I met withal, and for the love of the high order of knighthood let us joust once again."

"I assent me," said Arthur.

And then there were brought two great spears, and each gat one; and therewith they ran together, so that Arthur's spear all beshivered. But the knight hit him so hard in the middle of the shield that horse and man fell to the ground. And thereupon Arthur drew his sword and said,—

"I will assay thee, Sir Knight, on foot, for I have lost the honour on horseback."

"I will be on horseback," said the knight.

Then was King Arthur wroth; and he dressed his shield towards him with his sword drawn.

When the knight saw this attack he alighted, for he thought it was no worship to have a knight at such advantage—he to be on horseback and he on foot. And so he alighted, and dressed his shield unto King Arthur.

And then began a strong battle with many strokes. And they so hewed at each other that the cantels [pieces] flew in the fields, and so much blood they both bled, that all the place there, as they fought, was over-bled with blood. And thus they fought long; then rested them; and then went to battle again, and so hustled together like two rams, that either fell to the earth.

At the last they smote together, and the swords met even together. But the sword of the knight smote King Arthur's sword in two pieces, whereof he was heavy. Then said the knight unto Arthur,—

"Thou art in my danger whether me list to save thee or slay thee; and but thou yield thee as recreant and overcome, thou shalt die."

"As for death," replied King Arthur, "welcome be it when it cometh; but to yield me recreant, I had liever die than be so ashamed."

Thereupon the King leaped unto Pellinore, and took him by the middle, and tore off his helm.

When the knight felt he was adread—for he was a passing big man of might—he brought Arthur under him, and razed off his helm, and would have smitten off his head, when therewithal came Merlin, and said,—

"Knight, hold thy hand! An thou slay this knight thou puttest the kingdom in the greatest danger that ever realm was in, for this man is a knight of more worship than thou wottest of."

"Why, who is he?" said the knight.

"It is King Arthur," said Merlin.

Then would the armed knight have slain him, because he feared his wrath. And he heaved up his sword, when Merlin cast an enchantment upon him, that he fell to the earth in a deep sleep.

Then did Merlin take up King Arthur, and rode forth upon the knight's horse.

"Alas!" said Arthur; "what hast thou done, Merlin? Hast thou slain this good knight by thy crafts? There lived not so worshipful a knight as he was, and I had liever than the stint of my land a year, that he were on live."

"Care ye not," said Merlin, "for he is wholer than ye; he is but on sleep, and will waken within three hours. I told ye what a knight he was: here had ye been slain had I not been. Also there liveth not a bigger knight than he is one, and he shall hereafter do you right good service. His name is Pellinore, and he shall have two sons who shall be passing good men; save one they shall have no fellow in prowess and good living. Their names shall be Percivale of Wales and Lamerake of Wales, and he shall tell you the name of your sister's son, that shall be the destruction of all this realm."

So the King and he departed and went unto a hermit, a good man and a great leech, who searched all the King's wounds and gave him good salves. And the King was there three days; then were his hurts well amended that he might ride and go. So Merlin and Arthur departed on their way.

CHAPTER VI

HOW ARTHUR, BY THE MEANS OF MERLIN, GOT THE SWORD EXCALIBUR OF THE LADY OF THE LAKE

AS Merlin and Arthur rode on the King said, "I have no sword."

"No force," said Merlin; "hard by is a sword that shall be thine, an I may gain it for thee."

So they rode on until they came to a lake fair and broad, and in the midst of it King Arthur beheld an arm, clothed in white samite, that held a fair sword in that hand.

"So yonder is the sword I spake of," said Merlin.

Then they saw a damsel floating on the lake, and said the King, "What damsel is that?"

"That is the Lady of the Lake," said Merlin; "and within that lake is a rock, and on the rock a noble palace, as fair a place as any on earth, and richly beseen. This damsel will come to you anon, then speak ye fair to her that she will give you the sword."

Anon came the damsel unto Arthur, and saluted him, and he her again.

"Damsel," said the King, "what sword is that the arm holdeth yonder above the water? I would it were mine, for I have no sword."

"Sir Arthur, King," replied the Lady of the Lake, "that sword is mine; and if ye will give me a gift when I ask it, ye shall have the sword."

"By my faith," said Arthur, "I will give you what gift ever ye ask."

"Well," said the Lady of the Lake, "go ye into yonder barge, and row thyself to the sword, and take it and the scabbard with you, and I will ask my gift when I see my time."

So King Arthur and Merlin alighted, and tied their horses

to two trees, and went into the barge. And when they came to the sword, which the hand held, King Arthur took it by the handle and took it with him. Then the arm and the hand went under the water; and so they came unto the land again, and rode forth.

As they passed onward, King Arthur saw a rich pavilion, and said to Merlin,—

"What signifieth yonder pavilion?"

"It is the knight's pavilion," said Merlin, "that ye fought with last—Sir Pellinore; but he is out: he is not there. He hath had to do with a knight of yours—Knight Egglame—and they have fought. But at last Sir Egglame fled—an else he had been dead—and he hath chased him to Caerleon. We shall meet with him anon on the highway."

"That is well," said Arthur. "Now have I a sword, and I will wage battle with him, and be avenged on him."

"Sir, ye shall not do so," quoth Merlin, "for the knight is a-weary of fighting and chasing, so that ye shall have no worship to have to do with him. Beside, he will not lightly be matched by one knight living. Therefore my counsel is, let him pass, for he shall do you good service in a short time, and his sons after his days. You shall see that day in short space, and ye shall be right glad to give him your sister to wife."

"When I see him," replied King Arthur, "I will do as ye advise me."

Then King Arthur examined his sword, which he liked passing well.

"Whether liketh you the better," said Merlin, "the sword or the scabbard?"

"I like better the sword," replied Arthur.

"Ye are the more unwise," said Merlin. "The scabbard is worth ten of the sword; for while ye have the scabbard upon ye, ye shall lose no blood, be ye never so sorely wounded. Therefore keep well the scabbard always with you."

So they rode on to Caerleon, and by the way they met Sir Pellinore, who passed them by without any words, because he saw not Arthur, as Merlin had cast such a spell upon him.

"I marvel," said Arthur, "that the knight did not speak."

"Sir," said Merlin, "he saw ye not. Had he seen ye, ye had not lightly departed."

Then they came into Caerleon, whereby the knights were passing glad; but when they all heard of his adventures, they marvelled that he would jeopardize himself so greatly alone. But all men of worship agreed that it were merry to be under such a chieftain, who would put his person in adventure as poor knights did.

BOOK THE SECOND

CHAPTER I

THE MESSAGE FROM KING RYENCE OF WALES AND IRELAND, AND HOW HE DESIRED ARTHUR'S BEARD TO TRIM HIS MANTLE; AND OF THE DAMSEL WITH THE SWORD, WHO CAME TO FIND A MAN TO DRAW IT FROM ITS SCABBARD

IN A short while there came a messenger from Ryence, the King of North Wales and Ireland, bearing a message greeting King Arthur, saying,—

"That King Ryence had discomfited and overcome eleven Kings, and they all did him homage, and they gave him their beards clean shaven, 'flayn off,' as much as there was; wherefore he came for King Arthur's beard. For the King Ryence had trimmed a mantle with the Kings' beards, and there lacked one place in the mantle; wherefore he sent for the beard of Arthur, else he would enter the land and slay and spare not, and never leave them till he had by force, not his beard, but his head also."

"Well," said Arthur, as he rose in great wrath, "thou hast said thy message, which is the most insolent and villainous that ever man heard sent unto a King; also thou mayst see that my beard is full young yet to make a trimming of it. But tell thou thy King this. I owe him none homage, nor none of my elders; but ere it be long he shall do me homage on both his knees, or else he shall lose his head, by the faith of my body, for this message is the shamefullest I ever heard speak of. I see well thy King never yet met with a merciful man; but tell him I will have his head without he do me homage."

Then the messengers departed, and King Arthur, looking round upon his knights, asked them,—

"Is there any one here that knoweth King Ryence?"

Then answered a knight called Naram, and said,—

"Sir, I know the King well: he is a passing good knight of

his body as few living, and a passing proud man. And, sir, I doubt me not he will make war with a mighty puissance."

"Well," replied Arthur, "I shall be ready for him, and that he shall find."

And afterward it befell, when King Arthur was in London, that tidings came unto him that King Ryence of Wales had raised a great number of people, who were entered into the land, and had burnt and slain the King's true lieges.

"If this be true," said Arthur, "it were great shame unto mine estate but that he were mightily withstood."

"It is truth," replied the messenger knight, "for I myself saw the host."

"Well," said the King, "let us make a cry that all the lords, knights, and gentlemen-at-arms shall draw unto a castle called Camelot, and there let make a counsel and a great joust."

So when the King was come thither with all his baronage, and had lodged them as they seemed best, there was come a damsel who was sent on a message by the great Lile of Arabon. And when she came before the great King Arthur she told him whence she came, and how she was sent on message unto him for these causes.

Then letting her richly-furred mantle fall open, it was seen she was girded with a noble sword, whereof the King had marvel.

"Damsel," he said, "wherefore are ye girt with that sword? It beseemeth ye not."

"Now shall I tell you," replied the damsel. "This sword that I am girt withal doth me great sorrow and cumbrance, for I may not be delivered of this sword save by a good knight; but he must be a passing good man of his hands and of his deeds, without villainy or treachery or treason. If I can find one who hath all these virtues, he shall be able to draw it from the scabbard. For I have been to King Ryence, where I was told there were some passing good knights, and all have assayed to draw it forth, but none can speed."

"This is a great marvel," said Arthur. "If this be sooth I will myself assay to draw out the sword, not presuming that

I am the best knight, but that I will begin and give an example to all the barons, that they may assay every one after the other when I have assayed it."

So saying, King Arthur took the sword by the sheath and pulled at it eagerly, but the sword would not come out.

"Thou needest not strive so hard, lord," said the damsel, "for he that shall pull it out shall do it with little might."

"Thou sayest well," replied Arthur, who remembered the stone and sword at St. Paul's Church. "Now assay ye, my barons, but beware that ye be not stained with shame or treachery or guile."

And Arthur turned away his face, for he mused heavily of sins which he knew of, which had led to his failure in drawing the sword out of its sheath.

"It will not avail," said the damsel, "unless he be a clean knight without villainy, and of a gentle stock of father and mother side."

Then many barons that were there assayed all in turn, but there might non speed; wherefore the damsel made great sorrow out of measure, for she said,—

"Alas, alas! I thought in this Court to have found the best knights without treachery or treason."

"By my faith," said Arthur, "here be good knights as I deem any have been in the world, but their grace is not to help you, wherefore am I displeased."

CHAPTER II

HOW SIR BALIN, A POOR KNIGHT, PULLED OUT THE SWORD,
WHICH CAUSED HIS DEATH; AND HOW THE LADY OF THE LAKE
DEMANDED HIS HEAD OR THE MAIDEN'S

NOW by chance it fell out that there was at that time at
King Arthur's Court a poor knight, that had been
prisoner with him half a year or more for slaying a knight
who was cousin to the King. The name of this knight was
Balin; and by the good means of the barons he was delivered
out of prison, for he was a good man of his body, and born
in Northumberland, where he was named Balin le Savage.

So he went privily into the presence, and saw this adventure, whereof his heart rose high within him, and he would
assay it as the other knights did. But for he was poor, and
badly arrayed, he put him not forward in the press of the
knights and barons. But he felt assured he could accomplish
it as well as any other.

As the damsel took leave of King Arthur and the barons,
the knight called to her, and said,—

"Damsel, I pray you of your courtesy suffer me to assay as
well as these lords, though I be poorly clad. In my heart I
feel assured as these others, and me seemeth to speed right
well."

The damsel, beholding the poor knight, saw he was a likely
man; yet, because of his poor array, she thought he was no
knight of worship. So she said unto the poor knight,—

"Sir, there is no need to put me to any more pain or labour,
for it seemeth not you to succeed where others have failed."

"Ah, damsel," replied Balin, "worthiness and good quali-
ties are not only in array. Manhood and worship are hid in a
man's person, and many a worshipful knight is not known

unto all; and therefore worship and hardiness are not in arrayment."

"Ye say sooth," replied the damsel, "and therefore ye shall assay to do what ye may."

Then Balin took the sword by the girdle and the sheath, and drew the weapon lightly out; and when he looked upon the sword, it pleased him mightily.

Then had the King and the barons all great marvel at Balin, because he had done that adventure; and many knights were envious and had spite against him.

"Certes," said the damsel, "this is a passing good knight, and the best man that ever I found, and most worshipful, without treason, treachery, or villainy; and many wonders shall he achieve. Now, gentle and courteous knight, give me the sword again."

"Nay," replied Balin, "this sword will I keep, unless it be taken from me by force."

"Thou art not wise," said the damsel, "to keep it from me, for with this sword ye shall slay the best friend that ye have, and the man ye love most in the world; and so shall the sword be your destruction."

"I will take what adventure God may send me," replied Balin; "but the sword ye shall not have at this time, by the faith of my body."

"Ye shall repent it within a short time," said the damsel, "for I would have the sword more for your avail than for mine. I am passing heavy for your sake, for ye will not believe that sword will be your destruction, and that will be a great pity."

And with this saying the damsel departed, making a great sorrow and lamentation. Anon Balin sent for his horse and his arms, and so would depart from the Court, and took leave of King Arthur.

"Nay," said the King; "will ye depart? I suppose thou art annoyed by the manner in which thou hast been treated, and that I have showed thee unkindness? Blame me not overmuch, for I had been misinformed against thee; but I wist not thou wert such a knight as ye are, of worship and prowess; and if thou wilt abide at my Court I will advance thee so that thou shalt be well pleased."

"God thank thee, lord!" said Balin, "for no man can reward your bounty and your nobleness. But at this time I must needs depart, beseeching you always of your good grace."

"In good sooth," replied the King, "I am right wroth at your departing. I pray ye, fair knight, that ye tarry not long, and ye shall be right welcome to me and to my barons. And I shall amend all I said against ye."

"God thank your lordship," said Balin again, and therewith made him ready to depart.

Then the most part of the knights said that Balin did not this adventure all by might, but only by witchcraft.

But while the knight was preparing to depart there came unto the Court of King Arthur a lady named the Lady of the Lake. She came on horseback, richly beseen, and saluted the King. Then she demanded the gift that Arthur had promised her when she gave him the sword.

"Truly," said the King, "a gift I did promise you, but the name of the sword you gave me I have forgotten."

"The name of it," said the Lady of the Lake, "is EXCALIBUR—that is, Cut-steel."

"Ye say well," replied Arthur; "ask what ye will, and ye shall have it an it be in my power."

Then said the Lady of the Lake, "I ask the head of the knight who won the sword, or else the damsel's head who brought it, or both their heads; for he slew my brother, a full good knight, and that gentlewoman was causer of my father's death."

"Truly," said King Arthur, "I may not grant either of their heads with my worship; therefore ask what ye will else, and I will fulfill your wishes."

"I will ask no other thing," said the Lady of the Lake.

As Balin was now about to depart he saw the Lady of the

Lake, by whose means his mother had been slain, and for three years he had sought her. When therefore it was told to him that she had demanded his head of King Arthur, he advanced straight to her, and said,—

"Evil be with thee! Ye would have my head! Now therefore ye shall lose yours." And with the sword he lightly smote off her head before the King.

"For shame!" cried Arthur. "Why have ye done this? ye have shamed me and all my Court, for she was a lady I was beholden to, and she came hither on my safe conduct. I shall never forgive you this trespass and villainy."

"Sir," said Balin, "I am grieved at your displeasure. But this same lady was the untruest living. By enchantment and sorcery she hath destroyed many good knights, and she was the cause of my mother being burnt by her treachery and falsehood."

"Whatsoever cause ye had, ye should have forborne her in my presence," said King Arthur. "Therefore think not the contrary ye shall repent this, for such shame was never brought upon my Court. Therefore withdraw ye in such haste as ye may."

Then Balin took up the head of the Lady of the Lake, and bare it with him to the hostelry, where he met with his squire, who was sorry that the King had been so displeased. Then they rode forth from the town.

"Now," said Balin to his squire, "we must part. Do thou take this head and bear it to my friends in Northumberland. Tell them how I have sped, and that my greatest foe is dead. Also tell them I am out of prison, and what adventure befell me in the getting of this sword."

"Alas!" said the squire, "are ye not greatly to blame to displease King Arthur?"

"As for that," replied the knight, "I will at once hie me in all haste to King Ryence, and destroy him or else die therefor; and if it may hap that I defeat him, then will Arthur be my good and gracious lord again."

"Where shall I meet with you?" asked the squire.

"At King Arthur's Court," said Balin.

So the squire and he departed from each other. Then King Arthur and all the Court made great dole, and had shame at the death of the Lady of the Lake. And the King buried her with riches.

CHAPTER III

HOW MERLIN REVEALED THE STORY OF THE DAMSEL OF THE
SWORD, AND HOW BALIN WAS PURSUED BY SIR LANCEOR, A
KNIGHT OF IRELAND, AND HOW BALIN SLEW HIM

AT THAT time there happened at King Arthur's Court a
knight, the son of the King of Ireland. His name was
Lanceor, and he was a proud knight. He counted himself as
one of the best of the Court, and had much spite against Balin
for winning the sword; for he was jealous that any should be
considered better than he was, and he asked King Arthur to
give him leave to avenge the shame which had been put upon
him by Balin.

"Do your best," said King Arthur. "I am right wroth with
Balin; I would he were quit of the despite he hath done to
me and my Court."

Then Lanceor went into his hostelrie to make him ready,
and in the meantime Merlin came into the Court of King
Arthur, when he was informed of the adventure of the sword
and of the death of the Lady of the Lake.

"Now," said Merlin, "concerning this strange damsel that
came into your Court, shall I tell you the cause of her coming? She is the falsest damsel that ever lived. She hath a
brother, a passing good knight of prowess, and this damsel
loved a knight; and the brother met the lover of the damsel,
and slew him by force of his hands.

"When the false damsel understood this, she went to the
Lady Lyle of Avalon, and besought her help to be revenged
on her own brother. So the Lady of Avalon gave her that
sword she brought with her, and told her there should be no
man pull it out of the sheath, an he be not one of the best
knights in the realm. But he should be hardy, and with that
sword he should slay her brother.

38

"This was the reason that brought the damsel hither. Would she had not come! But she never came in fellowship to do good, but rather to do harm. And the knight that hath achieved the sword shall perish with the sword, for which it were a great pity, for there liveth not a knight of more prowess than he is; and he shall do my lord Arthur great honour and kindness. It is great pity he will endure but for a while, for of his strength and hardiness I know not his match."

The Knight of Ireland having armed himself as he had permission of King Arthur, dressed his shield upon his shoulder, and mounted his horse. Taking his spear in his hand, he rode as fast as his horse could go; and when, after a little time, he caught sight of Sir Balin on a mountain, he cried after him in a loud voice,—

"Abide, knight! Ye shall abide whether ye will or not; and the shield which is before you shall not help you."

When Balin heard this cry, he turned his horse angrily, and said,—

"Fair knight, what will you with me? Will you joust with me?"

"Yes," replied the Irish Knight; "for that reason have I come after you."

"Peradventure," replied Balin, "it had been better for you to have remained at home; for many a man thinks to joust his enemy to rebuke, and oft it falleth on himself. Of what Court be you sent from?"

"I am come from the Court of King Arthur," replied the Irish Knight. "And I came here to avenge the slight you have put upon the King and his Court this day."

"Well," said Balin, "I see I must have to do with you, though it paineth me to have shamed King Arthur or any of his Court; and your quarrel is full simple. The lady who is dead did great harm, else would I have been loth as any living knight to slay a lady."

"Make ready, then," replied Lanceor, "and address you to me; for one of us shall abide in the field."

They they grasped their spears, and met together as hard as their horses might drive. The Irish Knight struck Balin so upon the shield that his spear went all to shivers. But Balin hit him with such might that the spear went through his shield and hauberk, and so pierced through his body and his horse's croup. Then Balin drew his sword, and wist not the Irish Knight was dead until he turned and saw him lying on the earth a dead corpse.

CHAPTER IV

HOW A DAMSEL WHO WAS IN LOVE WITH LANCEOR SLEW HER-SELF FOR LOVE; HOW BALIN MET HIS BROTHER, AND WAS REPROVED BY A DWARF; HOW MARK OF CORNWALL FOUND THEM, AND MADE A TOMB OVER THE LOVERS

WHEN Sir Balin looked around him, he became aware of a damsel who came riding full speed on a fair palfrey. When she espied Lanceor dead, she made great lamentation, and cried aloud,—

"Oh, Balin! two bodies hast thou slain and one heart, two hearts in one body, and two souls thou hast lost!"

Thereupon she took the sword from her love Lanceor, and fell to the ground in a swoon.

Whenafter she arose, she made a great dole, and her sorrow grieved Balin passing sore. He went to her to take the sword from her hand; but she held it so fast that he could not have taken it unless he had hurt her, when suddenly she set the pommel on the ground, and pierced herself through the body.

When Balin saw this he was passing heavy in his heart, and ashamed that so fair a damsel had destroyed herself for the death of her love.

"Alas!" said Sir Balin to himself, "I repent me sore the death of this damsel for the love of this knight, for there was much true love between them."

Then because he could no longer remain there for sorrow, he turned his horse's head and faced towards a great forest, where he was made aware, by the arms, of his brother Balan. And when the brothers met they put off their helms, and kissed each other and wept for joy and pity.

Then said Balan, "I little thought to have met with you thus suddenly in adventure, but I am right glad of your deliverance out of your dolorous imprisonment; for a man of the

Castle of Four Stones told me you were delivered, and he had seen you at the Court of King Arthur. Therefore I came into this country, for here I supposed to find you."

Anon the knight Balin told his brother of his adventure with the sword, of the death of the Lady of the Lake, and how King Arthur was displeased at him.

"Wherefore," he continued, "he sent the knight after me who lieth dead yonder, and the death of the damsel grieveth me sore."

"So it doth me," replied Balan; "but ye must take such adventures as God may send you."

"Truly," said Balin, "I am right heavy that my lord Arthur is so displeased with me, for he is the most worshipful knight that now reigneth upon earth, and his love will I get, else I put my life in peril. King Ryence lieth at a siege at the Castle Tereabil; thither will we draw in all haste, to prove our worship and prowess upon him."

"I will well," replied Balan, "that we do, and we will help one another as beseemeth brethren."

"Well," said Balin, after a time, "let us go hence; it is good we have met."

Meanwhile, while they were talking, there came upon them a dwarf from the city of Camelot. He was on horseback, and rode as fast as he could. When he came to the dead bodies he made great lamentation, pulled his hair in his sorrow, and said,—

"Which of you knights has done this deed?"

"Wherefore do you ask?" said Balin.

"Because I would know," replied the dwarf.

"It was I," replied Balin, "that slew the knight in my own defence, for hither came he in chase of me; and either he must have slain me or I him. This damsel slew herself for love of him, which repenteth me sore; and for her sake I shall owe all women the better love."

"Alas!" replied the dwarf, "you have done great damage unto thyself, for this knight who lieth here was one of the most valiant living. Believe it well, Balin: the kin of this knight will chase thee through the world until they have slain thee."

"As for that," replied Balin, "I am not concerned; but I am right heavy in that I have displeased my lord King Arthur for the death of this knight."

Then it happened, as they talked thus together, there came by a ruler of Cornwall, named King Mark. And when he saw the dead bodies, and understood how they had been slain, he made great sorrow for the true lovers, and said, "I will not depart hence until I have made them a tomb."

So he pitched his pavilion; and they sought through all the country to find a tomb. And in a church they found one which was rich and fair. Then the King put both the bodies in the ground, and placed the tomb over them. On the tomb also were written the names, and how "here lieth Lanceor the King's son of Ireland, who at his own request was slain by the hands of Balin; and his Lady Calombe slew herself, with her love's sword, for dole and sorrow."

CHAPTER V

HOW MERLIN FORETOLD THE FIGHT THAT WOULD TAKE PLACE IN THAT SPOT; AND HOW BALIN AND HIS BROTHER, BY MERLIN'S COUNSEL, TOOK KING RYENCE PRISONER TO KING ARTHUR

WHILE these things were being done, Merlin appeared to King Mark of Cornwall, and having seen all he had achieved, said,—

"Here shall be the greatest battle between two knights that ever was or ever shall be, and yet neither shall slay the other."

Then Merlin wrote their names that should fight in that place in letters of gold. The names were Lancelot du Lake and Tristram.

"Thou art a marvellous man," said King Mark unto Merlin, "to tell of such things; a rude man and unlikely to tell of such deeds. What is thy name?"

"At this time," said Merlin, "I will not tell. But when Sir Tristram is taken with his sovereign lady, then shall ye know my name, and then also ye shall hear tidings which shall not please you."

Then continued Merlin to Balin, "Thou hast done thyself great hurt, because of the death of this lady, when thou mightest have saved her, an thou wouldst."

"By my faith!" said Balin, "I could not save her. She slew herself suddenly."

"For the death of that lady," continued Merlin, "thou shalt strike the most dolorous stroke that ever was struck, except the stroke of our Lord; for thou shalt hurt the truest knight, and the man of greatest worship, that now liveth. Through that stroke three kingdoms shall become to great poverty and misery twelve years, and the knight shall not recover that wound for many years."

With that Merlin took his leave of Balin.

Then said Balin, "If I knew this were true, that ye say I will do such a perilous deed, I would slay myself to prove thee a liar."

At this Merlin suddenly vanished and disappeared.

When he had gone Balin and his brother took leave of King Mark of Cornwall.

"First," said the King, "tell me your name."

"Sir," said Balan, "ye may see my brother beareth two swords. Thereby you may call him the Knight of the Two Swords."

So King Mark departed, and went to Camelot unto King Arthur, while Balin and his brother took the way to King Ryence. As they rode onward they met Merlin disguised, so that they knew him not.

"Whither ride ye?" inquired Merlin, as he joined with them.

"We have little to do to tell thee," replied the knight.

"But what is thy name?" said Balin.

"At this time," said Merlin, "I will not tell thee."

"It is evil seen thou art a true man when thou wilt not tell us thy name," said the knight, with a sneer.

"As for that," replied Merlin, "be it as it may. But I can tell you why you ride this way: it is to meet with King Ryence, but ye will not prevail without my counsel."

"Then," said Balin, "you are Merlin, and we will be ruled by your counsel."

"Come on," said Merlin, "ye shall have great worship; and look you do knightly, for indeed ye shall have need."

"As for that, fear you not," replied Sir Balin; "we will do what we may."

So they proceeded on their journey together till night came on.

When darkness approached, Merlin, who knew the movements of King Ryence, hid his companions in a wood near the highway. They unbridled their horses and put them to grass, and then they all lay down to rest.

But when it was near midnight Merlin bade them rise up and make ready, for the King was nigh with threescore of his horsemen, twenty of whom rode on before to advise Lady de Vance of the coming of the King.

"Which is the King?" inquired Balin.

"Wait where you are," said Merlin; "here in a narrow path ye shall meet with him."

And therewith he showed Balin and his brother the direction in which the King was riding.

Anon Balin and his brother met with the King, smote him down, and wounded him sore. As he lay upon the ground, the knights, slaying right and left, killed forty of his men, and the remnant fled.

Then went Balin and his brother unto King Ryence, who remained upon the ground, and would have slain him as he lay had he not implored their grace.

"Knights full of prowess," said he, "slay me not, for by my life ye may gain something, while by my death ye shall avail nought."

Then said the knights, "Ye say sooth."

So they laid him on a horse-litter, and, travelling all through the night, they carried him to King Arthur's castle at cock-crow.

Meanwhile Merlin had vanished and come to the King. Then he told him how his enemy had been discomfited and taken.

"By whom?" said Arthur.

"By two knights," said Merlin. "And to-morrow ye shall know what knights they are."

So at cock-crow came the two knights, the Knight of the Two Swords and Balan his brother and they carried with them King Ryence of North Wales. They delivered him to the porters to take charge of him, and they themselves returned at the dawning of the day.

When King Arthur heard that Ryence was at the castle, he came to him and said, "Sir King, ye are welcome. By what adventure came ye hither?"

"Sir," replied Ryence, "by a hard adventure came I hither."

"Who won you?" inquired Arthur.

"Sir," replied King Ryence, "the Knight of the Two Swords and his brother, who are two knights of marvellous prowess."

"I know them not," replied Arthur; "but I am much beholden to them."

"Shall I tell you," said Merlin, "that it is Balin that achieved the sword, and his brother Balan—a good knight—that did this? There liveth not a better of prowess and worthiness; and it shall be the greatest dole for him that ever I knew of knight, for he shall not long endure."

"Alas!" replied King Arthur, "that is a great pity, for I am much beholden to him, and I have ill deserved his kindness."

"Nay," said Merlin, "he shall do much more for you, as ye shall learn speedily. But, sir, are you prepared?—for to-morrow the hosts of Nero, King Ryence's brother, will set on you before noon. Therefore make you ready, for I will depart."

With that Merlin vanished again, and carried himself away to help the King in other matters.

CHAPTER VI

HOW KING ARTHUR HAD A BATTLE AGAINST NERO AND KING
LOT; AND HOW TWELVE KINGS WERE SLAIN; AND OF THE
PROPHECY OF MERLIN CONCERNING THE DOLOROUS STROKE

THEN Arthur, being warned by Merlin, arrayed his men
in ten divisions; and King Nero made ready in the field
before the castle, for he had ten divisions, but many more people than King Arthur had. Nero himself led the vanguard;
but Merlin came to King Lot of the island of Orkney, and
held him with a tale of prophecy till Nero and his people had
been destroyed by Arthur and his host.

In those days did Sir Kay passing well, so that all the days
of his life he had great worship. And Sir Hervis de Revel did
fine deeds also with King Arthur, who that day slew twenty
knights and wounded forty.

At the same time came in the Knight with the Two Swords
and his brother Balan. They did so marvellously that the
King and all his knights were greatly surprised at them; and
those who saw their deeds considered they were either angels
sent from heaven or devils from the pit. King Arthur himself
said they were the best knights ever he saw, for they gave such
strokes that all men had wonder at them.

In the meantime came a messenger to King Lot, and told
him that while he tarried there King Nero and his men were
all destroyed.

"Alas!" cried King Lot, "I am ashamed; for by my fault
there is many a worshipful man slain, for had we been together there had been none host under heaven that could have
matched us. This man with his prophecy has deceived and
mocked me."

That did Merlin, for he well knew that if King Lot and his

people had been with King Nero in the battle, King Arthur and his knights would all have been slain. He knew that one of the Kings must be slain, and though he was loth any of them should be killed, he had liever King Lot had been slain than King Arthur.

"What am I to do?" said King Lot; "whether is it better to treat with King Arthur or to fight with him—for the most part of our people are slain and destroyed?"

"Sir," said one of his knights, "set now upon Arthur, for he and his force are weary with fighting, and we be fresh."

"As for me," replied the King, "I would that every knight would do his part as I will do mine."

Then King Lot and his people advanced their banners against King Arthur, and the hosts met together and smote each other. The lances were all shivered, and King Arthur's knights, with the help of the Knight of the Two Swords and his brother Balan, put King Lot and his host to the rout.

But King Lot was always foremost, and did great deeds of arms. All his host was borne up by him and did great deeds of arms, for he abode and withstood his knights. Alas! he sought not life, which was a great pity for so worthy a knight as he was to be overmatched. Of late time afore he had been a knight of Arthur's, and had wedded the King's sister.

There was a knight in King Arthur's host called the Knight of the Strange Beast, whose name was Pellinore, who was a good man of prowess. He smote King Lot as he fought with his enemies, but failing of his stroke, he smote the horse's neck, so that it fell to the ground, carrying King Lot with it. Thereupon Pellinore smote the King through the helm, and hewed him to the brows, so he died.

Then all the host of the King of Orkney fled for the death of King Lot, and many were slain. Knight Pellinore bore the blame of the death of King Lot, wherefore Sir Gawaine revenged the death of his father ten years after he was made knight, and he slew Sir Pellinore with his own hands.

There were slain in that battle twelve Kings on the side of King Lot, and all of the twelve were buried in the church of Saint Stephen in Camelot, while the remnant of the knights and others were buried in a great rock.

At this interment came the wife of King Lot, Morgawse, with her four sons, Gawaine, Agravaine, Gaheris, and Gareth. Also came thither King Uriens, the father of Sir Ewaine, and Morgan le Fay, his wife, who was King Arthur's sister. All these came to the "entertainment." But of the twelve Kings Arthur made the tomb of King Lot most richly, and formed it by his own. And the King caused to be made twelve images of laton [brass] and copper, which he overgilt with gold in the likeness of the twelve kings, and each held a wax taper that burned day and night. King Arthur was made in the likeness of a figure standing above them, with his sword drawn in his hand; and all the twelve figures had countenances like conquered men.

This did Merlin by his subtlety, and he said to the King,— "These tapers will no longer burn when I am dead, and soon afterwards the adventures of the Sangreal shall come on you, and be achieved."

He also told Arthur concerning the knight who should give the Dolorous Stroke, whereof shall fall great vengeance.

"But where are Balin, Balan, and Pellinore?" said Arthur.

"Sir Pellinore will meet you soon," replied Merlin; "and as for Balin, he will not be long away from you. But the brother will depart, and ye shall see him no more."

"By my faith," said Arthur, "they are two marvellous men; and Balin surpasseth any knight I ever found, for much beholden am I to him. I would he would abide with me."

"Sir," said Merlin, "keep ye well the sheath of Excalibur, for ye shall lose no blood so long as ye retain it upon you, although you may have many wounds on you."

So afterwards, for great safety, Arthur took the scabbard to Morgan le Fay, his sister; and she loved a knight, and would have had Arthur slain. Therefore she had another scabbard made like it by enchantment, and she gave the sheath of Excalibur to her lover. This knight's name was Accolon, who afterwards nearly slew King Arthur.

After this converse, Merlin told King Arthur the prophecy that there should be a great battle by Salisbury, and that Mordred, his sister's son, should fight against him; and other things besides.

CHAPTER VII

HOW A SORROWFUL KNIGHT CAME BEFORE KING ARTHUR, AND HOW BALIN FETCHED HIM, AND HOW THAT KNIGHT WAS SLAIN BY AN INVISIBLE KNIGHT, A CURIOUS CUSTOM OF THE CASTLE

SOME time after these events was King Arthur taken sick, and had his pavilion pitched in a meadow, and laid him down to sleep; but he could get no rest. And as he lay there, he heard a great noise of a horse, and looking out of the tent door, he saw a knight coming by, and making great lamentation.

"Abide, fair sir," said Arthur, "and tell me why you make this great sorrow."

"You may little amend it," replied the knight, gloomily, as he passed on to the Castle of Meliot.

Anon afterward came Balin, and when he saw King Arthur, he lighted off his horse, and came to the King on foot to salute him.

"By my head," said King Arthur, "but ye are welcome, Sir Balin." He thanked him, and then said, "Sir, right now there came riding this way a knight, making great dole, for what cause I cannot tell. Wherefore I would desire of you to follow after, and of your courtesy and gentleness or by force to fetch again that knight, or by his goodwill."

"I will do more for your lordship than that," replied Balin.

So he rode on at a pace, and found the knight talking with a damsel in the forest, and said to him,—

"Sir Knight, you must come with me to King Arthur, for to tell him of your sorrow."

"That will not I," replied the knight, "for it will trouble me greatly, and to him avail nothing."

"Sir," said Balin, "I pray you make ready, for you must

go with me, else I must fight with you, and bring you by force, which were loth in me to do."

"I will go with you," said the knight, "if ye will be my warrant?"

"Yea," said Balin, "or I will die therefor."

So the knight made him ready to go with Balin, and left the damsel. And as they came before King Arthur's pavilion, there came up one invisible, and smote the knight that went with Sir Balin throughout his body with a spear.

"Alas!" said the knight, "I am slain under your conduct and guard by a treacherous knight Garlon, who by magic and witchcraft rides invisible. Take therefore my horse," said Sir Herlens, for so he was named, "as he is better than yours, and ride to the damsel; follow the quest I was in, where she will lead you, and revenge my death when best ye may."

"That will I do," said Sir Balin, "by my knighthood I vow it to you."

So he departed from the Sorrowful Knight, making great lamentation, and King Arthur caused Sir Herlens to be buried richly, and put upon the tomb how there was slain Herlens de Berbens, and also how the treachery was done by the knight Garlon. But the damsel who was in the wood ever bare the truncheon of the spear with her by which Sir Herlens had been slain.

After this Balin and the damsel rode on together, and as they went they were joined company by a good knight, Perin de Montbelgard, who vowed to take adventure with them wherever they might go.

And this knight asked Balin why he made such sorrow, and Balin told him; and the knight determined to remain with Sir Balin.

But presently, as they were passing by a hermitage and near a churchyard, there came upon them the knight Garlon, invisible, and smote Perin de Montbelgard throughout the body, as he had slain the Sorrowful Knight, with a spear.

"Alas!" said Perin de Montbelgard, "I am slain by the traitorous knight that rides invisible."

"Ah," said Balin, "it is not the first despite he hath done me." And Sir Balin was wroth, swearing to have Sir Garlon's life wherever he might encounter him.

Then the hermit and Sir Balin buried the knight Perin under a rich stone and a tomb royal. So Balin and the damsel continued their journey till they arrived at a castle, and there Balin alighted to enter it. But as Balin came within the gate the portcullis fell down behind him, and a party of men fell upon the damsel and made as if to slay her.

When Balin perceived this he was sore grieved, for he could not help the damsel as he was. But he ran up into the gate-tower and leaped over the walls into the moat, and hurt himself not, going to the damsel's assistance.

Anon he pulled out his sword, and would have fought with the men who restrained the damsel; but they cried out they would not fight with him, for they did nothing but act an old custom of the castle.

They then told the knight how their lady was sick, and had lain so for many years, and she might not be whole until a dish of silver, full of the blood of a pure maiden and a King's daughter, might be had. Therefore it was the custom of the castle that no damsel should pass that way without bleeding a silver dish full of her blood.

"Well," said Balin, "she may bleed with her own consent, an she will; but I will not lose her life so long as my life lasteth."

So Balin made her bleed by her goodwill; but the blood did not help the lady.

Balin and the damsel remained in the castle that night, and had good cheer, and in the morn they passed on their way.

[It telleth in the Sangreal how Sir Percevale's sister helped the lady, but she died after.]

CHAPTER VIII

HOW BALIN MET WITH GARLON AND SLEW HIM, AND HOW HE FOUGHT WITH KING PELLAM, AND SMOTE THE DOLOROUS STROKE

THE knight and the damsel rode on for some days without meeting with any adventure. And one evening they came and lodged with a rich man well at ease.

As they were sitting at supper, Balin heard some one close by him in a chair complaining bitterly.

"What is this noise?" he asked the host.

"I will tell you for sooth," replied the man. "Lately I was at a jousting, and there I jousted with a knight—brother unto King Pellam—and twice smote I him down; and then he promised to be revenged upon me through my best friend. So he wounded my son, that cannot be whole until I have had that knight's blood; but he rideth away invisible, and I know not his name."

"Ah!" said Balin, "I know that knight. His name is Garlon. He hath slain two knights, friends of mine, in the same manner; therefore I had rather meet with that knight than all the gold in the realm, for the spite he had put upon me."

"Well," said the host, "I will tell you a way you may meet him. King Pellam of Listeniss hath made cry of a great feast that shall be within these twenty days, and no knight may come there without a lady; and there we shall see your enemy and mine."

"Then," said Balin, "I promise you some of his blood to heal your son withal."

"We will set forward to-morrow," said the host.

So on the next day they departed and rode towards Listeniss, and they had fifteen days' journey ere they arrived there. On the day they came the great feast began.

Then they alighted and stabled their horses, and went into the castle. Balin's late host was not admitted, because he had with him no lady, but Balin was honourably received. They brought him into a chamber and unarmed him, and gave him robes, but would have had him leave his sword behind when he went in to the banquet.

"Nay," said Balin, "that do I not, for it is the custom of my country for a knight always to keep his weapon, and that custom will I observe, or else will I depart as I came."

Then they suffered him to retain his weapon, and he went into the castle. He was set with his lady before him amongst knights of worship and rank. Anon Balin asked of a knight near him if there were not at the castle a knight named Garlon.

"Yonder he goeth," replied the knight, "he with the black face. He is the most marvellous knight now living, for he destroyeth many good knights as he rideth invisible."

"Ah, well," said Balin, "is that he?"

Then Balin took counsel with himself long.

"If I slay him here I shall not escape, and if I leave him now, peradventure I shall never meet with him again in such a good time, and much harm he will do an he live."

So he looked at Garlon, and he espied that Balin had regard for him, so he came up, and, smiting Balin on the face with the back of his hand, said,—

"Knight, why beholdest thou me so? For shame. Therefore eat thy meat and do that thou came for."

"Thou sayest sooth," replied Balin. "This is not the first despite thou hast done me; therefore will I do that I came for."

So Balin quickly rose up fiercely, and, raising his sword, clave Garlon to the shoulders.

"Give me the truncheon," said Balin to the lady, "wherewith he slew your knight."

Anon she gave it to him—for she always bare it with her—and therewith Balin smote Garlon through the body, and said openly,—

"With that truncheon thou didst slay a good knight, and now it sticketh in thy body."

Then Balin called unto him his late host, and said, "Now may ye fetch blood enough to heal your son withal."

Then all the knights arose up from the tables to set on Balin, and King Pellam himself rose fiercely, and said,—

"Knight, thou hast slain my brother! Thou shalt die therefore, for thou shalt not depart hence."

"Well," said Balin, "do it yourself."

"Yes," replied King Pellam; "that will I. There shall no man have to do with thee but myself, for the love of my brother."

Then King Pellam seized in his hand a grim weapon, and smote eagerly at Sir Balin, who put up his sword to save the blow, but his sword brake in sunder.

And when Balin saw he was weaponless, he ran into another room to find a sword, and so from chamber to chamber, but no weapon could he find: and King Pellam pursued after him.

At last he entered a chamber which was marvellously well decked, and the bed was arranged with cloth of gold the richest that might be made; and thereby stood a table of pure gold, supported by four pillars of silver, and on the table lay a spear of marvellous make, strangely wrought.

When Balin saw that spear he gat it in his hand, and, turning on King Pellam, smote him passing sore, so that he fell down insensible. But at the same moment the walls and roof of the castle brake, and fell to the earth, and carried Balin with them, so that he was embedded in the ruins, and could not stir foot or hand. And so the castle fell down, and fell upon Pellam, and Balin, who had struck the Dolorous Stroke. There they lay three days, powerless to move.

CHAPTER IX

HOW MERLIN DELIVERED BALIN, AND HOW THE KNIGHT RODE TOWARDS A CASTLE, WHERE HE FOUGHT WITH HIS BROTHER BALAN TILL THEY DIED

AFTER the three days had passed, Merlin came to the ruins of the castle, and took up Balin. He also gat him a good horse, for his own was killed, and bade him ride out of that country.

"I wish the damsel to come with me," said Sir Balin.

"Lo," said Merlin, "where she lieth dead."

And King Pellam lay many years sore wounded, and could never be whole, until Sir Galahad came in the quest of the Sangreal and healed him.

"Ah!" said Merlin to Sir Balin, "little know you what you have done. In that chamber was the most holy cup—the Sangreal—wherefrom the wine was taken at the Last Supper of our Lord. Joseph of Arimathæa brought it to this land when he first came hither to convert and save it. The strange spear with which you dealt that very Dolorous Stroke was that by which the soldier Longus smote our Lord. King Pellam is the nearest of kin to Joseph in direct descent, therefore he held all these holy things in trust; but now have they gone at thy Dolorous Stroke no man knoweth whither, and great is the damage to the land, which until now has been the happiest of all lands. By that stroke thou hast slain thousands, and by the loss and parting of the Sangreal the safety of this realm is put in peril, and its great happiness is gone forevermore."

Then Balin departed from Merlin, struck to his heart with dole and sorrow, saying, as he went his way, "In this world we shall never meet more."

So Sir Balin rode forth through the country, and found

the people lying dead on every side. And those who remained alive cried out at him as he passed,—

"O Balin! all this misery hast thou done. For the Dolorous Stroke thou gavest King Pellam three countries are destroyed, and doubt not revenge will fall on thee at last."

Thus Balin rode on through the country; and when he had passed the boundaries of the land he was comforted.

He rode for about eight days without adventure; and at last he came to a forest in a valley, and was aware of a tower, and there beside he saw a great horse tied to a tree, and a fair knight on the ground, making great mourning.

Balin said, "God save you! Why be you so heavy? Tell me, and I will amend it."

"Sir Knight," said he, "thou dost me great grief, for I was not in merry thoughts, and now thou dost put me to more pain."

"What is your name?" said Balin.

"My name is Garish of the Mount; and my lady has broken her promise to meet me here by noon."

"How far is she hence?" asked Balin.

"But six miles," said the knight.

And then they rode on apace to the castle, and found her not as they hoped. So in his anger and despair Garish ran himself through with his own sword.

When Balin saw that, he got away as fast as he might, deeming folk would say he had slain him. So he rode on, and within three days he came to a cross, whereupon was written in letters of gold,—

It Is Not For A Knight Alone To Ride Towards This Castle

At this time he perceived a hoary-headed gentleman coming towards him, who said, "Balin le Savage, thou passeth thy bounds to come this way. Turn again; it will be better for thee."

Then he vanished away, and Balin heard a horn blown as if it had been at the death of a beast.

"That blast," said Balin, "is blown for me; yet am I not dead."

But even as he said this there came out to meet him a hundred ladies and many knights, who welcomed him with fair appearance, and made him good cheer, leading him into the castle, where was all manner of dancing and minstrelsy and joy.

Then the chief lady of the castle said to Balin, "Knight of the Two Swords, ye must have a to-do with a knight that keepeth an island, for there may no one pass this way unless he joust, or he pass not."

"This is an unhappy custom," said Balin, "that a knight may not pass this way unless he fight."

"Ye shall have only to do with one knight," said the lady.

"Well," said Balin, "since I shall I am ready; though travellers are oft weary, and their horses are weary. But though it be so with me, my heart is not weary. I would fain there my death shall be."

"Sir," said a knight to Balin, "methinks your shield is not good; let me lend you, I pray you, a bigger."

So Balin took the shield that was unknown, and left his own, and rode to the water, where he and his horse were put in a great boat. And when he had come across to the other side, a damsel accosted him, and said,—

"O Knight Balin! wherefore have you left your shield? for by it you should have been known. You have put yourself in great danger. It is a great pity of you; for of thy prowess and valour thou hast no fellow living."

"Indeed," replied Balin, "me repenteth that ever I came within this country; but I may not turn now again for shame. And what adventure shall fall to me, be it life or death, I will take the adventure that shall befall."

So he looked on his armour and saw he was well armed. Then he blessed himself and mounted upon his horse, for before him he saw coming riding towards him a knight trapped all in red, and his horse in the same colour.

When the Red Knight beheld Sir Balin, he bethought it was his brother Balin, because he had two swords; but when he saw his shield he deemed not it was he. So they adventured, and came marvellously fast together, smiting each other in the shields; but their speed was so great that it bare down horse and man, so that they lay in a swoon. Balin was also much bruised with the fall of his horse, because he was weary with travel.

Balan was the first to rise, and he drew his sword and went against Balin, who also arose. Sir Balan smote Balin first; but he put up his shield—yet the stroke clave his shield and his helm. Then Balin smote Balan again, and wellnigh felled him. And so they fought together until their breaths failed them.

Then Balin looked at the castle, and saw the towers were filled with ladies that witnessed the fight.

When the knights were rested, they went to battle again, and wounded each other dolefully. They paused again and took breath oftentimes, and battled again; and all the ground was red with blood. Both had received seven severe wounds, each of which might have destroyed the mightiest giant in the world. But they went to battle again, though their hauberks were now unmailed, and they were smiting at each other's naked bodies with their sharp swords.

At last Balan, the younger brother, withdrew a little, and laid him down. Then said Balin the Savage,—

"What knight art thou? for till now never have I found knight that matched me."

"My name," said he, "is Balan, brother to the good knight Balin."

"Alas!" cried Balin, "that I should see this day!" And thereupon he fell backwards in a swoon.

Then Balan roused himself, and went upon "all-four" feet and hands, and put off his brother's helm, and scarce could know him, because his visage was so full hewn and bleeding. But presently, when Balin awoke, he said,—

"O Balan, my brother, thou hast slain me, and I thee, therefore all the wide world shall speak of us both."

"Alas!" said Balan, "that ever I saw this day! Through mishap I did not know you, for, though I espied well your two swords, because ye had another shield I deemed you had been another knight."

"Alas!" replied Balin, "all this did an unhappy knight at the castle, for he caused me to leave my own shield—to our destruction—and if I might live, I would destroy that castle for its evil customs."

"That were well done," replied Balan, "for since I first came hither, I have had no chance to depart; for here it happened me to slay the knight that kept the island, and since I can never depart—no more should you, brother, had ye slain me, and escaped yourself with life."

At this time came out the lady of the castle, with four knights and six ladies and yeomen, and when she heard them make moan to each other, she wrung her hands and wept.

"We both came of one mother," said the brothers; "and so let us both lie in one grave."

So Balan prayed the lady of her gentleness, for his true service, that she would bury them both in that same place, where the battle had been fought. She, weeping, granted the request, and that it should be done in the best manner.

"Now, will ye send for a priest, that we may receive our sacrament and the blessed body of our Lord?"

"Yea," said the lady, "it shall be done."

And so she sent for a priest, who gave them the rites.

"Now," said Balin, "when we are buried in one tomb, and the mention made over us how two brethren slew each other, then will never a good man or good knight see our tomb but they will pray for our souls."

Anon all the ladies and gentlemen wept for pity, and soon Balan died; but Balin died not until the midnight after. So they were buried both; and the lady made mention of how

Balan had been slain by his brother's hands. But she knew not Balin's name.

Then, in the morning, came Merlin, and wrote Balin's name upon the tomb with letters of gold, that,—

Here Lieth Balin Le Savage, That Was The Knight Of The Two Swords, And He That Smote The Dolorous Stroke

Besides Merlin caused a bed to be made, and no man might lie thereon but he went out of his wit; yet Lancelot du Lake succeeded, through his nobleness, in overcoming the enchantment.

Now that Balin was dead Merlin took his sword, and, taking off the pommel, put thereon another pommel. And then he bade a knight who stood by to handle that sword; but when he essayed he could not handle it.

Then Merlin laughed at him, and the knight asked why he laughed.

"Because," said Merlin, "never shall man handle that sword unless it be Sir Lancelot, or Galahad his son. And with that sword shall Lancelot slay the man he loveth best in the world, which shall be Sir Gawaine."

So Merlin put the sword into a marble stone, and the sword swam in the water and floated down the river to Camelot (Winchester), where, as is told in the book of the Sangreal, Sir Galahad achieved the sword.

After these things were done by Merlin he returned to King Arthur, and told him of the Dolorous Stroke that had been achieved by Balin; how Balan and Balin had fought and killed each other; and how they were buried in one tomb.

"Alas!" said King Arthur, "this is the greatest pity that ever I heard tell of two knights."

Thus endeth the tale of Balin and Balan, two brethren and good knights, born in Northumberland.

CHAPTER I

HOW ARTHUR WEDDED GUENEVER, DAUGHTER OF LEODEGRANCE,
OF THE LAND OF CAMELIARD; AND HOW THEY FOUNDED THE
ROUND TABLE

UPON a certain day Arthur said to Merlin, "My lords
and knights let me have no rest, but I needs must take a
wife. But I will have none without thy counsel and advice."

"It is well done," said Merlin, "for thou shouldst have a
wife. A man of your bounty and nobleness should not be
without one. Is there any lady ye love more than another?"

"Yea," replied King Arthur, "I love Guenever, the daughter of King Leodegrance of Cameliard; which Leodegrance
holdeth in his house the Table Round that ye told me he had
of my father Uther. And this damsel is the gentlest and fairest
lady that I know living, or yet ever shall find."

"Sir," said Merlin, "as for her beauty, she is one of the
fairest that live; but did ye not love her so well as ye do, I
could find you a damsel of pureness and goodness that would
please you, were your heart not set. But where a man's heart
is set he will be loth to leave."

This said Merlin to dissuade King Arthur; for Merlin
knew the trouble that would thereafter arise from the marriage. Then Merlin desired to have men to go to King Leodegrance, to tell him the desire of the King, who would wed
his daughter Guenever.

"This is to me," said King Leodegrance, "the best tidings
I ever heard, that so worthy a knight will wed my daughter.
As for my lands, I will give him what would please him, but
he hath enough; and I have a gift that will please him more,
for I will give him the Round Table which Uther Pendragon
gave me, and when it is full complete there is a hundred
knights and fifty. As for the hundred good knights, I have

them myself; but I lack fifty, for so many have been slain."

And thus King Leodegrance delivered his daughter Guenever, and the Table Round with the hundred knights; and so they rode rapidly with great royalty. And what by land and what by water, they came that night to London.

When King Arthur heard of the coming of Guenever, and the hundred knights with the Table Round, he was very joyous, and said openly, "This fair lady is very welcome to me; and these knights of the Round Table please me more than riches."

So in all haste the King commanded the coronation to be prepared, and the marriage with all speed, with the most honourable pomp that may be devised.

"Now," said King Arthur to Merlin, "go then and find for me in all this land fifty knights of the greatest prowess and worship."

And within a short time Merlin had found twenty-eight such knights, but no more could he find. Then the Bishop of Canterbury was fetched, and he blessed them all in their places, and when they rose up to pay homage to King Arthur, upon the back of each knight's seat was his name written in letters of gold. But upon one seat was written, "This is the Siege Perilous"; for there were two seats which were unoccupied.

"What is the cause of these vacant seats?" said Arthur to Merlin.

"Sir," replied Merlin, "there shall no man sit in either of those seats but he shall be of the most worship. But in the Seat Perilous there shall no man sit but one, and if there be any so hardy to do it he shall be destroyed. He that shall sit there shall have no fellow."

Thereupon Merlin took Pellinore by the hand, and said, standing near to the Siege Perilous, "This is your place, for best be ye worthy to sit thereon of any that are here."

At that time came a young man to King Arthur, whose name was Gawaine, and he asked of him a boon.

"Ask," said the King, "and I will grant it to you."

"Sir," said Gawaine, "I ask that ye make me a fair knight the day ye wed fair Guenever."

"I will do it with a goodwill," replied King Arthur, "and do unto you all the worship that I may, for you are my nephew —my sister's son."

CHAPTER II

HOW A POOR MAN CAME AND DESIRED HIS SON BE MADE A
KNIGHT; HOW SIR TOR WAS FOUND TO BE THE SON OF KING
PELLINORE, AND THE ROUND TABLE WAS INSTITUTED

AFTER these things there came an old man to the King's
Court, and brought with him his son riding upon a
lean mare, who desired audience of Arthur, inquiring continually where he might find him. And being directed by the
knights, anon he came before the King, and falling at his feet,
said,—

"O King Arthur, the flower of all knights and Kings! it
was told me that at the time of your marriage you would give
any one the gift he should ask an it were reasonable."

"That is true," replied the King; "such I did say, and to
that will I hold, so it impair not my realm nor mine estate."

"Ye say well," replied the poor man; "and I ask nothing
but that you should make my son a knight."

"It is a great thing thou asketh of me," said the King.
"What is thy name?"

"Sir, my name is Aries, the cowherd," he replied.

"Cometh this prayer from thee or thy son?" said the King.

"Nay, sir; the desire cometh from my son, and not of me.
For I have thirteen sons, and all they will do what labour I
put them to, but this lad will not do anything that my wife
and I may desire; but he will be always shooting, or casting
arrows, or looking at jousting. Day and night he desireth me
to be made a knight."

"What is thy name?" said the King to the young man.

"Sir, my name is Tor," he replied.

Then the King looked at him steadily, and perceived that
he was well favoured. He was pleased with his countenance,
and said to Aries the cowherd, "Fetch all thy sons before me."

So the poor man did; but none of them were like Tor, neither in shape nor in countenance.

"Now," said King Arthur unto the cowherd, "where is the sword to make him a knight?"

"Here it is," replied Tor.

And then, at the King's desire, he unsheathed it, and kneeling, required the King to make him a Knight of the Table Round.

"A knight I will make you," said the King; and he smote him on the neck, saying, "Be ye a good knight, and so I pray to God ye may be; and if ye be of prowess and worthiness ye shall be a Knight of the Table Round."

Then Arthur inquired of Merlin whether Tor would prove a good knight.

"Yes, sir," replied Merlin, "he ought to be, for he comes of good stock. Aries is not his father; he is nothing to him. King Pellinore is his father."

Then when King Pellinore came in he recognized Tor for his son, and was very joyful when he heard how he had been made a knight by King Arthur. Then the King made Gawaine also a knight; but Tor was the first.

Afterward Arthur said to Merlin, "What is now the cause that two places are held vacant at this feast?"

"Sir," replied Merlin, "there shall no man sit in those places unless they have the greatest worship, as I said. In the Seat Perilous there shall sit no man but one; if any be so bold to attempt it, he shall be destroyed by fire."

Thereupon Merlin took King Pellinore by the hand, and led him to a place next the two vacant places near the Perilous Seat.

Sir Gawaine was very wroth at the great honour done to King Pellinore, and he said to Gaheris his brother,—

"Yonder knight is put to great worship, which grieveth me, for he slew our father Lot, therefore will I slay him."

"Not at this time," said Gaheris, "for I am but a squire. When I am also a knight, then will we be revenged on him."

Therefore let him go this time, and do not trouble the feast with bloodshedding."

"As ye will," replied Sir Gawaine, "will I do."

Then up rose the King and spake to all the Table Round, and charged them all present to be true and faithful knights; to do neither murder nor outrage, nor any unjust violence, and always to avoid treason. Never to be cruel, but to give money to him that asketh it, upon pain of forfeiting the liberty of the Court. At all times, on pain of death, to succour all ladies and damsels, and never to take any part in wrongful quarrel for reward or payment. And to all this Arthur swore his men, knight by knight.

Then the King ordained that every year at Pentecost all should come before him, no matter where he was, and give account of all their doings during the twelve months. So thus, with prayer and blessing, and high words of cheer, he instituted the most noble Round Table, whereto the best and bravest knights in the world sought to obtain admission.

CHAPTER III

HOW THE FEAST WAS INTERRUPTED BY A WHITE HART THAT
CAME INTO THE HALL; AND HOW SIR GAWAINE RODE TO FETCH
IT, WHEN IT WAS TAKEN AWAY; OF THE FIGHT OF THE TWO
BRETHREN FOR THE HART

THEN was the marriage feast made ready, and when the
King had been wedded to Guenever at the church of
St. Stephen, at Camelot, with great pomp, the assembly sat
down at the banquet. And Merlin bade them all remain still
to see a marvellous thing that would happen.

Accordingly, as they remained seated, a hart came running
into the hall, and a small white hound next him, with thirty
couple of hounds after him in full cry. He ran about the Table
Round, and past the other tables, when suddenly the white
hound sprang upon him, and bit him, and pulled a piece from
his haunch. Then the hart sprang up with a great leap, and
overthrew a knight sitting at the table, who at once arose,
and taking up the hound, mounted his horse and rode away
with it.

Immediately after there came in a lady, seated upon a white
palfrey, and cried unto King Arthur,—

"Sir, suffer me not to have this despite put upon me, for the
hound was mine which the knight carried away."

But almost as she spoke, there came in a knight, who with
force took the lady away, though she made a great cry.

When she had departed the King was glad, for she made
a great lamentation and noise. But Merlin said,—

"Ye must not treat these things so lightly, for these adventures must be pursued, else it will be to your disworship."

So the King commanded that it should be done as Merlin
had said; and Merlin cried for Sir Gawaine, for he must
bring back the white hart.

"Also, sir," he said, "you must let me call Sir Tor, for he must bring back the hound and the knight, or else slay him. Also Sir Pellinore, for he must bring again the lady and the knight, or else slay him. And these knights shall do marvellous adventures ere they come again."

Then they were called all three, and each one took his charge and armed him carefully. Sir Gawaine being the first called upon, we will follow him first and recount his adventure.

Sir Gawaine, followed by his brother Gaheris, for he had no squire, rode fast after the hart, and as they rode on they saw two knights battling with each other, and so Sir Gawaine inquired why they fought.

"We fight for a very simple matter," said one of the knights, "even though we be two brethren. There came a white hart this way, and many hounds were chasing him, and a white 'brachet' was always next him; and I would have gone after, but my younger brother said he would, for he was the better knight. In this cause we fell into dispute, and fought to find which is the better knight."

"That is indeed a simple cause," said Sir Gawaine. "It is strange that ye should thus dispute, being brethren; ye should dispute with strangers. Ye must have to do with me, unless ye will go to King Arthur and yield to his grace."

"Sir," replied the knights, "we have fought hard, and much blood have we lost, therefore would be loth to do with you."

"Then do ye as I said," replied Sir Gawaine.

"We will agree," said the knight; "but who shall we say sent us?"

"Ye may say the knight that followeth the quest of the white hart. Now what are your names?" said Sir Gawaine.

"Sorlons and Brian of the Forest," said the knights.

So they departed and came to King Arthur's Court, while Sir Gawaine followed his quest.

As he proceeded after the hart, he came to a river, led thereto by the crying of the hounds. And as Sir Gawaine was about to cross the river, there came a knight and stood on the opposite bank, and called to him and said,—

"Sir Knight, come not thou after the hart unless thou wilt joust with me."

"I will not fail for that," replied Sir Gawaine, "to follow the quest."

And at once he swam his horse over. When he came to the opposite side, the knight advanced against him, and they met in full career. But Sir Gawaine smote the knight off his horse, then turned and bade him yield.

"Nay," replied the knight. "But I pray thee alight, and I will match thee with swords."

"What is your name?" said Sir Gawaine.

"Allardin of the Isles," said the knight.

Then they made ready, and smote each other; but Sir Gawaine smote so hard that his sword clave Sir Allardin's helm and head, and he fell dead.

"That was a mighty stroke," said Gaheris.

CHAPTER IV

HOW THE HART WAS HUNTED INTO A CASTLE AND SLAIN; AND HOW GAWAINE KILLED A LADY BY MISADVENTURE; ALSO, HOW SIR GAWAINE AND GAHERIS WERE TAKEN PRISONERS, BUT THEIR LIVES WERE SPARED AT THE REQUEST OF FOUR LADIES

SIR GAWAINE and Gaheris continued to follow the quest of the hart, and let slip three couple of greyhounds, which they had brought with them. So they chased the hart into the courtyard of a castle, where they overtook him and slew him.

Right then came out of the castle a knight, and slew two of the greyhounds before Sir Gawaine, and chased the remnant with his sword out of the castle-yard. When he came back again he began to upbraid Sir Gawaine, and lamented greatly the dead white hart which had been given to him by his lady.

Then he retired and armed himself, and came quickly out to encounter Sir Gawaine, who inquired why he had slain the hounds, for they did but after their nature.

"I had liever ye wreaked your vengeance on me than upon the dumb beasts," said he.

"Thou sayest sooth," said the knight; "I will avenge myself on thee, now I have done so on thy hounds."

Then Sir Gawaine made ready afoot, and they struck together mightily, and fought until the blood ran down at their feet, for their hauberks were all torn and broken. At last Sir Gawaine smote the other knight very hard, and he fell to the earth. So he yielded him, and begged for mercy of Sir Gawaine, as he was a knight and gentle.

But Sir Gawaine said, "Nay, thou shalt die for the slaying of my hounds."

"I will make amends," said the knight, "unto my power."

But Sir Gawaine would show no mercy, and unlaced his foe's helm to strike off his head, when immediately came his lady, and fell upon him as Sir Gawaine was smiting him, and he cut off the lady's head by misadventure.

"Alas!" exclaimed Gaheris, "that were a foul stroke, and the shame of it shall cling to you for ever. Also, you should give mercy to them that ask mercy, for a knight without mercy is without worship."

Sir Gawaine was so astonied at the death of the lady, that he did not know what to do. He bade the knight arise for mercy. But the knight said he did not care to live now his dear lady had been slain, for he loved her above all earthly things.

"Me repenteth it," said Sir Gawaine, "for I thought to have smitten thee. But now shalt thou go to King Arthur and tell him thy adventures, and how thou hast been overcome by the knight in quest of the hart."

"I care not," replied the knight, "whether I live or die!"

But he agreed to go to King Arthur; and he was made to bear one greyhound, which he had killed, on the saddle before him, and the other behind him. So he departed.

"What is thy name?" asked Sir Gawaine, as he was riding away.

"Ablamor of the Marsh," he said. So he departed towards Camelot, but Sir Gawaine entered into the castle, and would have unarmed himself, had not Gaheris warned him to desist, "for," said he, "ye may have many enemies here."

Scarce had he spoken when there came upon them four knights, and said to Sir Gawaine, "Thou newly-created knight, thou hast stained thy knighthood, for thou hadst no mercy and art therefore dishonoured. Also thou hast slain a fair lady to thy great and universal shame, and thou wilt have great need of mercy ere thou depart from us."

Therewith one of the knights smote Sir Gawaine with a mighty stroke, so that he nigh fell to the earth, but Gaheris struck the assailant, and so they continued fighting, and Sir

Gawaine with his brother were in jeopardy of their lives. One of the men with a bow then discharged a bolt at Sir Gawaine, and wounded him in the arm, so that the brothers were in great peril of their lives.

Then, when they might have been slain, there appeared four ladies, and they besought the knights for Sir Gawaine and Gaheris; and the knights spared their lives at the ladies' beseeching, but made them yield as prisoners. Then Gawaine and his brother were very sorrowful.

"Alas!" cried Gawaine, "my arm grieveth me sore; I am like to be maimed."

But in the morning came the four ladies to him, and inquired of him, "what cheer?"

"Not good cheer," replied the knight.

"It is your own fault," they said: "ye did a passing foul deed in the slaying of the lady, which will always be a villainy to you. Are ye not of Arthur's kin?"

"Yea," replied Sir Gawaine, "truly am I."

"You must tell me your name," continued the lady, "or ye cannot pass hence."

"My name," he replied, "is Gawaine; I am the King of Orkney's son; my mother is the sister of King Arthur."

"Then are ye nephew unto King Arthur," said she, "and I shall so speak for ye that for his sake ye shall have conduct to his Court in safety."

So she spoke for him to the four knights and told who he was. Then they gave him the head of the white hart, which was his quest, and delivered him on the condition that he would bear the dead lady before him upon his saddle, and her head hanging around his neck. And so rode he forth to Camelot.

Anon, when he had come, Merlin said to the King, "Now Sir Gawaine must tell his adventures, how he slew this lady, and gave no mercy unto the knight by whom the lady was slain."

Then the King and Queen were heartily displeased with Sir Gawaine, and the Queen decided that Sir Gawaine should ever be the ladies' knight in their quarrels, and be most courteous—never refusing mercy to any who asked it.

Then was Gawaine sworn never to be against lady nor gentlewoman, unless he was fighting against a lady's champion. Thus ends the adventure of Sir Gawaine and his quest.

CHAPTER V

OF THE ADVENTURE OF SIR TOR; HOW HE FOUND THE BRACHET WITH A LADY, AND HOW HE OVERCAME A KNIGHT WHO LOST HIS HEAD

SIR TOR, the son of King Pellinore, left the Court, as already said, and hastened after the brachet [hound], which the knight had carried away in his arms. As he rode on rapidly he encountered a dwarf, which suddenly smote his horse on the head with a staff, so that the animal recoiled.

"Why dost thou so?" inquired Sir Tor.

"Because thou canst not pass this way, unless thou joust with the knights of these pavilions," replied the dwarf.

Then Sir Tor became aware of two tents, whence great spears stood out, and shields were hanging from trees close by.

"I may not tarry," replied Sir Tor, "for I am in quest which I must needs follow."

"Thou shalt not pass," said the dwarf, and therewithal he blew his horn; and then came one on horseback, and made at Sir Tor, who met him and bore him from his horse. And anon the knight yielded to him.

"But, sir," he said, "I have a fellow in yonder pavilion who will also have to do with you."

"He shall be welcome," replied Sir Tor.

And as he spake he was aware of another knight, who came upon him. Each of them then came together with marvellous speed; but the knight smote Sir Tor a great stroke, and shivered his own spear upon his enemy's shield. And Sir Tor smote him in return through his shield, and thence through his side, but low down, so it hurt him not, though he was borne from his horse.

Therewith Sir Tor dismounted, and smote the knight upon the helm, so that he yielded and besought mercy. Sir Tor gave it, but on condition that the two knights went prisoners to King Arthur, and tell him that the knight in quest of the white brachet sent them thither.

"Now what be your names?" said Sir Tor.

"My name," said the one, "is Sir Felot of Langduc."

"And mine is Sir Petipare of Winchelsea," said the other.

"Go ye forth, then," said Sir Tor, "and God speed ye."

So they departed.

Then came the dwarf unto Sir Tor, and begged of him a gift. Sir Tor assented, and the dwarf begged to take service with him, for he said, "I will serve no more recreant knights."

"Take a horse, then," said Sir Tor, "and ride along with me."

"I wot ye ride after the knight with the white brachet," said the dwarf, "and I will bring you where he is."

So they rode on throughout a forest; and at length they became aware of two pavilions, standing by a priory, with two shields hanging—one white and the other red—in either pavilion.

When he saw them, Sir Tor alighted, and came into the white pavilion, and found therein three damsels sleeping, and in the other pavilion he found a lady asleep, and with her was the white brachet, which rose and bayed, so that the lady awoke and quitted the pavilion, and went to her three damsels.

"Will ye take my brachet from me?" said the lady, as Sir Tor seized the hound.

"Yes," replied he, "this brachet have I sought from King Arthur's Court hither."

"Well," said the lady, "ye shall not go far hence but ye shall be met and grieved."

"I will accept what adventure cometh," said Sir Tor.

And so he mounted his horse and rode away towards Camelot. But night came on, and he could proceed no farther. And the knight inquired of the dwarf whether he knew of any place of shelter for the night.

"There is a hermitage here," said the dwarf; "and there ye must take lodging as ye find it, for I know of none other."

So they came to the hermitage, and stayed, and found grass and oats for the horses, and some food for themselves; but full hard was their supper. There they rested, however, till morning, and having heard mass, proceeded on their way to Camelot a long while.

As they were riding along, a knight called aloud after them, saying, "Knight, abide, and restore me the brachet thou hast taken from my lady."

Sir Tor turned round, and beheld a seemly knight well armed. So he dressed his shield, took his spear in his hand, and then the knights came fiercely upon each other, and both fell to the earth.

But they rose again, and then, drawing their swords, advanced against each other, covering their bodies with their shields, while they struck and hewed at each other mightily. They suffered much, and a great deal of blood was spilt on both sides. Their hauberks were riven and slashed to pieces, and both knights were passing weary.

But at length Sir Tor perceived that the other knight was fainting, and then he pursued him, doubling his strokes till he had felled him to the earth. Then Sir Tor bade him yield.

"That I will not," replied Abellius, "not while my life lasteth, and my soul is in my body, unless first thou deliverest me the hound."

"I cannot do so," replied Sir Tor, "and I will not, for it was my quest to bring that brachet, or thee, or both, to King Arthur, or else I must slay thee."

Just then there came up a damsel riding on a palfrey very fast, and she cried out to Sir Tor.

"What will ye?" said he, as she called to him.

"I beseech thee," said the damsel, "for the love of King Arthur, give me a gift I require thee, knight, as thou art a gentleman."

"Well," said Sir Tor, "ask a gift, and I will give it thee."

"Gramercy," replied the damsel. "Now I require the head of the false knight Abellius, the most outrageous murderer living."

"I repent of that I promised you," replied Sir Tor: "let him make amends."

"He cannot now make amends," replied the damsel, "for he has slain my brother before my eyes, who was a better knight than he. He scorned to give him mercy, though I kneeled to him in the mire to beg my brother's life. He had done him no damage, but fought with him by chance, without quarrel; yet he struck off his head for all I could do. Therefore I require of thee, as thou art a true knight, to perform thy promise, else I shall shame thee before all the Court of King Arthur."

When Abellius heard this he was greatly afraid, and yielding to Sir Tor, he implored his grace.

"I may not now," said Sir Tor, "else I should be false to my promise. I would have taken you to mercy, but you refused it; now it is too late."

So saying, he unlaced his helmet and took it off, while Abellius in fear arose and fled, pursued by Sir Tor; who overtook him and smote off his head with a single stroke.

"Now, sir," said the lady, "as night is at hand, I pray you come to my place and lodge with us, for we live hard by."

"That will I," replied Sir Tor, gladly; for his horse and he had need of rest and food, and had fared but ill since they had departed from Camelot.

So he rode with the lady, and she gave him good cheer. A fair knight was her husband, and they treated Sir Tor well and urged him to return.

On the morrow, as he was departing, they inquired his name, and he told them; also how it was his first quest of arms to bring back the knight Abellius. So Sir Tor departed, and arrived at King Arthur's Court. The King and Queen and all were very glad at his appearance, for he had had no assistance but what armour and a sorry charger had been given him there.

Then he told them of his adventures, and the King made great joy concerning him; but Merlin said the knight would do much greater things in time to come, "for," said he, "he shall prove a noble knight of prowess, as good as any living, as gentle and courteous, passing true of his word, and shall never commit outrage."

So depending upon Merlin's word, the King presented Sir Tor with an earldom of lands. And thus happily ended the adventure of Sir Tor.

CHAPTER VI

THE ADVENTURE OF KING PELLINORE, AND HOW HE FOUGHT WITH TWO KNIGHTS, AND GAT THE LADY HE WAS IN QUEST OF, AND BROUGHT HER TO THE COURT AT CAMELOT

MEANTIME, while Sir Gawaine and Sir Tor were pursuing their adventures as related, King Pellinore had also set forth in pursuit of the lady and the knight who led her away from the feast. And as he rode on by the forest, he came to a valley, in which was seated a damsel by a well, with a wounded knight in her arms.

When the damsel was aware of King Pellinore riding by, she cried out for his help. But he would not tarry, he was so eager in his quest, although she cried again and again for his assistance. At which neglect she prayed that King Pellinore would have need of so much as she before he died.

Afterwards it came to pass that the knight died of his wounds, and the damsel in her sorrow slew herself with his sword.

But King Pellinore, riding on, met a poor man in the valley, and inquired whether he had seen a knight leading away a lady by force.

"Yea," replied the man, "I saw the knight, and the lady made great lamentation. And in the valley yonder, as ye go on, ye shall see two pavilions, and one of the knights challenged the knight who was bearing off the lady, who is his cousin. They quarrelled over this matter, and a little while ago I left them fighting, as ye will find them if ye ride on apace. The lady was left with the squires in the pavilion."

"I thank thee," said King Pellinore. And he rode on as fast as he could, until he came in sight of the two pavilions and the knights, who were still fighting.

Anon he rode into the pavilion where the lady was, and

said, "Fair lady, you must come with me to King Arthur's Court."

"Sir Knight," said one of the squires with her, "yonder are two knights fighting for this lady. Go ye and obtain their consent ere ye take her hence."

"Ye say well," said King Pellinore. And immediately he spurred his horse between the contending knights, and inquired why they fought.

"I will tell you, Sir Knight," replied one of them. "This lady is my near kinswoman, and when I heard her complain that she was being carried away against her will, I assayed to fight with this knight."

"Sir Knight," said the other, who was called Hontzlake of Wentland, "this lady I got by prowess of arms at King Arthur's Court."

"That is untruly said," replied King Pellinore, "for ye came in suddenly as we were at the feast, and fled away with her ere any man could stay you. Therefore it was my quest to bring you and her back again, else one of us must abide in the field. So the lady shall go with me, or I will die for it, for I have promised King Arthur. Therefore fight ye no more, for none of you shall have any part with her. But if ye will fight for her, fight now with me. I will defend her."

"Well, then," said the knights, "make you ready, for we will assail you."

As King Pellinore would have separated from them, Sir Hontzlake ran his horse through with his sword, and said, "Now thou art on foot as well as we."

King Pellinore immediately freed himself from his fallen steed, and drawing his sword, holding his shield before him, said, "Sir Knight, guard well thy head, for thou shalt have a buffet for my horse." So King Pellinore set upon him, and with one stroke clave his helm and his head down to the chin; so he fell dead.

Then turned he to the other knight, the kinsman of the lady, who was sorely wounded. But when he saw the stroke that King Pellinore had dealt, he kneeled down and begged for mercy, saying, "Take my cousin the lady with you as you request, and I require of you as a true knight to put her to no shame."

"Will ye not fight for her?" said King Pellinore.

"No," replied the knight, "I will not fight with a knight of such prowess as ye be."

Then replied Pellinore, "Ye say well. She shall suffer no wrong, as I am a true knight. But," he continued, "I lack a horse: I will have Hontzlake's steed."

"Ye shall not want it," replied the knight: "if ye will tarry with me this night, I will give you such a horse as will please you."

So King Pellinore consented to remain that night, and had with him right good cheer, and fared of the best.

On the morrow, after a good night's rest, there was brought to King Pellinore a fine bay courser, and his saddle upon him.

"Now what shall I call you?" said the knight, "inasmuch as you have my cousin in the desire of your quest."

"My name is King Pellinore of the Isles," he replied, "and I am one of the Knights of the Table Round."

"Now am I glad," returned the knight, "that such a noble man should have the care of my cousin."

"Tell me your name," said King Pellinore.

"I am Sir Meliot of Logurs, and this lady is called Nimue. The knight who was in the other pavilion is my sworn brother; his name is Brian of the Isles. He is loth to do wrong, or to fight with any man unless he be sore pressed."

"It is a marvel," said King Pellinore, "that he will not encounter me. Bring him to Court some day."

"Sir," replied the knight, "we will come together."

"Ye shall be welcome," said the King.

Then he and the lady departed together, and he brought her to Camelot. And as they rode in the valley full of stones, the lady's horse stumbled and fell with her, and her arm was sore bruised and hurt. She was near swooning with pain, and cried,—

"Ah, sir, mine arm is out of joint, and I must needs rest me."

So Pellinore lighted off his horse under a tree, and tying up the steeds, he slept till it was nigh night. And when he would have continued his journey, the lady said,—

"Sir, ye may as well ride backward as forward in the dark."

So King Pellinore put off his armour, and under the tree they made their lodging for the night. About midnight they heard the sound of a trotting horse, and King Pellinore said to the lady,—

"Be still, for now we shall hear of more adventure."

Then he armed himself, and found right before him were two men who had met in the dark; one riding from Camelot, and the other towards it. They saluted each other, and the one said,—

"What news from Camelot?"

"By my head," said the other, "I have been there and espied King Arthur's Court; and such a fellowship is there that it will never be broken, for all the chivalry of the world holdeth to Arthur. So now am I riding into the north to tell our chieftain of it."

"For that," replied the other knight, "I have brought a remedy. It is the deadliest poison that ever ye heard speak of, and I will with it to Camelot, where I have a friend near the King, who hath received great gifts from us to poison him, as he hath promised."

"Beware ye of Merlin," said the first knight, "for he hath all manner of craft."

"I will not fear for him," replied the other.

And so they parted on their several ways.

Anon, when Sir Pellinore and the lady were made ready, they departed and went towards Camelot. And when they had come to the valley, in which the lady had cried to King Pellinore, they found only the lady's head; both she and the knight had been else entirely devoured by wild beasts.

When King Pellinore perceived this he wept and made great dole, saying, "Alas! I might have saved her life; but I was so intent upon my quest I would not abide."

"Wherefore make ye such dole?" said the lady.

"I know not," he replied, "but my heart mourneth for her, for she was young, and a passing fair damsel."

"Now will ye take my advice?" said the lady. "Let the knight be buried here in his bones, but take you the lady's head and bear it to King Arthur."

So the remains of the knight and the damsel were buried, and King Pellinore carried the head of the damsel to take unto the Court of the King at Camelot. The hermit who buried the remains was to make the service for the souls of the dead.

So the knight and the lady continued their journey; but King Pellinore was very sad whenever he looked at the fair face and yellow hair of the lady's head, which he carried before him on the saddle. Thus they came to Camelot at noonday.

When they arrived, King Pellinore was sworn to tell the truth of his quest.

"Ah, Sir Pellinore," said Queen Guenever, "ye were greatly to blame that ye saved not the lady's life."

"Madam," said he, "saving your pleasure, I was so furious in my quest that I could not abide, and I shall repent it all my life."

"Truly," said Merlin, "ye ought to repent it, for the lady was your own daughter, and the knight that is dead was her love, and he was to wed her. He was a right good man and knight, to this Court was he coming, and his name was Sir Miles of the Lands. A knight came behind him and wounded him with a spear. The assailant's name is Loraine de Savage, a false and coward knight. She slew herself for sorrow, and her name was Elaine. So because ye would not remain and help her whom ye have not seen since her infancy, ye shall see your best friend fail you when ye are in the greatest distress. That penance God hath ordained you for that deed, and he that you shall most trust shall leave you in your distress; he shall leave you to be slain."

"This may betide," said King Pellinore; "but God can conquer destiny."

Then did Sir Pellinore tell Merlin of the knight who had come to poison the King, and Merlin by his craft so managed it that the knight fell by his own poison, and the King was saved.

And so the three quests were done. And then came the true celebration and establishment of the Table Round, with the conditions afore mentioned. To these all were sworn, and so every year at the Feast of Pentecost.

BOOK THE FOURTH

CHAPTER I

HOW MERLIN WAS INFATUATED WITH ONE OF THE LADIES OF THE LAKE, AND HOW BY HIS OWN ENCHANTMENT SHE SHUT HIM IN A ROCK AND KEPT HIM THERE

IT WAS after the return of Sir Tor, King Pellinore, and Sir Gawaine from their quests, that Merlin fell in love with the damsel Nimue, who was the lady brought to Court by King Pellinore, and Merlin was ever after her. She did not care for him, but was anxious to learn the enchantments which she feared; so she was at first kind to him, and made him good cheer, till she had learned of him all manner of thing which she desired. But he was so besotted of her that he could in no way break his chain of love, and could not remain without her for any long time.

Then he went to King Arthur, and told him that the enchantments and power he himself possessed would not endure for long, but for all his crafts he would be put in the earth living. And he continued to tell the King many things that should befall. But in all his warnings he insisted that Arthur should keep the Sword and the scabbard, and advised him that they would both be stolen from him by the woman he most trusted if he did not guard them.

Thus Merlin prophesied his own departure, and thought that the King would miss him and his counsels when he had gone. He knew full well he should be put into the earth quick, yet for love of the Lady of the Lake, called by some Viviane, he could not deliver himself. He said to Arthur, "You would rather than all your lands have me again."

"Ah," said the King, "since you know of your adventure, forestall it, and put it away by your crafts."

"Nay," said Merlin, "it will not be so." And thus he departed from King Arthur.

Soon after this, the Damsel of the Lake also departed, and Merlin followed her, wherever she went, for love. And after-times, Merlin would do enchantments upon her, until she made him swear he would never do so more if she would consent to be his bride. So he sware it, and she consented, and in pursuance thereof they crossed over the sea into the land of Benwick (or Brenliande), in Brittany, where King Ban was ruler, who aforetime had had great war with King Claudas, as related in the foregoing books.

Then Merlin was well received, and found King Ban's wife, whose name was Elaine, and young Launcelot. The Queen was very sorry for the great and terrible war which King Claudas had made upon her dominion, but Merlin tried to comfort her.

"Take none heaviness," he said, "for this same child shall, within twenty years, revenge you upon King Claudas, so that all Christendom shall speak of it. This same child shall be the man of most worship in the world. His first name is Galahad, but ye have confirmed him Launcelot."

"O Merlin," said the Queen, "shall I indeed live to behold my son a man of such prowess as you say?"

"Yea, lady," answered Merlin, "ye shall see it, and shall live long after also."

So was the Queen comforted by Merlin.

After these things came again Merlin and the Lady of the Lake into Britain, and they travelled into Cornwall together. Then the lady was passing weary of Merlin, and wished to be rid of him; but she was afraid of him for his enchantments, and could put him away by no means.

So in the way to attain her freedom she pretended much affection; and she, by her arts and caresses, persuaded Merlin to reveal to her an enchantment that he knew, by means of which any one, no matter what his power, might be imprisoned in any place without walls, and could not release himself.

For a long time Merlin would not, for all her blandishments, reveal to her the charm, because, as he had told King Arthur, he knew the Lady of the Lake would use his arts against himself. But at length the lady prevailed. And so in time Merlin showed to her a rock, whereat was a great wonder, and wrought by enchantment, which went under a great stone.

So by her subtle working she made Merlin go under the rock; and when he had gone under she made use of the enchantment which she had learned, and enclosed him living within the magic circle she had drawn, so that he could not move. And there she left Merlin alive; and in aftertime she even came to see him. But she would never release him from the stone, and he remained there as it were dead, but quick.[1]

So Merlin disappeared off the face of the earth, and he was no more seen at the Court of Arthur, as he had foretold concerning himself. But the Lady of the Lake lived, and will appear many times in the books of this chronicle of the Knights of the Table Round.

---

[1]The version of this tale adopted by the Poet Laureate makes Vivien enclose Merlin in the tree under which they sat in the Forest of Brenliande.

AND SO IN TIME MERLIN SHOWED VIVIEN A ROCK
WHEREAT WAS A GREAT WONDER

CHAPTER II

HOW FIVE KINGS WARRED AGAINST ARTHUR, AND HOW HE
OVERTHREW THEM; AND HOW KING ARTHUR FOUNDED AN
ABBEY IN THE PLACE THE BATTLE WAS FOUGHT; WITH OTHER
MATTERS PERTAINING TO THE TABLE ROUND

IN THOSE days there came tidings to King Arthur that
five Kings were entered into his land to burn and destroy
it, slaying the people in the castles and in the cities, so that
it was a great pity to hear concerning them. These Kings who
had thus invaded his land were the King of Ireland and his
brother the King of Denmark, the King of the Vale, the King
of Soleise, and the King of the Island of Longtainse.

"Alas!" cried Arthur, when he heard of the doings of these
Kings and their hosts, "shall I never have rest? I have had
no peace since I was King of this land, and now I must meet
these Kings in fair field, for my people must not be destroyed.
Let him who will go with me, and let them abide who desire it."

Then Arthur sent unto King Pellinore, and bade him bring
what men he could and unite with him; and other knights
were also bidden. Arthur then requested his Queen Guenever
to accompany him, and she replied she was at his orders;
whereby they departed with their attendants, and came up as
far as Humber.

When the news came to the five Kings that King Arthur
was there, they hastened to meet him, fearing that the longer
they tarried the more formidable would the King become. So
they hastened to set upon him, and attack him, and the small
following he had.

The five Kings therefore assembled, and passing through
North Wales, came upon Arthur in the night-time, as he and
his men were at rest. Arthur was unarmed and in bed, though

Sir Kay had protested against putting off their armour, but had been overborne by Sir Gawaine and Sir Griflet.

Suddenly there came a great noise, and the knights called out that they had been betrayed, while Arthur called out, "To arms! to arms!" and hastened to assume his defence.

Anon they were all armed, and then there came a wounded knight unto the King, and implored him and the Queen to save themselves, for said he, "Our host is destroyed, and our men are nearly slain."

Upon this the King and Guenever mounted, and rode away across to the Humber; but the water was so rough that they were not able to pass it.

"Now," said Arthur, "we must choose whether shall we attempt the water, or remain on this side to be slain by our enemies."

"It were better," said Guenever, "to die in the water than in the hands of the enemy."

But as they talked thus, Sir Kay saw the five Kings by themselves, spurring hard, with spears, and coming towards them.

"So here are the five Kings," he said. "Let us go and match them."

"That were folly," said Sir Gawaine; "we are but four."

"Never mind," said Sir Kay; "I will give you an account for two of them, and you three may undertake the other three."

Therewithal Sir Kay set his horse at his best pace, and smote one of the Kings right through his shield and his body, and the spear came out a fathom behind him. So he fell upon the earth stark dead.

King Arthur also, and Sir Gawaine, attacked each another, and both smote their adversaries to the ground. Then Sir Griflet charged the remaining King, and gave him such a fall from his horse that he brake his neck, while Sir Kay undertook the fifth King, and clave him through the helm and head.

"That were a good stroke," cried King Arthur; "and honourably hast thou kept thy promise; therefore will I honour thee while I live."

Queen Guenever also greatly praised Sir Kay for his deeds, and said she would bear his noble fame amongst ladies. So they sent the Queen across the Humber in safety in a barge, while Arthur and his brave knights remained upon the hither side, and rode into the forest again, where Arthur met near all his people. He then told them concerning the death of the five Kings.

"Now," said he, "let us remain together until the day; and when the hosts shall perceive that the Kings be dead, they shall make such lamentation that they will be able to do nothing at all."

So as the King said they did, and it turned out as Arthur had predicted. The men made great dole, and fell from their horses in their grief. Then came King Arthur and his following, and slew them left and right to the number of thirty thousand, until scarce one was left to tell of the disaster.

When the battle was ended, the King kneeled down and thanked God for his preservation. The Queen was quickly sent for, and came, and was greatly rejoiced because of the issue of the battle.

After this battle had been happily ended, there came a messenger from King Pellinore, announcing that he was near at hand, and advancing with a great host. So Arthur bade the messenger return and tell King Pellinore how they had sped in his absence. Then in a while he came with his men, and saluting the King and his men, there was great joy in the camp.

Search was then made to see how many men of Arthur's force had been slain, and they found but two hundred men, and eight knights of the Table Round, who had been killed in their pavilions. Then the King commanded that a fair abbey should be founded and built, and endowed richly, and it was to be called the Abbey of la Belle Adventure.

And afterwards, when the news came into the countries of the five Kings how they had been slain, there was great mourning, and all Arthur's enemies were greatly moved when they heard of the result of the battle.

Arthur then returned to Camelot, and when he had arrived there, he called King Pellinore to an audience, and said,—

"Ye know we have lost eight knights who were of the Table Round, and with your advice we will choose eight more for them."

"Sir," said Pellinore, "there are in your Court many excellent knights both old and young, so my advice is that ye choose half from the old and half from the young knights."

Then said Arthur, "Which of the old knights will you choose?"

And Sir Pellinore told him that Uriens, his brother-in-law (who wedded Arthur's sister), the King of the Lake, Sir Hervaise de Revel, and Sir Galagars.

"Then," continued Arthur, "tell me the four young knights."

"Sir," said Pellinore, "the first is Sir Gawaine, your nephew; as good knight as any in the land. Secondly, Sir Griflet. The third seemeth to me to be your Seneschal, Sir Kay, for many times he hath done full worshipfully."

"By my head," replied Arthur, "he is the most worthy of all, had he done no more prowess all his days than he hath but now. He is worthy to be a knight of the Table Round."

The fourth knight had yet to be chosen, so King Pellinore put it to the King to choose which he would have of two knights, viz.: Sir Bagdemagus, or Sir Tor the son of the King Pellinore.

"Because he is my son," said Pellinore, "I may not praise him; but were he not, I would proclaim him, that of his age there is no better knight than he, nor of better condition."

"He is a passing good knight," said King Arthur, "for I have seen him. He saith little, but he doth much, and well I know him to be highly born. So we will leave Sir Bagdemagus till another time."

Thus it was all arranged, and every man's name was found in his chair, when the barons had approved the King's choice.

But Sir Bagdemagus was greatly wroth because Sir Tor had been placed at the Round Table before him; so he quitted the Court in a rage, with his squire; and riding into the forest, he sat down under a tree, and then said his prayers devoutly.

There was a cross there, and while Sir Bagdemagus was praying, his squire found a writing, saying that his master should never be made a knight of the Round Table until he had slain one of the existing knights thereof, body for body.

So said the squire, "Here, sir, is the writing. Return ye now into the Court."

"That never will I do," replied Bagdemagus, "until men speak highly of me, and until I be considered worthy of the Table Round."

As he rode on, he found a hart, which is a token of the Sangreal, and only found by such knights as are of good living, and he went in the hope of adventures. He had not gone very far when he happened to arrive at the place where Merlin had been imprisoned by the Lady of the Lake, and Sir Bagdemagus heard him making great dole under the stone in the rock. Whereupon the knight would have helped him, but the stone was too heavy and he could not move it. When Merlin wist he was there, he bade him leave his labour, for it were all in vain—he could never be holpen but by her who had put him there.

After this Sir Bagdemagus went on, and had many adventures; and when he had proved himself a good and worshipful knight, he returned to King Arthur's Court, and was made a knight of the Table Round, when other adventures were done.

CHAPTER III

HOW ARTHUR, WITH URIENS AND SIR ACCOLON OF GAUL, CHASED A HART; OF THEIR ADVENTURES, AND HOW ARTHUR FOUGHT FOR TWENTY KNIGHTS

ONE time Arthur and his knights rode into the forest, hunting; and he, with King Uriens and Sir Accolon of Gaul, followed a great hart, and, being well mounted, chased the deer a long way from their companions, so that their horses sank under them and died.

Thus it happened that the hart got away and hid in the bushes.

"What shall we do?" said Arthur. "We are hard put to it."

"Let us go on foot," said Uriens, "until we meet with some lodgment."

So they proceeded, and at length came in sight of a hart, with a hound biting at its throat, and other hounds baying round, all upon the bank of a great lake.

Then the King blew the taking—or prize—for the capture of the hart; and suddenly in the water appeared a little ship, which came direct towards them, and landed on the sands. Arthur looked into it, and finding no earthly creatures therein, said, "Sirs, come hither, and let us examine what is in this ship."

So they all went, and found it richly decked and hanged about with cloth of silk. By this time night had come on, and suddenly there came about them a great number of torches upon all sides of the ship, which gave a bright light. Then came there out twelve fair damsels, and saluting Arthur, set forth good cheer for him and bade him welcome.

The King thanked them, and then he and his companions were led into a rich chamber and feasted with wines and meats—they had never fared better at any supper. They were then led into their respective rooms, and slept well that night. But, behold! when Uriens awoke he found himself at home at Camelot, and marvelled how he came thither to his wife, Morgan le Fay. But when King Arthur awoke he found himself in prison, hearing about him many complaints of captive knights. King Arthur inquired of what they were complaining, so one replied to him,—

"We be here twenty prisoners, and some of us have lain here seven years and some less."

"For what cause?" said Arthur.

"We shall tell you," replied the knights. "Sir Damas is the lord of this castle: the most false knight that ever lived, full of treason, and a great coward. He hath a younger brother, whose name is Sir Ontzlake, and the elder one will give him nothing, but he keepeth for himself his fair manor and lands by his prowess. But Sir Damas is ever troubling his brother, and will not fight him body for body, but has agreed to find a knight to encounter for him; but he is so disliked, and in such ill favour, no one will fight for him. When, therefore, Damas had found that none will adventure for him, he with his followers lay in wait and captured all the knights he could, and kept them here by force, so that many good men have died of hunger. If any of us would engage his brother, Sir Damas would deliver us; but we would rather die than fight for such a man, full of treason as he is. But we be so lean with hunger that we scarce can stand upon our feet."

"God deliver you," said King Arthur.

Then came up a damsel and asked him what cheer.

"I cannot tell," replied Arthur.

"Sir," said she, "will you fight for my lord? If so ye will be delivered from prison—else ye shall never escape with your life."

"That is hard," replied Arthur; "but I had rather fight with a knight than die in a prison. And if I and all these shall be delivered if I do this, I will assay it."

"Yes," said the damsel.

"Then I am ready," said Arthur, "if I had horse and armour."

"Ye shall lack nothing," said the damsel.

"Damsel," said Arthur, "it seems to me I have seen you at Arthur's Court?"

"Nay," said she; "I am the daughter of the lord of this castle."

But this was false, because she was one of the waiting-women upon the King's sister, Morgan le Fay.

Then went she unto Sir Damas, and told him how Arthur would do battle for him; and Sir Damas sent for Arthur.

So when he appeared, the knight, seeing him so well made, said it was a pity he should die in prison.

Then an agreement was made with Sir Damas—that if Arthur fought for him, all the knights in prison would be delivered; and this was done. Then the twenty knights were brought out and released. But they all remained to see the battle between Arthur and the brother of Sir Damas.

CHAPTER IV

HOW ACCOLON FOUGHT WITH KING ARTHUR; AND HOW ARTHUR WAS NEARLY SPENT

FOR a space we must return to Sir Accolon of Gaul, who had been asleep; and when he awoke he found himself close by a very deep well, and in great danger of death. But a silver pipe ran from the well pure water into a stone, and Sir Accolon was glad when he saw it, for he thought he had been enchanted, as indeed he had been by the damsels. "They were devils," he said, as he blessed himself, "and no women; and if I may escape this misadventure, I will destroy all those damsels wherever I may find them."

While he was thinking these things there came up a horrible dwarf, with an immense mouth and a flat nose, and he saluted King Accolon. He then told the knight that he came from Morgan le Fay, with a message to bid him be of good heart, for on the morrow he should have to do with a knight at the hour of prime; and so she sent him Arthur's sword Excalibur and the scabbard therewith.

"And," continued the dwarf, "she biddeth you, as you love her, to do battle to the uttermost, without mercy, as ye have promised her; and any damsel who bringeth her the head of the knight with whom ye fight shall be made a queen."

"I understand you," said Sir Accolon. "Now I have the sword, I accept the promise. But when saw you my lady Morgan le Fay?"

"But lately," replied the dwarf.

Then Sir Accolon said, "Recommend me to my lady Queen, and tell her all that I have promised her shall be done, else I will die for it. I suppose she hath made all these enchantments for this battle?"

"Ye may believe so," replied the dwarf.

As he was speaking there came a lady, with six squires, and saluted Sir Accolon, and begged him to arise and come to rest himself at the manor. So he went with them, and had excellent cheer.

Then Sir Damas sent unto his brother, and bade him make ready to encounter a good knight, for he had found one ready to do battle at all points.

This message made Sir Ontzlake very troubled, for only a little time before he had been wounded through both his thighs with a spear; but even as he was he would have taken the battle in hand. However, it happened at that time, by the arts of Morgan le Fay, that Sir Accolon came to lodge with Sir Ontzlake; and when he heard of the battle, he said he would fight for Sir Ontzlake, as he was wounded.

As Morgan le Fay had sent him the sword Excalibur and the scabbard, he felt he could fight with the knight in the morn; and so he took the battle in hand. So Sir Ontzlake sent a message unto his brother Sir Damas, that he had a knight who would be in the field by the hour of prime.

In the morning, therefore, King Arthur was made ready, armed and well horsed, and he asked Sir Damas what he should do.

"We will hear Mass," said Sir Damas. So they did; and when Mass was over, a messenger came to say that the other knight was ready, and waiting in the field. Then Arthur mounted his horse amid all the people there; and twelve good men were chosen to wait upon the knights in the encounter.

Then just as King Arthur was on horseback another messenger came to him from his sister, Morgan le Fay, and brought him a sword, like his Excalibur, and a scabbard, saying, "Morgan le Fay sendeth you your sword Excalibur for great love."

He thanked the messenger for her, and addressed him to the fight; but the sword and the scabbard were counterfeit, and brittle, and false.

Then the knights made ready against each other in different

sides of the field, and they let their horses run so fast that the combatants smote each other in the midst of their shields with their spears, and both horses and men fell to the earth. So they arose on foot, and drawing their swords, fell upon each other furiously.

At this time came upon the field of battle the Lady of the Lake, who had put Merlin under the stone. She came, for love of King Arthur, to save his life; for she knew that Morgan le Fay had given Arthur's sword, and had intended Arthur to be slain that day.

The knights fought bravely, and dealt each other many great strokes; but King Arthur's sword did not cut like Sir Accolon's, for every stroke of Excalibur wounded King Arthur, so that it was a marvel he stood upright. He bled very much, and when Arthur beheld the blood falling from him so fast, he began to be dismayed concerning the virtues of the scabbard, and he feared some treason.

After a while he fancied that his sword had been changed, for it was no longer Cut-steel (Excalibur), as it had been, and he feared death, because it seemed to him that Sir Accolon had *his* sword, as every stroke drew blood.

"Keep thee well, Sir Knight," cried Accolon; but Arthur answered not, and dealt him such a buffet upon the helm that he stooped to earth with the blow. Then Sir Accolon replied with a stroke which made King Arthur reel, and both became very wroth with each other. They gave many sore strokes, and King Arthur continued to lose much blood, and yet he endured most marvellously still. But Sir Accolon did not lose blood like the King, because of the scabbard he wore; so King Arthur became very feeble, and felt like to die; though he held Accolon as short as he could.

But he was passing hardy because of Excalibur, and all men declared that they never saw a man fight as did Arthur, considering the blood he lost; so all were very sorry for him; but the brothers would not agree, and the battle continued.

At length Sir Arthur withdrew to rest a little, and Sir Accolon called him to the fight, saying, "It is no time for me to give you rest." Therewith he came fiercely upon King Arthur, and he, being wroth for all the blood he had lost, smote Accolon again so mightily that his sword broke in his hand.

When Arthur saw this, he was in great fear to die; but he held up his shield, and lost no ground, nor bated any cheer.

CHAPTER V

HOW ARTHUR RECOVERED HIS OWN SWORD EXCALIBUR, AND
HOW ACCOLON CONFESSED THE TREASON OF MORGAN LE FAY
TOWARDS THE KING

SIR ACCOLON then summoned King Arthur to yield
him. "Knight," said he, "thou art overcome, and mayest
not endure, yet thou hast lost so much blood, I am loth to slay
thee: yield thee, therefore, as recreant."

"Nay," replied Arthur, "I may not do so, for I have
promised to sustain this battle by my body while life lasteth,
and I would rather die with honour than live with shame.
Though I lack weapon, I shall lack no worship, and if thou
slayest me weaponless, it shall be to thy shame."

"As for the shame," replied Accolon, "I will not spare: so
keep thyself, for thou art but a dead man."

Therewith the fight recommenced, and Accolon struck
King Arthur nearly to the earth; but Sir Arthur pressed up
close under cover of his shield, and dealt Sir Accolon a tre-
mendous stroke, which made him fall three paces back from
the King, for he struck hard with the pommel of the sword.

Now, when the damsel, the Lady of the Lake, perceived
how Arthur fought, and how bravely he sustained all his
wounds, she had great pity for him, and was moved to assist
him by her enchantment. So when Sir Accolon again advanced and dealt a blow at the King, the sword Excalibur
flew out of his hand, and the King at once leaped upon it,
and found it was indeed his own sword.

"Thou hast been away from me too long," he cried, "and
much damage hast thou done me." Then espying the scabbard
by the side of Sir Accolon, he darted upon him, and threw it
as far away as he could, so Sir Accolon's blood was no longer
staunched by the enchantment of it.

"O knight," said King Arthur, "this day you have done me great damage by this sword, now are you come unto your death, for I will warrant you ye will be well rewarded with this sword ere we depart, as thou hast rewarded me, for much pain have ye made me endure, and much blood have I lost."

Therewith Sir Arthur rushed upon him, and pulled him to the earth. Then taking off his enemy's helm, he dealt him such a buffet that the blood flowed from his ears, and mouth, and nose.

"Now will I slay thee," cried Arthur.

"Slay me ye well may," replied Sir Accolon, "for ye are the best knight that ever I found, and I see well God is with you. But as I promised to do my might in this battle, therefore I will never yield with my mouth, let God do with my body what He will."

Then, considering, Sir Arthur remembered him, and thought he had seen him somewhere before.

"Tell me," he cried, "or I will slay thee, of what country art thou, and of what Court?"

"Sir Knight," replied Sir Accolon, "I am of the Court of King Arthur, and my name is Accolon of Gaul."

Then was Arthur sore dismayed, for he remembered the treachery of his sister, Morgan le Fay, and her enchantment of the ship.

"O Sir Knight," cried he, "tell me who gave you this sword, and by whom you had it?"

"Woe unto the sword," exclaimed Sir Accolon, "for by it I have got my death."

"That may well be," replied the King.

"Now, sir," said Sir Accolon, "I will tell you. This sword has been in my keeping the most part of this twelvemonth, and Morgan le Fay, the wife of King Uriens, sent it to me yesterday by a dwarf to the intent that I should slay her brother Arthur. For ye must understand she hateth her brother most of any in the world, because he is of most worship and prowess, and she would slay her husband and make me King, and would be my Queen. But all that is done now," continued Sir Accolon, "for I am as dead."

"So ye would have been King?" said Arthur. "It would have been great pity to have destroyed your lord Arthur."

"It is truth," said Sir Accolon. "I have told it to you: now, therefore, I pray you tell me whence you are, and of what Court?"

"O Accolon, I would have thee know that I am King Arthur, to whom thou hast done so great damage."

When Accolon heard that he cried aloud, "Fair lord, have mercy on me, for I knew you not."

"Sir Accolon," replied the King, "mercy shalt thou have, because I feel by your words ye knew not my person. But I understand also that thou hast consented unto my death and therefore thou art a traitor. But I blame thee less than my sister Morgan le Fay, and I shall be sore avenged upon her, an I live, so that all Christendom shall hear of it. God knoweth I have honoured her and worshipped her more than all my kin, and have trusted her more than my own wife."

Then Sir Arthur called the keepers of the field, and said unto them, "Come hither, for here are we two knights that have fought and done great damage unto each other; but had either of us known the other, there had been no damage nor blow stricken."

Sir Accolon then cried aloud to all the knights and people assembled, and said, "O lords, this noble knight that I have fought withal, the which it me sore repenteth, is the man of most worship, manhood, and prowess in the world, for he is himself King Arthur our liege lord. With mishap and misadventure have I done battle with the King and lord that I am beholden withal."

Then all the people fell down upon their knees, and cried King Arthur mercy.

CHAPTER VI

HOW ARTHUR ACCORDED THE TWO BRETHREN; HOW HE DELIVERED THE TWENTY KNIGHTS; AND OF THE DEATH OF SIR ACCOLON

THEN said Arthur, "Mercy shall ye have. Hereby ye may see what adventures errant knights may have, and now have I fought with a knight of my own Court to my great damage and his hurt. But, sirs, because I am so wounded with him, and have need of rest, ye shall understand the opinion betwixt these two brethren.

"As for thee, Sir Damas, for whom I have been champion and won the field, I will judge, because ye are called an orgulous knight, and full of villainy, and of no prowess of your deeds. Therefore will I give to your brother all the whole manor, with this condition only, that Sir Ontzlake hold the manor of you, and yearly give you a palfrey to ride upon, which will become you better than a courser.

"Also I charge thee, Sir Damas, on peril of thy death, never distress any knight-errants who ride past upon their adventures. And also that thou restore these twenty knights that thou hast long kept prisoners, of all their harness, that they may be content for; and if any of them come to my Court and complain of thee, by my head you shall die therefor.

"Sir Ontzlake, as for you, being a gentle and good knight, and full of prowess, this shall be your charge. I will give you that in all reasonable haste you come to me at my Court, and ye shall be knight of mine; and according to your deeds ye shall have preferment, so that in time you shall live as worshipfully as your brother Sir Damas."

Sir Ontzlake then thanked the King for his bounty, saying he would ever hold himself at his commandment. "For," said he, "sir, I was hurt but lately by an adventurous knight through my thighs, which injured me sore, else would I have done battle with you."

"I would you had," replied King Arthur; "for then had I not been hurt as I am—because in that case my sword would not have been stolen from me by treason; and by this battle I was intended to be slain by enchantment."

"Alas! it were a pity that any man or woman should work treason against you—such a knight of prowess as you are," said Sir Ontzlake.

"I will well reward them," replied King Arthur. "Now tell me, how far am I from Camelot?"

"Sir, ye are two days' journey therefrom."

"Then would I were at some place where I could rest," said Arthur.

Upon this Sir Ontzlake indicated an abbey of nuns at which the King might find shelter and attendance on account of his wounds. Then Arthur took leave of all the people, and with Sir Accolon he went to the abbey, where he was received, and leeches provided for the healing of his hurts and Sir Accolon's. But Sir Accolon died in four days, for he had bled very much, while King Arthur was healed.

When it was seen that Sir Accolon was dead, the King commanded that they should put the body in a horse-litter, and bear it to Morgan le Fay, "and tell her," said Arthur, "I send him as a present; but I have now my sword Excalibur, and my scabbard."

So the messengers departed with the body to Morgan le Fay.

CHAPTER VII

HOW MORGAN LE FAY TRIED TO SLAY HER HUSBAND, AND HOW SIR UWAINE, HER SON, SAVED HIM; HOW SHE MADE GREAT SORROW FOR THE DEATH OF SIR ACCOLON, AND STOLE THE SCABBARD FROM ARTHUR

MORGAN LE FAY made certain that Arthur was dead by the deed of enchantment she had done, and one day she espied her husband, King Uriens, sleeping, and said to one of her maidens, "Go, fetch my lord's sword, for I never saw a better time to slay him than now."

"Oh, madam!" said the damsel, "can ye slay my lord? You will never escape."

"Care not you," replied the Queen. "Now I perceive the time in which to do it; so hie thee fast, and fetch the sword."

Then the damsel departed, and finding Sir Uwaine was sleeping, she went unto him and waked him, saying, "Arise quickly, for my lady your mother would slay my lord your father, sleeping, and I am now going to fetch the sword."

"Go your way," said Sir Uwaine, "and let me deal with this matter."

So he arose, while the damsel departed to find the sword, and she brought it trembling to Morgan le Fay, who took the sword very lightly, and went boldly unto the bedside. She was about to smite the King her husband, when Uwaine leaped upon her and caught her hand.

"Fiend!" said he, "what wouldst thou do? Wert thou not my mother I would smite off thy head myself. Ah!" he continued, "people say that Merlin was begotten of a devil—surely an earthly devil bare me."

"Oh, fair sir!" exclaimed Morgan le Fay, "have mercy upon me. I was tempted by a devil, and cry thee mercy. I will never attempt such a thing more; save my worship, and betray me not."

"On this understanding," said Sir Uwaine, "I will forgive it you: so ye never be about to do such deeds again."

"Nay, son," she exclaimed; "of that I make you assurance."

Soon after these things came the message that Sir Accolon was dead, and his body was borne into the church; and Morgan le Fay was told how Arthur had gotten his sword again. The Queen was very sad when she heard of the failure of her crafts, and she begged permission of Guenever to ride a space into the country.

"Ye should abide," said Guenever, "until your brother the King comes home."

"I may not," replied Morgan le Fay; "for I have such hasty tidings, that I must not tarry."

"Well," said Guenever, "you may depart when you will."

Then Morgan hastened away at daybreak; and after riding all day and all the night, she came at last to the abbey where the King was lodged. Knowing he was there, she asked where he was, and they said he was asleep in his bed, having had but little rest for three nights.

"Well," said she, "I charge ye, none of you awake him until I do."

Then she alighted from her horse, and had it in her mind to steal away Excalibur, his sword; so she went straight into his chamber—for no one durst disobey her commandment. There she found Arthur sleeping, and Excalibur unsheathed in his hand. But Morgan wished he was dead, but she could not take the sword for fear of waking him; but she took the scabbard, and went her way on horseback.

When the King awoke he missed his scabbard, and was wroth, and demanded who had been there. Then they told him how Morgan le Fay had come in, and had put the scabbard under her mantle and departed.

"Alas!" cried Arthur, "falsely have ye watched me."

"Sir," they all said, "we durst not disobey your sister's commands"

"Fetch me the best horse ye can find," said the King, "and bid Sir Ontzlake arm him in all haste, and ride with me."

So anon the King and the good knight rode after the lady, and finding a poor man, they asked him had he seen the lady riding by.

"Sir," replied the man, "right late came a lady riding with forty horses, and to yonder forest she rode."

Then the King and Sir Ontzlake spurred their horses, and at length caught sight of Morgan le Fay. So they chased her with all their might. When she espied the King coming after her she rode faster across the plain, but finding she could not escape, she rode into a lake, and threw the scabbard into the water, saying, "Whatever becomes of me, my brother shall not have the scabbard." Then, the scabbard being thrown into the deepest part of the lake, it sank and disappeared.

Then Morgan rode with her following into a valley, where were many great stones, and when she perceived she must be overtaken, she by enchantment turned herself and her attendants into stones also. Anon, when King Arthur and the knight appeared, they did not know his sister or her men, or one knight from another.

"Ah," said the King, "here ye may see the vengeance of God; and now am I sorry this adventure has befallen."

Afterwards he and Sir Ontzlake sought for the scabbard, but could not find it. So they returned to the abbey; and when Arthur and Sir Ontzlake had departed, Morgan le Fay turned herself and her company back again, saying, "Sirs, now we may go where we will."

CHAPTER VIII

HOW MORGAN LE FAY SAVED A KNIGHT FROM DROWNING;
HOW KING ARTHUR RETURNED HOME; AND OF THE DAMSEL
OF THE LAKE WHO SAVED HIM FROM A MANTLE THAT WOULD
HAVE BURNT HIM

AS MORGAN LE FAY rode with her attendants, she met
a knight leading another bound hand and foot and blind-
fold, seated on his horse, for he was about to drown him in a
fountain. When the Queen saw the knight she asked his cap-
tor what he intended to do with the other knight.

"Lady," said he, "I will drown him."

"For what cause?" inquired Morgan le Fay.

And he told her how he had been false to him; but the
Queen said it were pity to drown him, and inquired of the
knight whether the accusation were true.

"Nay, madam," he said, "it is false of him. He saith not
right of me."

"Whence come ye?" said the Queen Morgan, "and of what
country?"

"I come from Arthur's Court," he replied, "and my name
is Manassen, cousin to Sir Accolon of Gaul."

"Ye say well," she replied, "and for love of Sir Accolon
I will release you, and ye shall have your enemy in the same
plight."

So Manassen was loosed, and the other knight bound hand
and foot. Anon, Manassen unarmed him, and arming himself
in his harness, mounted on horseback, with the knight before
him, and threw him into the fountain and drowned him. Then
he rode after Morgan again, and asked her if he could do anything for her with King Arthur.

"Tell him," replied Morgan, "that I have rescued thee, not
for love of him, but in memory of Accolon; and that I fear

him not so long as I have the power to turn myself and my men into stone when I please; and let him wit I can do much more when the time comes."

So she departed into the country of Gore, and was richly received. She made all her castles and towers passing strong, for she had fear of King Arthur.

Meantime the King had been resting himself at the abbey, and when he was well he rode on to Camelot, where the Queen and his barons welcomed him gladly. When they had heard of his adventures, and of the treachery of Morgan le Fay, they were wroth, and some of the knights wanted her burnt. Then Manassen arrived at the Court, and told the King his adventure.

"Well," said the King, "she *is* a kind sister! but I shall be avenged upon her, and, as I live, all Christendom shall speak of it."

It happened the very next morning that a damsel brought from Morgan le Fay to the King a present of the richest mantle that ever was seen in that Court, for it was set full of the most precious stones that ever the King had beheld. The damsel said, "Your sister sendeth you this mantle, and desireth you should take it as a gift of her; and in what manner she hath offended you, she will make amends at your own pleasure."

When the King beheld the mantle it pleased him very much, but withal he said but little. And as he was considering what it might mean, there came the Lady of the Lake and desired to speak with him in private.

"Say on," said the King, "what ye will."

"Sir," said the damsel, "put not on that mantle till ye have seen more; and in nowise permit yourself nor any of your knights to put it on until the bringer thereof hath first worn it."

"Well," said Arthur, "it shall be done as ye counsel me."

Then said he unto the damsel who had come to him from his sister, "Damsel, this mantle which ye have brought I will see it upon you."

"Sir," she replied, "it will not beseem me to wear a King's garment."

"By my head," said Arthur, "ye shall wear it before it come on my back, or on any man here."

So the King forced her to put it on; and forthwith she fell down dead. She never spake after, but burnt to cinders!

Then was the King terribly wroth, more than ever he had been, and said unto King Uriens, "My sister, your wife, is always ready to betray me; and well I wot that either you or my nephew is in her counsel with me to have me destroyed. As for you, I think you are of my mind, when I deem not greatly that ye be of her counsel, for Accolon told me that she would have you destroyed, as well as me. But as for Sir Uwaine, your son, I hold him suspected, therefore I charge you put him out of my Court."

In this manner was Sir Uwaine dismissed; and when Sir Gawaine understood it, he said he would go with him. "For," said he, "whoso banisheth my cousin-german, banisheth me."

So they departed, and reached a forest, wherein was an abbey of monks, where they were well lodged. And when the King heard that Sir Gawaine had departed, there was great sorrow among all the estates.

"Now," said Gaheris Gawaine's brother, "we have lost two good knights for the love of one."

In the morning the travellers heard mass in the abbey, and rode on again until they became aware of a castle and of two knights armed on horseback, but the damsels went to and fro by a tree. And when the damsels came to a white shield that was hanging upon the tree, they spat upon it, and some threw mire upon it, which made Sir Gawaine marvel.

CHAPTER IX

HOW SIR GAWAINE AND UWAINE MET TWELVE DAMSELS WHO COMPLAINED OF SIR MARHAUS, AND HOW HE OVERTHREW BOTH THE KNIGHTS

SIR GAWAINE and Sir Uwaine wondered why the damsels treated the shield so, and riding up, they saluted them and inquired why they did so.

"Sirs," said the damsels, "there is a knight in this country who owneth a white shield—a passing good man—but he hateth all ladies and gentlewomen, therefore do we despise his shield."

"It ill becometh a knight to despise all gentlewomen," said Sir Gawaine, "and peradventure he hath some cause. He loveth and is beloved in another place, if he be such a man of prowess. What is his name?"

"His name is Marhaus, the son of the King of Ireland."

"I know him well," said Sir Uwaine; "he is as passing good knight as any on live, for I saw him proved, and none could then withstand him."

"Ah, damsels," said Sir Gawaine, "I think ye are to blame, for if he hung that shield there he will not be long away from it; and for my part I should not remain to see any knight's shield so dishonoured."

Therewith the knights departed, and at a little distance they met with Sir Marhaus; and when the damsels caught sight of him they ran away into the turret as fast as they could go, and so quickly that some of them fell by the way.

Then one of the Knights of the Tower made him ready, and called upon Sir Marhaus to defend himself. So they ran together, and the knight's spear brake upon Sir Marhaus, who smote the knight so hard that he brake his neck and his horse's back. Then the other knight came forward, and they met together so eagerly that the Knight of the Turret was quickly smitten to the earth, and rolled over, horse and man stark dead together.

Sir Marhaus then rode up to his shield, and perceived how it had been despoiled, and he said, "Of their despite I am in part avenged, but for her love that gave me this white shield I will wear thee, and hang mine where thou wast." So he hanged it about his neck. Then espying Sir Gawaine and Sir Uwaine, he asked what brought them there.

They told him; and then said Marhaus, "Here am I ready to fulfil any adventure that ye will desire." So they separated to pitch the range.

"Let him go," said Sir Uwaine to his cousin; "he is a passing good knight, and I have no desire to match with him."

"Nay," said Sir Gawaine; "it were a shame he were not assayed."

"Well, then," said Sir Uwaine, "I am weaker than you. Let me assay first, and if he smite me down you can avenge me."

So Sir Marhaus and Sir Uwaine came together with great violence, and Sir Uwaine smote his enemy upon the shield with such violence that it brake in pieces, and Sir Marhaus smote him so that he bare him and his horse to the ground.

Then Sir Marhaus turned his horse, and he and Sir Gawaine assayed; and his spear also brake, but he leaped down and drew his sword. When Sir Marhaus saw that, he did likewise, and came upon Sir Gawaine on horseback; thereupon he cried out, "Sir Knight, alight, or I will slay thine horse."

"Gramercy! ye teach me courtesy," said Sir Marhaus; "for it is not for one knight to be on horseback when the other is on foot."

So he alighted, and they attacked each other fiercely, so that their shields flew in cantels, and they bruised their helms and gashed their hauberks, wounding each other sorely. But Sir Gawaine—as it was past nine of the clock—waxed stronger and stronger, till noon; and thrice his might was increased. Sir Marhaus perceived this and wondered at it; but they continued their battle past noon. And towards evensong Sir Gawaine began to feel faint, while Sir Marhaus increased.

"Sir Knight," said the latter, "I have felt well ye are a passing good man, and as marvellous man of might as any. Our quarrels are not great, and I am loth to do you any hurt, for I feel ye are very feeble."

"Ah, gentle knight! ye say the word I would say."

Therefore they took off their helms and kissed each other, swearing to be true as brethren.

Then Sir Marhaus begged Sir Gawaine to remain with him that night, and Sir Uwaine also; so they accompanied him. And as they rode to his house Sir Gawaine said,—

"I marvel, Sir Knight, that so valiant a man as you loves no ladies nor damsels."

"Sir," replied Sir Marhaus, "they say wrongfully who give me such a name; but I wit the damsels in the turret have told you so. Now I hate them because they are sorceresses and enchanters, and be a knight never so brave they will make a coward of him; and this is the principal cause I hate them. To all good ladies I owe knightly service."

They now came to Sir Marhaus's house, which was a little priory; and there ladies and damsels came out and unarmed them, looking also to their hurts, for they were all wounded. So they had good lodging with Sir Marhaus and good cheer, for when he knew they were King Arthur's sisters' sons, he did all that lay in his power. There they sojourned seven days, until they were well eased of their wounds, and at last they made ready for departure.

"Now," said Sir Marhaus, "we will not part so lightly, for I will bring ye through the forest."

So they rode together for some days, but without meeting any adventure. At last they came to a great forest in the country of Arroy—a place of strange adventures.

"In this country," said Sir Marhaus, "came never knight, since it was christened, without meeting strange adventure."

So they rode on, and after awhile they came to a place where was a stream of water and a fountain, and three damsels sitting thereby. Then they rode to them, and either saluted the other.

The oldest of these damsels had a garland of gold about her head; and she was threescore winter of age or more, and her hair was white under the garland. The second damsel was of thirty winter of age, with a circlet of gold about her head; and the third was about fifteen years, with a garland of flowers about her head. When the knights had beheld them, they asked the cause why they sat at the fountain.

"We be here," said the damsels, "to see any knights-errant, and to lead them to strange adventures. Ye be three knights that seek adventures; we be three damsels. Therefore you must each choose one of us. And when ye have done so, we will lead you by three highways, and each shall choose a way, and his damsel with him. And this day twelvemonth ye must meet here again, and God send ye your lives. Now thereto ye must plight your troth."

"That is well said," replied Sir Marhaus; "now shall each of us choose a damsel."

CHAPTER X

HOW THE THREE KNIGHTS CHOSE EACH A DAMSEL, AND OF THE ADVENTURES OF SIR GAWAINE

I WILL tell you," said Sir Uwaine, "what we shall do. I am the youngest and the weakest of all, and therefore I will have the eldest damsel, for she hath seen much, and can help me in my need."

"Very well," said Sir Marhaus, "then I will have the damsel of thirty years, for she falleth best to me."

"I thank you both," said Sir Gawaine, "that you have left me the youngest damsel, and the fairest, for she is most welcome to me."

Then every damsel took the bridle-rein of her knight and brought them to the cross roads, and there they made oaths to return to the fountain that day twelvemonth an they were alive. So they kissed and departed, every knight setting his lady behind him. Sir Uwaine took the westward road, Sir Marhaus the south, and Gawaine took the road that lay north, and him we follow first.

Sir Gawaine held his way until he came to a fair manor, where lived a good old knight, and Sir Gawaine asked him if there were any adventures in the country.

"I shall show you some marvels in the morn," replied the old knight. Accordingly in the morning they rode forth, and reached a place where was a cross on a lawn, and there there came a seemly and comely knight, who made great dole. He saluted Sir Gawaine, and prayed God to send him worship; Sir Gawaine thanked him, and returned the good wish.

"Ah," said the knight, "I may lay that aside, for sorrow and shame cometh to me after worship."

So saying, he passed to the other side of the lawn, and there Sir Gawaine saw ten knights, who made ready their spears against the one knight who spoke to Sir Gawaine. Then one of them adventured against him, and the woeful knight smote him, so that he fell over his horse's tail. Thus did the same dolorous knight to them all as they came before him, and all with one spear. Then when they were all apart they went to the dolorous knight, and bound him securely under his horse's belly, and led him with them.

"Oh!" said Sir Gawaine, "this is a doleful sight, to see yonder knight so entreated; and it seemeth that he suffereth them to bind him so, and maketh no resistance."

"No," said the host. "That is truth."

"Sir," said the damsel unto Sir Gawaine, "it seemeth it were to your worship that you went to the assistance of the dolorous knight, for he is one of the best knights I ever saw."

"I would," replied Sir Gawaine, "only it seemeth to me he will have no help."

"Yes," said the damsel; "and ye have no desire to help him."

As they were speaking thus a knight appeared at the other side of the lawn, armed,—all save his head; and there came also a dwarf, with a great mouth and short nose, riding, and also armed, all save his head. And when the dwarf came near he said, "Where is the lady which should meet us here?" And forthwith she came out of the wood, and immediately the knight and the dwarf strove for her. But at length they agreed to allow Sir Gawaine to decide between them, and then they told him why they strove.

"Well, sirs," said he, "will ye put the matter into my hand?"

"Yes," said they.

"Now, damsel," said Sir Gawaine, "ye shall stand betwixt them, and whichever ye list better to go to he shall have you."

And when she was set between them both she went to the dwarf. Then the dwarf took her away singing, and the knight went his way with great mourning. Soon there appeared two other knights, who came on to attack Sir Gawaine; so one of them made ready, and he and Sir Gawaine met, and both fell. Then they addressed them with their swords, and fought full actually.

While they were engaged the other knight came to the young damsel, and said to her, "Why remain you with yonder knight? If ye abide with me, I will be your faithful defender."

"And with you I will be," said the damsel, "for I cannot find it in my heart to be with him; for now here was one knight who discomfited ten knights, and at the last he was cowardly led away, and Sir Gawaine helped him not. Therefore let us two go our way while they fight."

Sir Gawaine fought long with the other knight; but at last they accorded both, and the knight prayed Gawaine to lodge with him that night; and as they proceeded, Sir Gawaine inquired what knight he was who permitted himself to be taken prisoner by the others, after having done so manfully.

"Ah," said the knight, "he is the manfullest I know, and yet hath been served so ten times. His name is Sir Pelleas, and he loveth a great lady in this country whose name is Ettard. And at the jousts she gave he bore down all knights for her sake, and won the prize, which he bestowed upon the Lady Ettard, and chose her for his sovereign lady. But she is so proud, she has scorn of him, and said she would never love him, though he will die for her. Wherefore all had scorn of her, she was so proud, for there are fairer than she; but there were none to whom Sir Pelleas would proffer love, though they would have loved him for his noble conduct. He will never leave her, and comes hither after her; but she sends knights to fight him, whom he vanquishes, and then he permits himself to be taken prisoner only for a sight of the lady. But she always does him great despite, for she hath him tied sometimes to the horse's tail, and sometimes under its belly, and is carried to her in the shamefullest manner.

"Yet all this doth not cure him; she cannot make him leave the country; and had he found the ten knights on foot as well as on horseback, he would equally have had the better of them."

"Alas!" said Sir Gawaine, "it is a great pity. I will seek him to-morrow, and do him what help I can."

So next day they met with each other, and the sorrowful knight told him all as he had heard, when Sir Gawaine promised to get him the love of his lady, and told him who he was, and swore he would not betray him. This did Sir Gawaine treacherously. And he said, "I will take your horse and armour, and tell her I have slain you; and when I have gained her confidence I will do all I can on my part, that ye shall not fail to have the true love of her."

It came to pass, however, that Sir Gawaine, when he had told his tale, persuaded the Lady Ettard to love him, and to promise to be his wife. When Sir Pelleas heard this he was exceedingly wroth, and would have slain them both, but the Lady of the Lake, Nimue, met with an attendant of Sir Pelleas, and said,—

"Bring me to your master, and I will warrant his life; he shall not die of love. She that caused him all this sorrow shall be in an evil plight ere long, for she had no mercy upon so valiant a knight."

Anon that knight brought her to Sir Pelleas, and when she beheld him she had never seen so valiant a knight, she thought, and she threw an enchantment upon him till he fell asleep. Then she rode to the Lady Ettard, charging them not to wake the knight until she came again. So she returned with the lady, and told her she ought to have been ashamed to wrong so good a knight. Thereupon the Lady of the Lake threw an enchantment upon Ettard, so that she fell violently in love with Sir Pelleas; and she said, "Woe is me! that now I love the man I most hated in the world."

Soon Sir Pelleas awaked, and when he beheld Ettard he hated her more than any woman alive. "Away, traitress!" said he, "come never in my sight."

And when she heard him say so she wept, and made great sorrow out of measure.

But the Lady of the Lake said, "Sir Knight Pelleas, take your horse and come forth with me out of this country, and I will show you a damsel that shall love you."

"I will well," said Sir Pelleas, "for this Lady Ettard hath done me great despite and shame."

Then he told her all, and how he had been betrayed by Sir Gawaine. "And now," he said, "I hate her as much as I before loved her."

"Thank me," said the Damsel of the Lake.

Anon Sir Pelleas armed him, took his horse, and commanded his men to bring his pavilions and stuff where the Lady of the Lake might assign. So the Lady Ettard died for sorrow, and the Damsel of the Lake led Sir Pelleas to the Court of King Arthur, by the Feast of Pentecost.

CHAPTER XI

HOW SIR MARHAUS PROSPERED, AND CAME TO THE DUKE OF THE SOUTH MARCHES; HOW HE CONQUERED HIM AND HIS SIX SONS

WE MUST now turn our attention to the adventures of Sir Marhaus, who rode with the damsel of thirty years of age by the south way. The pair continued their journey until they also reached a deep forest, and became benighted; so they were compelled to ask for shelter from a man in a courtelage, who would not lodge them for any consideration whatever. "But," said he, "if ye will take adventure of your lodging, I will lead you where ye may find it."

"What adventure," said Sir Marhaus, "shall I have to do for my lodging?"

"Ye shall know when ye get there," replied the man.

"No matter for the adventure," said Sir Marhaus; "bring me thither, I pray you, for this damsel and I are faint and weary, and my horse is tired."

So the man led them away, and anon they came to a castle. Then he called to the porter, and was admitted. So he told the lord of the castle how a knight-errant and a damsel desired to be lodged there.

"Let him in," said the lord of the castle. "It may event that they will repent having sought lodging here."

So Sir Marhaus was admitted by torchlight, and was welcomed by a number of goodly young men. His horse was led to the stable, while he and the damsel were admitted to the presence of the mighty duke who ruled in the castle. Then he inquired his name, whence he came, and with whom he dwelt.

"Sir," replied Sir Marhaus, "I am a knight of King Arthur's and of the Table Round. My name is Sir Marhaus, and I was born in Ireland."

"Then," said the Duke, "I repent me sore, for I love not thy lord, nor thy fellows of the Table Round. So, therefore, rest thyself this night as thou mayest; but to-morrow I and my six sons shall match thee."

"Is there no remedy?" said Sir Marhaus; "must I match myself with thee and thy six sons at once?"

"There is no remedy," replied the duke. "For this cause I made a vow, because Sir Gawaine slew my seven sons in an encounter, I would never lodge a knight of King Arthur's Court, but I would have to do with him, to have the revenging of my sons' death."

"What is your name?" inquired Sir Marhaus. "I require you to tell me, if it so please you."

"Wit ye well that I am the Duke of the South Marches," he replied.

"Shall I have to do with you?" inquired Sir Marhaus. "I have heard that you are a great foe to Arthur and his knights."

"Yea," said the duke; "you will feel that in the morn. Wherefore hie you to your chamber, and ye shall have all that is needful."

So Sir Marhaus was led unto his chamber, and the damsel unto hers. And in the morn the duke sent unto Sir Marhaus, and bade him make ready; so the knight arose and armed him. Then there was mass said before him; and when he had broken his fast he mounted on horseback in the court of the castle where they were to do battle.

There the duke was already on horseback, armed, and his six sons by him—each had a spear in his hand. So they encountered him, when the duke and his sons brake their spears upon Sir Marhaus, but he touched none of them.

After this came four of the duke's sons in couples, and they all brake their spears upon Sir Marhaus, while he touched them not. But then he ran at the duke and smote him with his spear, so that horse and man fell to the earth; and likewise he served his sons. Then Sir Marhaus alighted, and would have the duke yield or he would slay him; but some of the sons recovered, and were about to set upon Sir Marhaus, who said to the duke,—

"Cease thy sons, or I will do my uttermost to you all."

So the duke, seeing the plight he was in, cried to his sons to yield them to Sir Marhaus, and they all kneeled down and put the pommels of their swords to the knight, and he received them. Then they helped their father up, and promised never to be enemies unto King Arthur, and to come at Whitsuntide and accept the King's grace.

After this Sir Marhaus departed, and the damsel led him to a great tournament which had been proclaimed by the Lady de Vawse. He that did the best was to have a rich circlet of gold worth a thousand bezants. In this tournament Sir Marhaus did so nobly that he bore down forty knights, and the circlet of gold was awarded to him. So he departed with great honour.

Again, within seven nights, the damsel led him to the place of Earl Fergus, that after was Sir Tristram's knight. This young earl had only of late come to his lands; and there was a giant fast by him called Taulurd, who had a brother in Cornwall named Taulas, whom Sir Tristram slew when out of his mind. This earl made a complaint to Sir Marhaus that there was near by him a giant that destroyed his lands, and the earl said he was afraid to ride far for fear of him.

"Doth he ride on horseback or go afoot?" said Sir Marhaus.

"There is no horse that can bear him," replied the earl.

"Well, then," said Sir Marhaus, "I will go to him on foot and fight with him."

So on the morrow Sir Marhaus caused one of the earl's men to lead him where the giant was; and the knight perceived the giant sitting under a tree of holly, with many iron clubs around him. Then Sir Marhaus prepared for the battle, and put his shield before him; but the giant, at the first onset, clave the shield into two pieces, so the knight was in great danger, for the giant was a wily fighter. But after a while Sir

Marhaus managed to strike off the giant's right arm above the elbow; and then the giant fled into a pool of water, and the knight followed him as far as he could. But the giant being so tall, Sir Marhaus could not wade far enough to reach him, as the water was deep.

So Sir Marhaus made the attendant, who had shown him the way, fetch a number of great stones, and with these weapons the knight gave the giant many sore knocks, till at last he fell down in the water and died.

Then Sir Marhaus went into the giant's castle and delivered twelve knights and twenty-four ladies out of their prison, and found in the castle great riches, so that he was never again a poor man all the rest of his life. So Sir Marhaus returned to Earl Fergus, who would have given him half his land, but the knight would none of it, and at length he took his leave.

As he proceeded on his journey he met Sir Gawaine and Sir Uwaine, and also four other knights of King Arthur's Court, and overcame them all four. So he departed to meet at his day aforeset.

CHAPTER XII

THE ADVENTURES OF SIR UWAINE; HOW HE WON THE PRIZE AT THE TOURNEYING, AND FOUGHT TWO KNIGHTS

SIR UWAINE and the damsel of threescore winters rode on westward together, and in time she brought him to a place where a tournament was holden, nigh the Marches of Wales. At that tournament Sir Uwaine smote down thirty knights, and won the prize, which was a ger-falcon, and a white steed trapped with cloth of gold.

Then, by the means of the old damsel his companion, Sir Uwaine did many bold deeds, and had strange adventures, until she led him unto a lady called the Lady of the Rock, who was very courteous. There were in that country two knights, brothers, called the Two Perilous Knights, the one knight, Sir Edward of the Red Castle, the other, Sir Hue of the Red Castle; these two had disinherited the Lady of the Rock of a barony of lands by their extortion.

As Sir Uwaine was lodged with the lady, she naturally complained to him of the conduct of the two knights.

"Madam," said Sir Uwaine, "they are to blame, for they do against the high order of knighthood, and the oath that they made, and if it like you I will speak with them, because I am a knight of King Arthur's. I will entreat them with fairness; and if they will not, I will do battle with them in defence of your rights."

"Gramercy," said the lady; "and if I cannot requite you, God will."

In the morn the two knights were sent for, so that they should come and speak with the Lady of the Rock. They failed not, for they came with a hundred horse. But when the lady saw them come thus escorted and in so big a manner, she would not suffer Sir Uwaine to go out to speak to them, but made him address them from a tower.

Finally, the two brethren would not be entreated, answering the knight that they would keep what they had.

"Well," said Sir Uwaine, "then I will fight with one of you, and prove that ye do this lady wrong."

"That will we not," replied the brothers. "When we do battle, we both fight at the same time with one knight; therefore, if ye will so fight, we will be ready at what hour ye may assign. If ye win the battle, the lady shall have her lands again."

"Ye say well," replied Sir Uwaine; "so make ye ready, that ye be here to-morn, in defence of the lady's right."

Thus the agreement was made by both parties, and that no treason should be wrought by either party. Then the knights departed, and made them ready, and that evening Sir Uwaine made great cheer. On the morn he rose and heard mass; and when he had broken his fast, he rode out into the plain without the gates, where he found the two brethren awaiting him.

Then they rode together passing sore, and in the encounter Sir Edward and Sir Hue brake their spears against Sir Uwaine, and he smote Sir Edward so sore that he fell over his horse; yet Sir Uwaine's spear brake not. Then he spurred his horse and came upon Sir Hue, and likewise overthrew him; but they both soon recovered, and dressing their shields, drew their swords, and bade Sir Uwaine alight and do battle to the uttermost.

Sir Uwaine suddenly dismounted, put his shield afore him, and they all engaged, and gave each such strokes, while the brethren wounded Sir Uwaine very grievously, and the Lady of the Rock thought he would have died. Thus for five hours they encountered, as men enraged out of all reason.

At last Sir Uwaine smote Sir Edward upon the helm, so that the sword clave his collar-bone, and he fell. Then Sir Hue abated his courage; and Sir Uwaine would have slain him, had he not begged for mercy and yielded to Sir Uwaine, who of his gentleness took him by the hand and led him into the castle.

The Lady of the Rock was thereupon passing glad, but Sir Hue made great dole for his brother, who was dead. So the lady was restored all her lands, and Sir Hue was commanded to appear at King Arthur's Court at the next Feast of Pentecost. But Sir Uwaine was obliged to remain at the castle of the Lady of the Rock nigh half a year, till his wounds were healed.

And when it drew nigh the term day that Sir Gawaine, Sir Marhaus, and Sir Uwaine had to meet at the crossway, every knight came thither according to promise. Sir Marhaus and Sir Uwaine brought their damsels with them, but Sir Gawaine had lost his attendant, as already related.

CHAPTER XIII

HOW AT THE END OF THE YEAR ALL THE KNIGHTS MET AT THE FOUNTAIN

RIGHT so at the end of the twelve months the three knights and the three damsels came to meet at the fountain, but the lady who had left Sir Gawaine could say but little in his favour. The knights then departed from the damsels, and rode through the great forest, where they encountered a messenger from the Court of King Arthur, who had sought them nigh a year through England, Wales, and Scotland, to bring Sir Uwaine and Sir Gawaine unto Court again.

Then were they all glad, and prayed Sir Marhaus to ride with them to Court. So within twelve days they came to Camelot, and the King with all his Court were right glad of their coming. Then they told all their adventures, and Sir Marhaus was welcomed. By the feast of Pentecost came also Sir Pelleas and the Lady of the Lake; and there was great jousting. And Sir Pelleas was victor of all the knights at the jousts, while Sir Marhaus came next.

At the next feast they were made knights of the Table Round, as two seats were vacant. But Pelleas would never like Sir Gawaine, though he spared him for love of King Arthur. Sir Marhaus after fought with Sir Tristram, and was slain by him. Sir Pelleas ofttimes at jousts quit Sir Gawaine. Sir Pelleas was a worshipful knight, and one of the four who achieved the Sangreal; but the Lady of the Lake would never let him have to do with Launcelot du Lake, nor suffer him to engage except on the side of Sir Launcelot.

BOOK THE FIFTH

CHAPTER I

HOW AMBASSADORS CAME FROM ROME TO ARTHUR TO DEMAND TRIBUTE, AND HOW THE KING GAINED HELP AGAINST THE EMPEROR

WHEN King Arthur was resting after his wars, there came to his Court, while he was seated upon the throne at the Round Table, twelve aged men, ambassadors from Lucius Tiberius, Emperor of Rome, demanding tribute under pain of war, and requiring the restoration of all Gaul, which he had won from the tribune Flollo.

King Arthur heard the message, and when he had caused the ambassadors to withdraw, he took counsel with his knights and lords as to the reply he should send. Some of the younger knights were for slaying the ambassadors, declaring that the King had been insulted by the arrival of such messengers; but the King commanded that none should molest them.

"Though their message please me not," he said, "yet must I remember mine honour."

So the ambassadors were entertained with due worship. After this the King called the knights of the Table Round to counsel, and asked their advice. Sir Cador of Cornwall spake first, and said,—

"Sir, this message liketh me well, for we have many days rested us and been idle; and now I hope ye will make sharp war upon the Romans, when I doubt not we shall obtain much honour."

"I believe," said Arthur, "that the matter pleaseth thee well; but these answers must not be said to the Emperor. Yet his demand doth grieve me sore, for truly I will pay no truage to Rome, wherefore I pray you counsel me. I have understood that Belinus and Brenius, Kings of Britain, held the Roman Emperor in their hands many days; and also Constantine, son of Queen Helen, which is open evidence that we owe no tribute to Rome, but that I being descended from them may rightly claim the empire."

King Anguish of Scotland then spake, and said, "Sir, ye ought of right to be above all other Kings, for there is not thine equal in all Christendom, and I counsel thee never to obey the Romans. When they reigned here they grievously oppressed us, putting the land to great and heavy burdens, and for my own I swear to avenge myself when I may, and to strengthen your quarrel, I will furnish twenty thousand good men of war, and wage them at my own cost, which shall await on you when it please you."

Then the King of Little Britain rose and promised King Arthur thirty thousand men, and many others also. The Lord of West Wales, Sir Uwaine, and Sir Ider his son, Sir Launcelot, and all the other knights of the Table Round, promised assistance.

The King thanked them heartily for their goodwill, and then sent for the ambassadors to hear his answer, thus: "I will that ye now go back to your lord and Procuror of the Common Weal for the Romans, and say to him, 'Of his demand and commandment I set nothing, and I know of no truage nor tribute that I owe to him or any other earthly prince—Christian or heathen. But I pretend to have and occupy the sovereignty of the empire, wherein I am entitled by the right of my predecessors, sometime Kings of this land. I am fully and deliberately concluded to go with mine army with power and strength unto Rome, by the grace of God to take possession of the empire, and subdue them that be rebel. Wherefore, lastly, I command him and all the lords of Rome that they do me homage, and acknowledge me their Emperor, under pain of what shall ensue.' "

So Arthur dismissed the ambassadors with presents, paid all their expenses, and sent them out of the country under the care of Sir Cador. They took ship at Sandwich, and returned to Rome by Flanders, Almaine, and the mountains, until they came to Italy, and returned to Lucius.

The Emperor was much enraged when he heard the answer of Arthur, and when his ambassadors advised him to refrain—for they said, "We were all fearful at his majesty, and fearful to behold his countenance. Ye have made a rod for yourself, for he intendeth to be lord of this empire, and is another kind of man than thou supposest, and holdeth the most noble Court in the world."

Then Lucius sent messengers to all the subjects of Rome, and collected a mighty army—sixteen kings, and dukes, lords, and admirals, from Europe to India, with thousands of Spaniards. He had also fifty giants born of fiends, to guard his own person and break the front of the battle. Then he departed from Rome, and came down the mountains to destroy the lands King Arthur had conquered. He came to Cologne, and besieged a castle there, and subdued the territory Arthur had won from King Claudas. Then he advanced upon Little Britain.

CHAPTER II

HOW KING ARTHUR HELD A PARLIAMENT AT YORK; AND OF HIS MARVELLOUS DREAM, WITH ITS INTERPRETATION

MEANTIME King Arthur had holden a Parliament at York, and left the kingdom in charge of Sir Bawdwin of Britain, with Sir Constantine, son of Sir Cador of Cornwall, who, after Arthur's death, was King of the realm. Queen Guenever made great sorrow for the departure of her lord, and swooned, so that the ladies bore her to her chamber. Then the King, with the great army, departed, and embarked at Sandwich with all his following, in a great multitude of ships, galleys, cogges, and dromons, sailing on the sea.

As the King lay in his cabin in the ship he fell asleep and dreamed a marvellous dream. It seemed to him that a dreadful dragon did drown much of his people, and it came flying out of the west. His head was enamelled with azure, and his shoulders were as gold, and a hideous flame came out of his mouth. After him came from the East a grimly boar, black as a cloud, and his paws were as big as a post; he was rugged, and the most horrible beast ever conceived, and he roared and roamed so dreadfully that it was marvellous to hear. Then the terrible dragon came on flying, and gave great strokes to the boar, and the boar bit him again with his tusks till his breast was all bloody, and all the sea was red with it.

Then the dragon flew away high up, and came down with a swoop, and smote the boar all to powder, both flesh and bones, and it frittered away in the sea. Therewith the King awoke, and was sore alarmed at the dream. He sent for a wise philosopher to tell him the meaning, who said,—

"Sir, the dragon thou dreamest of betokeneth thine own person; the colours of his wings are the realms thou hast won, and his tail, which is all tattered, signifieth the Round Table.

The boar betokeneth some tyrant that tormenteth the people, or else thou art like to fight with some giant thyself, which is horrible and abominable, whose equal ye never saw in your days. Wherefore of this dreadful dream fear nothing, for thou shalt come forth conqueror."

Soon after this the ships came in sight of land, and they sailed until they arrived in Flanders; and when Arthur had landed, he found many of his lords awaiting him.

CHAPTER III

HOW A MAN OF THE COUNTRY TOLD OF A MARVELLOUS GIANT, AND HOW ARTHUR FOUGHT AND CONQUERED HIM

THEN there came to Arthur a husbandman, and told him there was in the country of Constantine a great giant, which had murdered and devoured many people of the country, and had lived on the children until they had all been slain and destroyed. "Now, lately, he hath taken the wife of thy cousin Sir Howell, and as thou art a rightful King, have pity on this lady, and revenge us all."

"Now, fellow," said King Arthur, "canst thou bring me where this giant haunteth?"

"Yea, sir," said the man; "yonder where thou seest those two fires, there shalt thou find him, and more treasure than I suppose there is in all France."

When the King had understood this, he returned to his tent, and called Sir Kay and Sir Bedivere, and commanded them secretly to make ready his horse and theirs, for at eventide he would ride with them to Saint Michael's Mount. So he armed him at all points, and took his horse and his shield. Then they departed, and rode to the foot of the Mount, where they alighted, and the King said he would himself go up into that Mount.

Accordingly he ascended the hill till he came to a great fire, when he found a widow wringing her hands and making great sorrow, sitting by a grave new made. King Arthur saluted her, and demanded wherefore she made such lamentation.

"Sir Knight," she said, "speak soft, for yonder is a devil. If he hear thee speak, he will come and destroy thee. What dost thou here in this mountain? Were ye fifty as ye be, ye were not able to make resistance against this fiend, which hath murdered the fairest lady of all the world, wife to Sir Howell, Duke of Britanny."

"Dame," replied the King, "I come from the noble conqueror Arthur to treat with that tyrant."

"Fie upon such treaty!" said the widow. "He hath no regard to the King or any man. He hath vanquished fifteen kings, and made him a coat of precious stones embroidered with their beards. If thou wilt, speak with him at yonder great fire at supper."

"Well," said Arthur, "I will accomplish my message, with all your fearful words."

So he went forth by the crest of the hill, and saw where the giant sat at supper, gnawing the limb of a man, while three damsels turned three spits, whereon were broached twelve young children, like young birds.

When King Arthur beheld this piteous sight he had great compassion, and cursing the giant, said, "Why hast thou murdered these young innocent children and this duchess? Therefore arise, and dress thee, thou glutton, for this day shalt thou die of my hand."

Then the giant started up, and taking a great club in his hand, smote at the King so that his coronal fell to the earth; but the King stabbed him, when the giant threw away his club, and catching the King in his arms, crushed his ribs. The three maidens knelt down and prayed for Arthur's success, while the combatants rolled over and over each other, and down the hill, till they came to the sea-mark. As they rolled, Arthur smote the giant with his dagger, and it fortuned they came to the place where the two knights were keeping Arthur's horse.

When they saw the King fast in the giant's arms they came and unloosed him, and the King commanded Sir Kay to smite off the giant's head and bear it to Sir Howell, and tell him that his enemy was dead.

Anon this was known through all the country, wherefore the people came and thanked the King, who said, "Give the thanks to God, and part the goods among you." After that

King Arthur commanded his cousin Howell that he should ordain for a church to be built on the same hill for the worship of St. Michael.

On the morn the King removed with his great army and came into Champagne, and in a valley they pitched their tents; but while the King was at dinner there came two messengers, of whom one was Marshal of France, and told the King that the Emperor had entered and destroyed a great part of it. He was then in Burgoyne, had destroyed and made great slaughter of people, and had burnt towns and boroughs; "wherefore," he added, "if thou come not hastily they must yield up their bodies and goods."

CHAPTER IV

HOW KING ARTHUR SENT EMBASSY TO LUCIUS; HOW THE
KNIGHTS WERE ASSAILED AND FOUGHT; OF THE PRISONERS
TAKEN, AND OF THE GREAT BATTLE WITH, AND THE DEFEAT OF,
THE EMPEROR BY KING ARTHUR

THEN the King called to Sir Gawaine, Sir Bors, Sir
Lionel, and Sir Bedivere, and commanded them to go
to the Emperor Lucius and tell him to move swiftly and in
haste out of the land, "And if he will not, bid him make ready
to battle, and not distress the poor people."

Then these noble knights set forth on horseback, and rode
on till they came to the Roman camp, with the Emperor's
pavilion in the middle, and an eagle set above it. To this tent
the knights approached, and ordained that Sir Gawaine and
Sir Bors should do the message, leaving Sir Lionel and Sir
Bedivere in ambush.

The two knights did their message, to which the Emperor
replied, "Ye may return to your lord, and tell him that I shall
subdue him and all his land."

Then Sir Gawaine was wroth, and said, "I would rather
than all France fight against thee." And Sir Bors said the
same.

And a knight named Sir Gainus, a cousin of the Emperor,
said, "Lo, how these Britons boast, and are full of pride!
bragging as though they bare up all the world."

Sir Gawaine was so grieved at these words that he pulled
out his sword, and with one blow smote off Sir Gainus' head;
and then, with Sir Bors, he turned his horse to where Sir
Lionel and Sir Bedivere were in ambush.

The Romans followed fast on horseback and on foot till
the knights turned to bay, when Sir Bors smote the foremost
of them through the body with a spear, and he fell dead to

the earth. Then came on Caliburn, one of the strongest men of Pavia, and smote bravely; but Sir Bors ran him through the breast, and he fell dead. Then Sir Feldenak thought to be revenged upon Sir Gawaine; but he smote him on the head, and the sword passed through to his breast. Then Sir Bedivere and Sir Lionel broke from their ambush, and, attacking the Romans, forced them to flee to their tents.

But the Romans gathering more force, there was a new battle, in which Sir Berel and Sir Bors were taken. When Sir Gawaine saw that, he drew his good sword Galatine and pursued those who had taken the knights. At length he smote him that led Sir Bors, and released him, while Sir Idrus rescued Sir Berel. Again the battle waged hot, and Sir Gawaine sent to Arthur for succour, which put the Romans to flight. Except Sir Gawaine, who was so hurt, no man of worship of Arthur's was lost.

This was the beginning of the first day's fighting of the Britons and Romans, when there were slain of the latter more than ten thousand; and great joy and mirth was made that night in King Arthur's camp. In the morning the King sent all his prisoners to Paris, under the guard of Sir Launcelot, with Sir Cador and many other knights.

As soon as the Emperor perceived the prisoners were to be sent to Paris, he made an ambushment of sixty thousand men to rescue them; and as on the morn Sir Launcelot and Sir Cador passed through a wood, they espied and perceived this ambush, so they returned and told Sir Launcelot of it. Then Launcelot put his men in array, and fought with them, in which battle the Romans and Saracens with them were defeated, and fled from him like sheep from the wolf.

These tidings came to King Arthur, and anon he made him ready and came out. When he saw how his knights had won the battle, he embraced them in his arms every one, and said, "Ye be worthy to bear all your honour and worship, for there was never King, save myself, who had so noble knights."

"Sir," said Cador, "there was none of us failed other, but the prowess and manhood of Sir Launcelot were more than wonder to tell; and also of his cousins, which did this day many noble feats of war."

Then Sir Cador told who of the knights had been slain, and the King wept, saying, "Your courage had near hand destroyed you: though ye had returned again, ye would have lost no worship, for I call it folly for knights to abide when they would be overmatched."

When the Emperor Lucius heard of this defeat, he rose with all his army to crush King Arthur, and met him in the vale of Sessoyne [Soissons], where he was surrounded by Arthur's troops. The Emperor addressed his men, and admonished them how Rome was chief over all the earth, and that they were not to suffer the barbarous and savage Britons to abide. At this the trumpets were blown so loud that the earth shook.

Then the forces approached, and when they closed together no tongue could tell the fury of their smiting, or the struggling and slaughter. Great strokes were smitten on both sides, many men overthrown, hurt, and slain, and great valiances, prowesses, and feats of war were that day showed, which were over long to recount the noble feats of every man, for they should contain a whole volume.

King Arthur with his bravest knights rode into the thickest of the battle. He drawing Excalibur, his sword, hewed and slew down right and left, and killed a great giant called Galapas, which was a man of huge quantity and height; so he shortened him by smiting off both his legs at the knees, and said, "Now art thou of a better size to deal with than thou wert." So saying he cut off his head, and as the body fell down it killed six men under it.

The battle continued long, and at last Arthur perceived where Lucius fought; so he rode to him, and either smote the other fiercely, till at the last Lucius smote Arthur athwart the visage, giving him a grievous wound. When Arthur felt himself hurt, he smote the Emperor again with Excalibur, so that he cleft his head down to the breast, and Lucius fell dead.

When the Romans knew that their Emperor was slain, they all took to flight, and King Arthur, with his host, followed them, slaying more than a hundred thousand in pursuit. Afterwards Arthur returned to the spot where Lucius lay dead, and found round him the Kings of Egypt and Ethiopia, and seventeen other Kings, with sixty Roman senators—all noble men.

These did King Arthur have embalmed and laid in chests of lead; upon their bodies he placed their arms and banners. After this, finding three senators alive, he said to them, "To save your lives, I will that ye carry these dead bodies unto Rome, and present them on my behalf as the tribute. Tell them I shall speedily be in Rome, and the Romans may be ware how they demand any more of me. If they are not content with these I shall pay more at my coming, for other tribute owe I none, and none other will I pay. Methinketh this sufficeth for Britain, Ireland, and all Almaine with Germany."

Laden with this charge and the dead bodies, the three senators departed. The body of Lucius was in a car all alone, and after, the bodies of the kings in chariots by pairs, and after all, the bodies of the senators. So they went towards Rome, where they showed all these things to the Senate, and advised them in no wise to move again against the noble conqueror Arthur, "to whom none earthly prince may compare."

CHAPTER V

HOW KING ARTHUR ENTERED ITALY; AND OF THE BATTLE DONE
BY SIR GAWAINE AGAINST A SARACEN, WHO YIELDED, AND
BECAME A CHRISTIAN

AFTER this King Arthur entered into Lorraine, Brabant,
and Flanders, and thence, subduing the country as he
went, he entered Germany. Thence he crossed the mountains
into Lombardy and Tuscany, where was a city that refused
to yield him, and he sat down to besiege it. But it was valiantly
defended. Then, after a long time, King Arthur called Sir
Florence, and said to him they lacked victual for the hosts.
"Not far from hence," said he, "there be great forests, wherein
are many of my enemies with much cattle. I will that thou go
thither in foraging; take with thee Sir Gawaine, Sir Wisshard, Sir Clegis, Sir Clairemonde, the Captain of Cardiff,
and others, and bring with you all the beasts you can get."

The knights made ready accordingly, and rode over holts
and hills, through forests and woods, till they came to a great
meadow, where they rested. At the dawn of day Sir Gawaine
took his horse and rode away from his fellows to seek adventure. Soon he saw a man armed, walking his horse by a wood-
side, sitting on a strong courser, without any attendant save
a page bearing a mighty spear. This knight bare on his shield
three golden griffins; and when Sir Gawaine perceived him
he put his spear in rest, and, riding to him, asked who he was.

The knight answered and said he was of Tuscany, "And
thou mayest prove me when thou wilt, for thou shalt be my
prisoner ere we part."

"Thou vauntest thee greatly, and speakest proud words,"
replied Gawaine; "yet I counsel thee for all thy boasting to
make ready ere grief befall thee."

Then they took their spears and ran at each other with

all their might, piercing each other through the shields into their shoulders, then they pulled out their swords and attacked each other fiercely, till fire sprang out of their helms. Sir Gawaine was much enraged, and with Galatine, his good sword, he smote his adversary through his mail, splintered all the precious stones of it, and made him such a large wound that both liver and lungs were visible.

"Ah, this wound!" the knight groaned heavily, but managed to deal Sir Gawaine a slanting stroke, which cut a vein, and he bled sore.

Then said the knight to Sir Gawaine, "Bind thy wound up quickly, for thou be-bleedest all thy horse and arms, nor can all the surgeons staunch the blood which is let with this sword."

"It grieves me but little," replied Gawaine: "thy words shall not make me afraid, but thou shalt suffer great grief and sorrow ere we part. Yet tell me who can staunch my bleeding."

"That may I do," said the knight; "and I will, if thou wilt aid and help me to become a Christian, which shall be great merit for thy soul."

"I grant it, God helping me to accomplish my desire," said Gawaine; "but tell me first, what soughtest thou here, and whence thou comest."

"Sir," he replied, "my name is Priamus; my father is a great prince, descended from Alexander and Hector. Of right I am King of Alexandria and Africa; yet would I believe on thy Lord, and for thy labour thou shalt have treasure enough. I was so proud to think no man my equal, but now thou hast given me of fighting my fill; wherefore, Sir Knight, I pray thee tell me what thou art."

"I am no knight," said Gawaine, "I have been brought up in the guard-robe of the noble King Arthur to mind his armour and array."

"Ah," said the Tuscan, "if his knaves be so keen, his knights must be passing good. Now, for the love of Heaven, tell me thy name."

"By Heaven," said Gawaine, "I will now tell thee the truth.

My name is Sir Gawaine, and I am a knight of the Round Table."

"Now I am better pleased," said Priamus, "than if thou hadst given me all the province. I had rather been torn by wild horses than any varlet had won such praise, or any page should have had the advantage of me. But now, Sir Knight, I warn thee close by is a Duke of Lorraine with his army of sixty thousand men, wherefore, if we hie us not hence it will harm us, both being sore wounded and not likely to recover. But take heed to my page that he blow no horn, for close by are a hundred of my knights, and if they take thee thou shalt never get free for gold or silver."

Then Sir Gawaine rode over the river to save himself, and Sir Priamus after him, so they fled till they rejoined Sir Gawaine's companions. But when Sir Wisshard saw his friend so hurt, he ran to him weeping, asking who had wounded him. Sir Gawaine then pointed to Priamus, who had salves to heal them both. "But we must be ready," he said, "for a great army is close upon us, and we shall have ado with many enemies."

Then Sir Priamus and Sir Gawaine alighted and unarmed themselves, while the blood ran freely from their wounds. Then Priamus took from his page a phial full of water from the four rivers which flow out of Paradise, and with certain balm anointed their wounds, washing them with the water; thus they were quickly healed.

A council was then called, when, after much talking, Priamus said, "Cease your words, for I warn you in yonder woods ye shall find many perilous knights, who will try to decoy you with cattle, when ye are so few to encounter so many."

"Nevertheless," said Sir Gawaine, "we will encounter them at once, and the best shall have the victory."

Then Sir Florence called Sir Floridas, with a hundred knights, and drove forth the herd of beasts; and the Saracens, with an earl named Ethelwold and the Duke of Dutchmen, came leaping out of the woods with many thousands, and the knights of Priamus, and came straight to battle. Sir Gawaine comforted his knights, and bade them be of good cheer, saying, "They are all ours." So the seven hundred knights rode fiercely amongst their enemies, smiting down all who opposed them. In and out pressed the knights of the Table Round, till their foes recoiled and fled.

Then entered into the battle Jubance, a giant, who fought and slew and distressed many of our knights, who returned and slew many Saracens, while Sir Priamus came with the knights of the Round Table to the rescue, and slew the Marquis of Moissesland. In this fight was Sir Chestelaine, a ward of Sir Gawaine, slain, wherefore much sorrow was made, and his death soon avenged. So the battle ended, many high lords of Lombardy, with Saracens, being left dead upon the field.

Then Sir Florence and Sir Gawaine collected their people, and having taken plenty of cattle, of gold and silver, and riches, they all returned to King Arthur, who still kept the siege. To him they recounted their adventures and presented their prisoners.

CHAPTER VI

HOW KING ARTHUR ENTERED ROME, AND WAS CROWNED EMPEROR BY THE POPE

"NOW God be thanked," said King Arthur. "But what man is he who standeth by himself? He appeareth no prisoner."

"Sir," said Gawaine, "he is a good man of arms, and hath matched me, but cometh hither to be made a Christian. But for him we never should have returned. Wherefore, I pray you, let him be christened, for there is no better knight of his hands."

Then the King let him be baptized, and made him a duke and knight of the Table Round.

Soon afterwards the King cried to the assault of the city, and they made ready to enter on every side. While yet the men were rushing in to pillage, came forth a duchess, and Clarisin the countess, with numerous ladies and damsels, came to request Arthur not to take the city by assault, for many of the guiltless would be slain.

"Madam," replied the King, "none of my people shall hurt you nor your damsels, but the duke shall abide my judgment."

Accordingly the assault was delayed, and anon the duke's son brought out the keys, so the town was taken by consent, and the duke was sent prisoner to Dover. Then Arthur, having made suitable arrangements, took his journey towards Rome.

And when they came to the city of Urbino, and laid an ambushment, while the townspeople skirmished with the vanguard, then the ambush was broken, and the town was won; but the King protected all the ladies and women, and comforted those in sorrow.

The people of Milan, when they heard this, yielded to

Arthur, and did him homage. Thence he proceeded into Tuscany, winning towns and castles on his way, and so on till he came to Viterbo, whence he sent messengers to Rome to know if they would have him for their lord.

In answer to this came out the senate and the cardinals with great treasure, and besought him to be crowned Emperor. The King assented, saying, "At Christmas I will be crowned, and hold my Round Table in your city."

Anon he entered Rome in great state, and was crowned Emperor by the Pope with all the royalty that could be made. After the coronation he remained in Rome for a time, distributing his lands and presents to his knights and people, so that every one, rich or poor, was satisfied. To Sir Priamus he gave the duchy of Lorraine. And when he had made every man rich, all his knights and lords addressed him, saying,—

"Blessed be God your war is over. None is so great or mighty to make war against you. Wherefore we beseech you, O Emperor, to return homeward, and give us licence to go home to our wives, from whom we have been long parted, and to rest us, for your journey is finished with honour and worship."

"Ye say truth," replied the King. "To tempt God is no wisdom; wherefore make you ready, and return we into England."

So the King made ready and came over the sea again, landing at Sandwich, where his wife Guenever came to meet him. He was nobly received of all his commons in every city, and great joy, such as no tongue can tell, was made at his home-coming to welcome him.

BOOK THE SIXTH: SIR LAUNCELOT DU LAKE

CHAPTER I

HOW SIR LAUNCELOT AND SIR LIONEL LEFT THE COURT TO SEEK ADVENTURES, AND HOW SIR LIONEL WAS TAKEN

AFTER King Arthur had come from Rome into England, all the knights of the Round Table resorted to the King, and made jousts and tournaments. In these were many good knights, who increased in arms and passed their fellows in prowess; but especially was Sir Launcelot du Lake renowned, for in all tournaments and deeds of arms for life or death he passed all other knights, and was not overcome save by treason or enchantment.

Wherefore Queen Guenever had him in favour above all other knights; and ever since he had escorted her to King Arthur, before her marriage, he had thought her the fairest of all ladies. She often sent for him, and bade him tell of his birth and strange adventures: how he was the only son of King Ban of Britanny, and when his parents fled from their burning castle, he was left wailing on the ground; how the Lady of the Lake then took him in her arms, and carried him into the midst of the waters, where, with his cousins Lionel and Bors, he had been cherished till he came to Arthur's Court. So he was called Launcelot du Lake.

He did also for the Queen many deeds of arms, and saved her from the fire through his chivalry. After that, he rested a long time with play and game, and then he thought to prove himself in strange adventures. So he bade his nephew Sir Lionel make him ready, "For," said he, "we two will seek adventure."

So they mounted their horses, and, well armed, rode through a deep forest into a plain, where the weather was hot, and Sir Launcelot greatly longed to sleep; so they lay down beneath an apple-tree to rest themselves and their

horses. Sir Lionel kept awake and watched, while Sir Launcelot fell asleep, and slept soundly, his head on his helm.

In the meanwhile came three knights riding as fast as they
could, but after them came only one knight. When Sir Lionel
beheld him, he thought he had never seen so great a knight,
neither one so well apparelled in all rights. But within a
while this strong knight overtook the hindmost of the three,
and smote him to the earth, and so with the second and the
foremost. Then alighting from his horse, he bound all three
knights together with the reins of their own bridles.

When Sir Lionel saw this, he thought to assay him, so he
made him ready, and quickly took his horse, so as not to
awaken Sir Launcelot. When he was mounted he overtook the
strong knight, and made him turn; but the other attacked
him so fiercely that he smote Sir Lionel to the earth, horse
and man. Then he alighted down, bound Sir Lionel, and
threw him over his horse's back, and carried him away with
the other three knights, all four together, unto his own castle.

When he arrived there he made them unarm and undress.
Then he beat them, all naked, with thorns, and put them into
a deep dungeon, where were many more knights, who made
great lamentation.

CHAPTER II

HOW SIR ECTOR FOLLOWED LAUNCELOT DU LAKE, AND HOW HE
WAS TAKEN PRISONER BY SIR TURQUINE

WHEN Sir Ector de Maris knew that Sir Launcelot had
left the Court and gone to seek adventures he was
wroth, and made him ready to seek Sir Launcelot; and when
he had ridden into a great forest, he met with a man like a
forester.

"Fair fellow," said Sir Ector, "knowest thou in this country any adventures that be here nigh hand?"

"Sir," said the forester, "this country I know well, and
close by is a strong manor, and on the left of it is a ford, and
over that ford groweth a tree, on which hang many fair
shields that good knights lately wore. At the bole of the tree
hangs a basin of copper and brass, and if thou strike on that
basin with the butt of thy spear three times, thou shalt soon
hear new tidings."

"Gramercy," said Sir Ector, and rode on.

When he came to the tree he saw the shields, and amongst
them his brother's, Sir Lionel's shield, with many more
which he knew belonged to the knights of the Round Table.
This grieved him sore, and he promised to revenge his
brother. So he beat on the basin fiercely, and gave his horse
drink at the ford, till a knight came out behind him, and bade
him make ready. At this Sir Ector turned round, and putting
his spear in rest, he smote the other knight a great buffet that
his horse turned twice about.

"That were well done," said the strong knight, whose name
was Sir Turquine, "and knightly hast thou stricken me."

Therewith rushed he on Sir Ector, caught him under his
right arm with his spear, bare him clean out of the saddle,

and rode away with him to his own hall, where he threw him down on the midst of the floor.

Then turning to Sir Ector, he said, "As thou hast done this day more than any knight did these twelve years I will grant thee thy life, so thou wilt be sworn to be my prisoner all thy life days."

"Nay," said Sir Ector, "that I will never promise, but that I will do mine advantage."

"I repent me," said Sir Turquine. So he made Sir Ector unarm, and beat him, all naked, with thorns; then he thrust him into the dungeon where were many of his fellows, and when Sir Ector saw Sir Lionel he made great sorrow.

"Alas!" said Sir Ector, "where is my brother Sir Launcelot?"

"Fair brother," said Sir Lionel, "I left him asleep under an apple-tree, and what is become of him I cannot tell."

"Alas!" said the knight, "unless Sir Launcelot help us, we may never be delivered, for we know no knight able to match with Turquine, our master."

CHAPTER III

HOW FOUR QUEENS FOUND SIR LAUNCELOT ASLEEP; AND HOW HE WAS TAKEN AND LED INTO A CASTLE BY ENCHANTMENT, AND DELIVERED BY MEANS OF A DAMSEL

WE MUST now return to Sir Launcelot du Lake, who was sleeping all this time under the apple-tree.

About noon there came by the place four Queens of great estate, and in order that the heat of the sun should not annoy them, there rode four knights with them, who carried a cloth of green silk on four spears betwixt them and the sun, while the Queens rode on four white mules.

As they rode thus along they heard a horse neigh, and then they were aware of the sleeping knight, who lay all armed under the apple-tree; and as soon as the Queens had looked in his face they knew it was Sir Launcelot. Then began they to strive for that knight which should have his love.

"We need not strive," said Morgan le Fay, who was King Arthur's sister. "I shall put an enchantment on him, so that he shall not wake for six hours. I will then lead him away into my castle, where I shall take the enchantment from him, and then let him choose which of us he will have for his love."

So the enchantment was cast upon Sir Launcelot, who was laid upon his shield and so borne by two knights, and brought into the castle named Chariot, where he was laid in a cold chamber, and at night they sent him his supper by a fair damsel. By that time the enchantment was passed, and when she came in she saluted him, saying, "What cheer?"

"I cannot say, fair damsel," replied Sir Launcelot; "for I wot not how I came to this castle, save it be by enchantment."

"Sir," said she, "ye must make good cheer; and if ye be such a knight as is said ye be, I will tell you more to-morn at prime of the day."

"Gramercy, fair damsel!" said Sir Launcelot; "of your good will I require you."

So she departed, and left him alone all the night; but on the morn early came the four Queens, all bidding him good morn, and he them again.

"Sir Knight," they said, "thou must understand thou art our prisoner. We know thee well that you are Sir Launcelot du Lake, King Ban's son, and truly we understand your worthiness to be the noblest knight living; therefore it behoveth thee to choose one of us four. I am Queen Morgan le Fay (Queen of the land of Gore), here is the Queen of North Galis, the Queen of Eastland, and the Queen of the Out Isles. Now choose ye one of us, which ye will have to thy love, for thou canst but choose, or else in this prison to die."

"This is a hard case," said Sir Launcelot, "that either I must die or choose one of you. Yet had I liever die in this prison with worship than have one of you to my love maugre my head. Therefore be ye thus answered, I will none of you, for ye be false enchantresses."

"Well," said the Queen, "is this your answer—that you will refuse us?"

"Yea, upon my life," replied Sir Launcelot; "refused ye be of me."

So they departed, and left him there alone that made great sorrow. At noon again came the damsel to him, bringing him his dinner, and she asked him what cheer.

"Truly, fair damsel," said Sir Launcelot, "in all my life never so ill."

"Sir," she said, "that grieveth me sore; but an ye will be ruled by me I will help ye out of your distress, and ye shall have no shame or villainy, so that ye hold me a promise."

"Fair damsel, that I will grant you; sore am I afraid of these Queen witches, who have destroyed many a good knight."

"Sir," said she, "that is sooth; yet for the renown they hear of you they would have your worship. They say your name is Sir Launcelot du Lake, the flower of all knights that are

living, and they have been passing wroth with you that ye
have refused them. But, sir, I would you promise me to help
my father on Tuesday next coming, who hath made a tournament between him and the King of North Galis, for on the
Tuesday last past my father lost the field through three knights
of King Arthur's Court; so if ye will be there on Tuesday
next coming, and help my father, by the grace of God I shall
deliver you clean to-morrow ere prime."

"Fair maiden," said Launcelot, "tell me what is your
father's name, and then I shall answer."

"Sir Knight," she said, "my father is King Bagdemagus,
who was foully rebuked at the last tournament."

"Well I know your father for a noble King and a good
knight," said Sir Launcelot; "and by my faith ye shall have
my body ready to do your father and you service at that day."

"Gramercy, sir," said the damsel; "to-morrow be ye ready
betimes, and I shall deliver you. Take you your armour, your
horse, shield, and spear. Hereby, within ten miles, is an abbey
of white monks; there, I pray thee, abide, and thither shall
I bring my father unto you."

"All this shall be done," said Sir Launcelot, "as I am a
true knight."

So she departed. On the morrow early she came again, and
found him ready; then she brought him out of twelve gates,
and found him his armour. When he was armed and arrayed
she brought him unto his own horse, which he saddled quickly.
Then taking a great spear in his hand, he rode forth, saying,
"Fair damsel, I will not fail you, by the grace of God."

So he rode into a great forest all that day, and could find
no highway; but as night fell he became aware in a valley of
a pavilion of red sendal.

"By my faith," said Sir Launcelot to himself, "in that
pavilion will I lodge to-night."

So he lighted down, and tied his horse to the pavilion, and
armed himself, and finding a rich bed in the pavilion, he laid
him therein, and anon he fell asleep.

Within an hour came there the knight to whom the pavilion

belonged, and lay down in the bed beside Sir Launcelot, who immediately leaped out of bed and gat his sword, the other knight following him, and went out of the pavilion, where they fought. Sir Launcelot wounded the other knight sore nigh unto death, who then yielded him, and Sir Launcelot spared his life on condition that he would tell him why he came into the bed.

"Sir," said the knight, "the pavilion is my own, and there this night would I have slept, but now am I likely to die of this wound."

"That me repenteth," said Sir Launcelot; "but I was afraid of treason, as lately I was beguiled. But come your way into the pavilion and take your rest, and I will staunch your blood."

So they both went into the pavilion, and anon Sir Launcelot staunched the knight's blood. While they talked the night passed away, and when the day appeared Sir Launcelot armed him, took his horse, and having been told the way to the abbey, thither he rode within the space of two hours.

CHAPTER IV

HOW SIR LAUNCELOT WAS RECEIVED OF KING BAGDEMAGUS'S DAUGHTER; HOW HE BEHAVED AT THE TOURNAMENT, AND MET SIR TURQUINE LEADING AWAY SIR GAHERIS

AS SOON as Sir Launcelot came within the abbey-yard, the daughter of King Bagdemagus heard a great horse move on the pavement, and, looking out, she perceived Sir Launcelot, and so she sent men to him, who led his horse to the stable and himself to a room, where they unarmed him. Afterwards she herself came to see him, making him good cheer, and told him he was the most welcome knight in the world to her.

Then in haste she sent for her father, and before eventide he came with a fair fellowship of knights. As soon as he had dismounted he went in and welcomed Sir Launcelot, who told him how he had been betrayed, and how the King's daughter had delivered him out of prison. "Wherefore," said he, "I shall, while I live, do her service, and all her friends and kindred."

"Then am I sure of your help," said the King, "on the Tuesday next coming?"

"Yea, sir," replied Sir Launcelot; "I will not fail you, for I have promised my lady your daughter. I hear say that the tournament will be held within three miles of this abbey: ye shall send unto me three knights you can trust, and take care that they all have white shields, such as I shall have. We four will then come out of a little wood in the midst of both parties, and shall fall on the front of our enemies as we may. Thus it shall not be known what knight I am."

The King then told him what knights of King Arthur's were with the King of North Galis; and, it being Sunday, they took their rest. So the King departed, and sent unto Sir

Launcelot the three knights and four white shields. On the Tuesday the four knights lodged in a little wood near where the tournament was to be holden. There were scaffolds whence lords and ladies might behold the jousting, and to give the prize.

First on the field came the King of North Galis with eight-score knights, and the three knights of Arthur stood by themselves. Then King Bagdemagus appeared with four-score men. These arrayed them against each other, and at the first encounter there were slain twelve of King Bagdemagus's party, six of the King of North Galis's party, and King Bagdemagus's forces were driven back.

With that came Sir Launcelot du Lake, thrusting into the thickest of the press, and there smote down five knights, and of four of them he brake their backs. He smote down also the King of North Galis, and brake his thigh. All these doings the three knights of Arthur saw.

"Yonder is a shrewd guest," said Sir Mador de la Porte; "therefore have at him."

So they encountered, and Sir Launcelot bare him down, horse and man, so that his shoulder went out of joint.

"Now it is my turn," said Sir Mordred; "for Sir Mador hath a sore fall."

Sir Launcelot was aware of him, and, having gotten a huge spear, he met him. Sir Mordred brake his spear upon him, and Sir Launcelot gave him such a buffet that the bow of his saddle brake; so he flew over his horse's tail, and his helm went into the earth a foot or more, that nigh his neck was broken, and he lay long in a swoon.

Then came the third knight, Sir Gahalantine, and encountered Sir Launcelot so fiercely that both their spears brake, and they fought hand to hand with swords, giving many a grim stroke. Sir Launcelot was wroth out of measure, and he smote Sir Gahalantine on the helm that his nose, ears, and mouth burst out bleeding, and his head hung low. Therewith his horse ran away with him, and he fell down to the earth.

Anon Sir Launcelot got a great spear in his hand, and ere

it brake he bore down sixteen knights, and there was none but he hit surely. He bare no device on his shield, and then got another spear, and smote down twelve knights, the most part of whom never throve after.

At this the knights of the King of North Galis would joust no more, and then the prize was given to King Bagdemagus. So each party departed into its own place, and Sir Launcelot returned with King Bagdemagus to the castle, where he had good cheer with the King and his daughter, who proffered him great gifts.

In the morn he took his leave, telling the King he would go and seek Sir Lionel, who had left him when he slept. "But," he added to the King's daughter, "if ye have need any time of my service, I pray you let me have knowledge, and I will not fail you, as I am a true knight."

Thus Sir Launcelot departed, and by adventure came into the same forest where he was taken sleeping; and in the midst of a path he met a damsel riding on a white palfrey, and they saluted each other.

"Fair damsel," said Sir Launcelot, "know ye in this country any adventures?"

"Sir Knight," said the damsel, "here are adventures at hand, an thou durst prove them."

"Why should I not prove adventures?" said he; "for that cause came I hither."

"Thou seemest well to be a good knight," she replied, "and if thou dare meet with a good knight I will bring thee where is best and the mightiest that ever thou foundest. Wilt thou tell me what is thy name, and what knight thou art?"

"Damsel, as for to tell thee my name I take no objection. Truly, I am Sir Launcelot du Lake."

"Sir, thou beseemest well. Here be adventures for thee, for near by dwelleth a knight who will not be overmatched by any man I know, unless ye overmatch him, and his name is Sir Turquine. And, as I understand, he hath in his prison threescore and four good knights of Arthur's Court that he hath won with his own hands. But when ye have done that day's work, ye shall promise as a true knight to go with me, to help me and other damsels that are daily distressed by a false knight."

"All your intent, damsel, and desire I will fulfil, if ye will bring me unto this knight."

"Well, now, fair knight, come on your way."

So she brought him to the ford where was the tree on which hung the basin; so Sir Launcelot let his horse drink, and then beat on the basin so hard with the butt of his spear that the bottom fell out; but no one appeared. He rode by the gates of the manor nigh half an hour, and then was he aware of a great knight who came, driving a horse before him, and over the horse there lay an armed knight bound. As soon as they came nearer Sir Launcelot thought he should know the captive knight, and he soon found that he was Sir Gaheris, Gawaine's brother, a knight of the Table Round.

"Now, fair damsel," said Sir Launcelot, "yonder knight fast bound is a fellow of mine and brother of Sir Gawaine. At the first beginning I promise you, by the leave of God, to rescue that knight; and unless his master sit better in the saddle, I shall deliver all the prisoners he hath, for I am sure there are two brethren of mine prisoners with him. Now, fair knight," said Sir Launcelot, "put that wounded knight off the horse, and let him rest awhile, and let us two prove our strength; for as it is informed me thou doest and hast done great despite and shame unto knights of the Round Table, therefore now defend thyself."

"An thou be of the Table Round," said Sir Turquine, "I defy thee and all thy fellowship."

"That is overmuch said," replied Sir Launcelot.

CHAPTER V

HOW SIR LAUNCELOT AND SIR TURQUINE FOUGHT TOGETHER

THEN they put their spears in rest, and came together as fast as their horses could run, and either smote the other so that both their horses' backs brake under them. The knights were both astonied, and as soon as they might avoid their horses, they took their shields and drew their swords and fought with many strong strokes, till within awhile they both had grimly wounds, and bled passing grievously.

Thus they fared for two hours or more, either endeavouring to hit any bare place; at last they both stood breathless, leaning on their swords.

"Now, fellow," said Sir Turquine, "hold thy breath awhile, and tell me what I shall ask thee."

"Say on," replied Sir Launcelot.

Then Turquine said, "Thou art the biggest man I ever met, and the best breathed. Thou art like one knight I hate above all others; so if thou be not he, I will deal lightly with them, and for thy sake will release all the prisoners that I have, so thou wilt tell me thy name. Then thou and I will be fellows together, and never fail as long as we live."

"It is well said," replied Sir Launcelot; "but since I may have thy friendship, what knight is he that thou hatest above all others?"

"Truly," said Sir Turquine, "his name is Sir Launcelot du Lake; for he slew my brother, Sir Carados, one of the best knights when alive, at the Dolorous Tower. Therefore Sir Launcelot I except of knights, for if I once meet with him, one of us shall make an end of the other, I avow. For Sir Launcelot's sake I have slain a hundred good knights, and as many I have maimed so utterly that they might never after, help themselves. Many have died in prison, and yet I have threescore and four who all shall be delivered if thou tell me thy name so it be not Sir Launcelot."

"Now see I well," said Sir Launcelot, "that such a man I might be and have peace, and such a man I might be that there should be war mortal betwixt us. Now, Sir Knight, I tell thee I am Launcelot du Lake, King Ban's son of Benwick, and very knight of the Table Round—so I defy thee; do thy best."

"Ah!" said Turquine, "thou art with me most welcome as ever was knight, for we shall never part till one of us be dead."

Then they hurtled together as two wild bulls, rashing and lashing with their shields and swords, that sometimes they both fell over on their faces. Thus they fought still for two hours or more, nor would have rest; and Sir Turquine gave Sir Launcelot so many wounds that all the ground where they fought was bespeckled with blood.

At last Sir Turquine waxed faint, and giving somewhat aback, held his shield low from very weariness. That espied Sir Launcelot, who leaped upon him fiercely and got him by the beaver of his helmet; he then pulled him down on his knees, and tearing off his helm, smote his neck in sunder.

Then Sir Launcelot turned to the lady, and said, "Damsel, I am ready to accompany thee, but I have no horse."

"Fair sir," said she, "take this knight's horse, and send him into the manor to deliver all the prisoners."

So Sir Launcelot went unto Sir Gaheris and begged his horse, which he accorded willingly; and when he had told Sir Gaheris his name, he advised him to free all the knights, and come to King Arthur's Court at Pentecost.

"Tell them from me," he said, "to take all the stuff they can find and abide me at the Court, for I must ride with this damsel to save my promise."

So he departed from Gaheris, who went into the manor and gained possession of the keys. Anon he loosed all the prisoners, and told them the message of Sir Launcelot, and how he had slain Sir Turquine. Then the knights sought their armour and their horses, and found all that belonged to them. After that they sat down to supper, but Sir Lionel, Ector de Maris, and Sir Kay rode after Sir Launcelot to find him if they might.

CHAPTER VI

HOW SIR LAUNCELOT SLEW A KNIGHT, A VILLAIN, AND TWO GIANTS; AND HOW HE SET A CASTLE FREE

AS SIR LAUNCELOT rode on with the damsel in the highway, she said, "Sir, by this way haunteth a knight that distresses and robs all ladies and gentlewomen."

"What," said Sir Launcelot, "is he a thief, and a knight? He doth shame unto the order of knighthood, and a contrary to his oath. It is a pity he liveth. Now do you ride on apace, and I will keep in covert, so if he molest you I will come to your rescue and teach him to be ruled as a knight."

So the maiden rode on, and presently the false knight came out of the wood, his page with him, and put the damsel from her horse. Then she cried out, and Sir Launcelot came riding up as fast as he might, rebuking her assailant.

When the knight saw Sir Launcelot he made no reply but drew his sword against him; but in a moment the good knight clave him through his head and neck saying, "Take the payment thou hast long deserved. Now, damsel, will ye any more service of me?"

"Nay, sir," she replied; "but God preserve thee wherever ye ride or go, for thou art the courtliest knight unto all ladies and gentlewomen that now liveth."

So Sir Launcelot and she departed.

Then he rode into a deep forest two days and more, and on the third day he reached a long bridge, whereon a churl came upon him suddenly and smote his horse on the nose, demanding why he rode over that bridge without his licence.

"Why should I not ride this way?" said Launcelot. "I may not ride beside."

"Thou shalt not choose," said the churl, and lashed at him

with a great club shod with iron. Then Sir Launcelot drew his sword and clave the churl's head to his breast.

At the end of the bridge was a village, and when the people saw what Sir Launcelot had done, they cried and said, "A worse deed didst thou never for thyself! thou hast slain the chief porter of our castle."

But Sir Launcelot paid no attention to them. He went into the castle, and tied his horse to a ring on the wall. Then he saw a fair green court, and advanced thither, for he thought it was a fair place to fight in. But as he looked about he saw many people at doors and windows, who said, "Fair knight, thou art unhappy [unfortunate]."

Anon came there upon him two great giants well armed, except their heads, with two horrible clubs in their hands. Sir Launcelot, with his shield, put aside the stroke of one giant, and clave his head asunder. When his fellow saw that, he ran away, and Sir Launcelot pursued him till he smote him down the middle.

The victor then entered the hall, and there came to him threescore ladies and damsels, who kneeled down and thanked him for their deliverance.

"Fair sir," said they, "the most part of us have been here this seven years, and have worked all kinds of silk work for our meat. We are all great gentlewomen born, and blessed be thou, knight, who hast done the most worshipful thing, as we will bear record. We pray thee tell us thy name, that we may tell our friends who delivered us out of prison."

"Fair damsels," he said, "my name is Sir Launcelot du Lake."

"Ah, sir, well mayest thou be he, for save yourself, as we deemed, never might knight have the better of these two giants; many knights have assayed it and failed. Many times have we wished for you, for these two giants dreaded never knight but yourself."

"Now ye may say," said Sir Launcelot, "unto your friends how and who has delivered you. Greet them all from me; and if I come into any of your marches, show me such cheer as ye have cause. I give you what treasure there is in this castle as a reward for your grievance, and I would the lord who is the owner of this castle received it as its right."

"Fair sir," said they, "the name of this castle is Tintagel; a duke owned it sometime, who wedded fair Igraine, who afterwards married Uther Pendragon, whose son was Arthur."

"Well," said Sir Launcelot, "I understand now to whom this castle belongs." So he departed from them, and commended them to God. Then he rode through many strange and wild countries, and badly was he lodged.

At last it happened that he came to a fair courtelage or enclosed domain, where he found an old gentlewoman who lodged him, and gave him a garret over the gate wherein to sleep. He was awaked soon after by one who came on horseback, and knocked at the gate in great haste. When Sir Launcelot heard this, he rose up, and looked out of the window, and beheld by the moonlight three knights coming after that one man, and attacking him with their swords, while the knight defended himself bravely.

"Truly," said Sir Launcelot, "yonder single knight will I help, for it were a shame for me to see three on one, and if he be slain I am partner with his death."

Therewith he took his harness, and went down from the window by a sheet to the four knights, and said, "Turn you unto me; leave your fighting with that knight."

Then they left Sir Kay, for it was he, and turned against Sir Launcelot, assailing him on every side. Then Sir Kay would have helped him; but Sir Launcelot said, "Nay, sir, I will none of your help. Therefore, as ye will have my help, let me alone with them."

Sir Kay, for the pleasure of the knight, suffered him to do his will, and stood aside. Then with six strokes Sir Launcelot had stricken his enemies to the earth.

Then they all three cried, "Sir Knight, we yield us to you as a man of might matchless."

"As to that," said Sir Launcelot, "I will not take your yielding unto me; but ye shall yield you to Sir Kay, the

Seneschal; on that covenant I will save your lives, or else not."

"Fair knight," said they, "that we are loth to do, for we chased Sir Kay hither, and would have overcome him had ye not been; therefore to yield us unto him it were no reason."

"Well, as to that," said Sir Launcelot, "advise ye well, for ye may choose whether ye will die or live, for an ye be yielden it shall be unto Sir Kay."

"Fair knight," they then said, "in saving our lives we will do as thou commandest us."

"Then shall ye," said Sir Launcelot, "on Whit Sunday next coming, go unto the Court of King Arthur, and there ye shall yield you unto Queen Guenever, and put you all three in her grace and mercy, saying that Sir Kay sent you there to be her prisoners."

"Sir," they said, "it shall be done, by the faith of our bodies, an we be living."

So there they swore every knight upon his sword, and then Sir Launcelot suffered them to depart.

He now turned to the gate, and knocked with the pommel of his sword. Thereupon came his host, and said, "Sir, I weened ye had been in your bed."

"So I was," replied Sir Launcelot, "but I rose and leaped out of window to help an old companion of mine."

So they entered. When they had come nigh to the knight, Sir Kay knew well that it was Sir Launcelot, and therewith he kneeled down and thanked him of all his kindness that he hath holpen him twice from death.

"Sir," he replied, "I have done nothing but what I ought to do, and ye are welcome. Here repose you and take your rest."

So when Sir Kay was unarmed he asked for meat, and when it was brought ate greedily; but after supper they were lodged together in one bed.

On the morn Sir Launcelot arose early and left Sir Kay sleeping, and armed him in Sir Kay's armour, went into the stable and took his horse; then taking leave of his host, he departed. Soon after arose Sir Kay, and missed Sir Launcelot; then he espied that he had taken his armour and his horse. "Now, by my faith, I know well that he will grieve some of the Court of King Arthur," said Sir Kay, "for on him knights will be bold and think it is I, while because of his armour and shield I am sure to ride in peace."

So soon after this departed Sir Kay, and thanked his host.

CHAPTER VII

HOW SIR LAUNCELOT RODE DISGUISED IN SIR KAY'S HARNESS; AND HOW HE JOUSTED AGAINST FOUR KNIGHTS OF THE ROUND TABLE

SIR LAUNCELOT rode along in a great forest, and came at last into a fair country, full of rivers and meadows. Afore him he saw a long bridge, and thereon stood three pavilions of silk and sendal in divers hues. Outside the pavilions hung three white shields on truncheons of spears, and great long spears stood upright beside the pavilions. At every pavilion's door stood three squires, but Sir Launcelot passed them and spake no word.

When he had passed, the three knights said he was the proud Sir Kay. "He weeneth no knight so good as he, and the contrary is ofttimes proved."

"By my faith," said Sir Gaunter, one of the knights, "I will ride after him and assay him for his pride, so ye may behold him how I speed."

So Sir Gaunter armed him, mounted his horse, and galloped after Sir Launcelot. When he came nigh him he cried, "Abide, thou proud knight, Sir Kay, for thou shalt not pass quit."

So Sir Launcelot turned him, and putting their spears in rest, they came together with all their might. Sir Gaunter's spear brake, and Sir Launcelot smote him down, horse and man.

When Sir Gaunter was on the ground, his brethren said each to other, "Yonder knight is not Sir Kay, for he is bigger than he."

"I dare lay my head," said Sir Gilmere, "yonder knight hath slain Sir Kay and taken his horse and harness."

"Whether it be so or no," said Sir Raynold, the third

brother, "let us now mount upon our horses, and go rescue our brother Sir Gaunter upon pain of death. We all shall have work enough to match that knight, for he seemeth, by his person, to be either Sir Launcelot or Sir Tristram, or Sir Pelleas the good knight."

Anon they took their horses and overtook Sir Launcelot; and Sir Gilmere put forth his spear and attacked him, and Sir Launcelot smote him down that he lay in a swoon; and the like fortune befell Sir Raynold. But he and Sir Gilmere and Sir Gaunter all arose, and came against Sir Launcelot, who overcame them a second time, till Sir Raynold started up with his head all bloody, and came straight to Sir Launcelot.

"Now let be!" said Sir Launcelot. "I was not far from thee when thou wast made knight, Sir Raynold. I know thou art a good knight, and loth I were to slay thee."

"Gramercy!" said Sir Raynold, "as for your goodness; and I daresay, as for me and my brethren, we shall not be loth to yield us unto you if we knew your name, for well we know you are not Sir Kay."

"As for that, be it as it may, for ye shall yield thee unto Dame Guenever on Whit Sunday, and say that Sir Kay sent you unto her."

Then they swore it should be done; so passed forth Sir Launcelot, and each one of the brethren helped each other as well as they might. So Launcelot rode on, and in a glade of the wood he saw four knights under the shade of an oak, who were of Arthur's Court. One was Sagramour le Desirous, with Sir Ector de Maris, Sir Gawaine, and Sir Uwaine. When these four knights espied Sir Launcelot, they thought it had been Sir Kay.

"Now, by my faith," said Sagramour, "I will prove Sir Kay's might." So he came near Sir Launcelot, spear in hand. Therewith Sir Launcelot was ware, so he advanced against him, and smote him so sore that Sir Sagramour and his horse fell to the earth.

"So, my fellows," said Sir Ector, "ye see what a buffet he

hath got. That knight is much bigger than ever was Sir Kay. Now shall ye see what I may do to him."

So Sir Ector gat his spear in his hand, and galloped towards Sir Launcelot, who smote him through shield and shoulder, and horse and man went to the earth.

"By my faith," said Sir Uwaine, "yonder is a strong knight; and I see it will be hard to match him."

Therewithal Sir Uwaine gat his spear in his hand and rode towards Sir Launcelot, who knew him well; so he met him on the plain, and gave him such a buffet that he was astonied so long he wist not where he was.

"Now see I well," said Sir Gawaine, "I must encounter with this knight."

Then he dressed his shield, and gat a good spear in his hand; and then they let run their horses with all their might, and either knight smote the other in midst of the shield. But Sir Gawaine's spear broke to pieces, and Sir Launcelot charged so sore upon him, that his horse was overturned, and much sorrow had Sir Gawaine to avoid his horse.

Sir Launcelot passed on at a pace smiling, and saying, "God give him joy that made this spear, for there came never a better in my hand."

Then the four knights met together, and comforted each other.

"What say ye by this?" said Sir Gawaine; "one spear hath felled us four,—he is a man of great might."

"Ye may well say it," said Sir Gawaine; "for I dare lay my head it is Sir Launcelot; I know him by his riding."

"Let him go, Sir Uwaine, for when we come to the Court, then shall we know."

And then they had much sorrow to get their horses again.

CHAPTER VIII

HOW SIR LAUNCELOT FOLLOWED A HOUND INTO A CASTLE,
WHERE HE FOUND A DEAD KNIGHT, AND HOW HE CAME TO THE
CHAPEL PERILOUS

SIR LAUNCELOT continued his journey in the forest,
and there met with a black brachet (or small hound)
scenting a trail, and when the knight examined it, he found
the marks of blood upon the ground. Then rode he after the
hound, which traversed a great marsh. Sir Launcelot followed, and soon became aware of an old manor, whither the
hound ran, and so over the bridge.

So Sir Launcelot rode over the bridge, which was old and
feeble, and up to the castle. He entered the great hall, where
he perceived a dead knight lying, and the hound licking his
wounds. Therewithal came out a lady, weeping and wringing
her hands, saying, "Oh, knight! too much sorrow hast thou
brought me!"

"Why say ye so?" said Sir Launcelot. "I never harmed this
knight; for hither by the track of blood the brachet brought
me. So be not displeased with me, fair lady, for I am sore
aggrieved at your sorrow."

"Truly, sir, I know you have not slain my husband," she
replied, "for he that did that deed is sore wounded and unlikely to recover."

"What was your husband's name?" asked Sir Launcelot.

"Sir," she replied, "he was called Sir Gilbert, one of the
best knights in the world; and he that has slain him I know
not his name."

"Now God send you better comfort," said Sir Launcelot.

So he departed, and entered the forest again, where he met
a damsel, who knew him, and cried unto him, "Well be ye

found, my lord, and now I require you on your knighthood keep my brother, who is sore wounded, and never stinteth bleeding. This day he fought with Sir Gilbert, and slew him in plain battle, and there is a lady, a sorceress, who dwelleth in a castle hard by, who tells me my brother will never be made whole until I can find a knight who will go into the Chapel Perilous, and find a sword and a bloody cloth which the knight was wrapped in. A piece of that cloth and sword shall heal my brother's wounds if they be touched with them."

"This is a marvellous thing," said Sir Launcelot. "What is your brother's name?"

"Sir," she said, "his name is Meliot de Logres."

"That repenteth me," said Sir Launcelot, "for he is a fellow of the Table Round; and to his help I will do my best."

"Then, sir," said she, "follow even this highway, and it will bring you unto the Chapel Perilous. Here I will abide till God send you here again, and unless you speed I know no knight living that may achieve the adventure."

Forthwith Sir Launcelot departed, and when he came to the Chapel Perilous he alighted down and tied his horse to the little gate. As soon as he was inside the churchyard, he saw on the front of the chapel many shields upside down, which Sir Launcelot had seen before carried by knights.

Immediately he saw stand beside him thirty great knights, taller by a yard than any man he had ever seen, and they all grinned and gnashed their teeth upon him. When he saw their faces he was sore afraid; but he put his shield before him, and took his sword in his hand ready to do battle. The great knights were all around in black harness, ready with their shields, and their swords drawn. And when Sir Launcelot would have gone through them, they scattered on every side of him, and gave way.

Therewith he waxed bold, and entered the chapel, where he saw only a dim lamp burning, and then he was ware of a corpse covered with a cloth of silk. So Sir Launcelot stooped down and cut a piece of that cloth away, and then the earth quaked a little, and he was afraid.

Then he perceived a fair sword lying beside the dead knight, and he gat it in his hand and hied him out of the chapel. But when he had got outside the chapel, the knights spake in a grimly voice, saying, "Knight Sir Launcelot, put that sword from thee, else thou shalt die."

"Whether I live or die," said Sir Launcelot, "no word will get it from me; therefore fight for it an ye list."

So he passed through them; and beyond the chapel-yard there met him a fair damsel, who said, "Sir Launcelot, leave that sword behind thee, or else thou shalt die for it."

"I leave it not," he replied, "for no entreaties."

"No," said she; "and if thou didst, Queen Guenever shouldst thou never see."

"Then were I a fool to leave the sword," said Sir Launcelot.

"Now, gentle knight," continued the damsel, "I require thee to kiss me but once."

"Nay," returned he, "that God forbid."

"Well, sir," she said, "hadst thou kissed me thy life days had been done; but, now, alas! I have lost all my labour, for I ordained this chapel for thy sake, Sir Launcelot, whom I have loved this seven year. But as I could not have thee living, I had kept the joy to have thy body dead. Then would I have balmed it, and kept it all my life days."

"Ye say well," replied Sir Launcelot. "God preserve me from thy wicked crafts."

Therewith he took his departure from her, whose name was Hellawes the Sorceress, lady of the Castle Nigramous.

Anon Sir Launcelot came to the damsel, Sir Meliot's sister, who clapped her hands joyfully when she saw him, and wept for joy. Then they rode to the castle where Sir Meliot lay pale from bleeding. When he saw Sir Launcelot he kneeled upon his knees and cried for his help. So Sir Launcelot hurried to him, and touched his wounds with Sir Gilbert's sword, and wiped them with the bloody cloth, and anon Sir Meliot became whole as ever.

Then there was great joy between them, and they made

Sir Launcelot as good cheer as they might. So on the morn he took his leave, and bade Sir Meliot hie him to the Court of King Arthur, for the Feast of Pentecost was drawing nigh.

"There," said Sir Launcelot, "by the grace of God ye shall find me." And therewith they parted from each other.

CHAPTER IX

HOW SIR LAUNCELOT RECOVERED A FALCON, AND HOW HE CAME AGAIN UNTO KING ARTHUR'S COURT

SIR LAUNCELOT rode through many strange countries, till, by fortune, he came to a fair castle, and as he passed he thought he heard two bells ring. Then was he aware of a falcon which came flying over his head into a high elm, and as she perched on the elm the lines hung down and about a bough; so when she would have taken her flight, she hung by the legs fast, and Sir Launcelot was sorry for her.

Meanwhile there came a lady out of the castle, exclaiming, "O Launcelot, Launcelot! the flower of all knights, aid me to recover my falcon: an my hawk be lost, my lord will destroy me."

"What is your lord's name?" said Sir Launcelot.

"Sir," she said, "his name is Sir Phelot, a knight of the King of North Galis."

"Well, fair lady, as ye require me of my knighthood to help you, I will do what I may to get your hawk; yet, truly, I am an ill climber. The tree is passing high, and there are few boughs to help withal."

Therewith Sir Launcelot alighted and tied his horse to the tree, and then begged the lady to unarm him. So when he was unarmed he put off all his upper clothing, and with his force he climbed up to the falcon, and tying the lines to a rotten branch, threw it and the branch down together.

Anon the lady secured the hawk, and just then came out her husband, all armed, carrying his naked sword in his hand, and said,—

"O Knight Launcelot, now have I found thee as I would." And he stood at the foot of the tree to slay him.

"Ah, lady," said Sir Launcelot, "why have ye betrayed me?"

"She hath done," said Sir Phelot, "but as I commanded her, therefore there is none other boot: thine hour has come, and thou must die."

"That were shame unto thee," said Sir Launcelot, "thou, an armed knight, to slay an unarmed man by treason."

"Thou gettest none other grace," said the armed knight; "therefore help thyself as thou canst."

"Truly," said Sir Launcelot, "that shall be thy shame; but since thou wilt do none otherwise, take mine harness with thee, and hang my sword upon a bough that I may get it, and then do thy best to slay me, if thou canst."

"Nay, nay," said Sir Phelot, "I know thee better than thou weenest, therefore gettest thou no weapon, an I may keep thee therefrom."

"Alas!" cried Sir Launcelot, "that a knight should die weaponless." And therewith he looked up and down, and espied a round spike upon a leafless bough, which he brake off. Then he came lower, and perceiving where his horse stood, he suddenly leaped down upon the side of his horse farthest from the knight.

Then Sir Phelot lashed at him to slap him, but Sir Launcelot put aside the stroke with his weapon, and therewith smote the knight on the side of his head and felled him to the ground. Taking his sword, Sir Launcelot struck off the armed knight's head as he lay.

"Alas," cried the lady, "why hast thou slain my husband?"

"I am not to blame," said Sir Launcelot, "with falsehood and treason ye would have slain me; now it has fallen on you both."

Then she swooned like to die. But Sir Launcelot got all his armour and put it on hastily for fear of more attack, for the castle was nigh; then as soon as he might he took his horse, and departed thence, thanking God that he had escaped such an adventure.

After divers other adventures Sir Launcelot came back to

King Arthur's Court two days afore the Feast of Pentecost. And all were glad of his coming. But when Sir Gawaine, Sir Ector, Sir Uwaine, and Sir Sagramour saw him, they knew who had smitten them all with one spear. Then was there much laughter among them.

Ever and anon came home the knights whom Sir Tarquine had held prisoners; they were all of them honoured, and worshipped Sir Launcelot. When Sir Gaheris heard them speak he said he had seen all the battle from the beginning.

King Arthur then was told concerning Sir Turquine; and Sir Kay informed him how he had been rescued by Sir Launcelot, and how he had made the knights yield to the name of Sir Kay, so he had ridden in peace, having the armour of Sir Launcelot. Then came the three knights who had fought on the bridge, and they yielded to Sir Kay; but he said,—

"I will ease your hearts: there is the knight who conquered you," pointing to Sir Launcelot.

So they were glad. Then came Sir Meliot, and told how he had been saved from death by Sir Launcelot, all whose deeds, as already recounted, were made known, concerning the four Queens and King Bagdemagus's daughter. And all his deeds of arms at the tournament were related by Sir Gahalantine, Sir Mador de la Porte, and Sir Mordred, who were there also.

Then came in the lady who knew Sir Launcelot when he had wounded Sir Belleus of the Pavilion; and at Sir Launcelot's request Sir Belleus was made a knight of the Round Table.

Thus was Sir Launcelot the greatest knight of that time in the world, and the most honoured by high and low, who met with other adventures, as may be told.

Here endeth the Tale of Sir Launcelot du Lake.

BOOK THE SEVENTH: THE TALE OF
SIR GARETH OF ORKNEY

CHAPTER I

HOW GARETH ENTERED KING ARTHUR'S COURT AND TOOK SERVICE IN THE KITCHEN AS "BEAUMAINS"

WHEN King Arthur held his Round Table most fully it fortuned that he commanded that the high Feast of Pentecost should be holden at a city and a castle which in those days was called Kinkenadon, on the sands bordering on Wales.

The King had a notion that he would not go to meat at that feast in particular, until he had heard or seen of a great marvel. So all manner of strange adventures came before him at that feast more than at any other. Sir Gawaine, on that Day of Pentecost, espied at a window three men upon horseback and a dwarf on foot. The three men alighted, while the dwarf kept their horses; and one of the three men was taller than the other two by a foot and a half.

Then Sir Gawaine went unto the King, and said, "Sir, go to your meat, for here at hand come strange adventures."

So Arthur went to meat with many other Kings, and all the knights of the Table Round were present, save the dead or those who had been made prisoners. Then came unto the hall two men well and richly clad, and upon their shoulders leaned the goodliest and fairest young man they had ever seen. He was large and long, broad in the shoulders, and well visaged; but he seemed as if he could not support himself unless he leaned upon men's shoulders.

There was silence in the room when he came in, and he, with his men, went up to Arthur, when the young man pulled himself up straight, and said, "King Arthur, God you bless and all your fair fellowship—in especial this fellowship of the Table Round! For this cause I am come hither to require and pray you to give me three gifts, which shall not be unreasonable. The first I will ask now, the other two this day twelvemonth, wheresoever ye hold your high feast."

"Now ask," said Arthur, "and ye shall have your asking."

"Sir, this is my petition for this feast: that ye will give me meat and drink sufficient for this twelvemonth, and at that day I will ask my other two gifts."

"My fair son," said Arthur, "ask better, I counsel thee, for this is but a simple asking. My heart telleth me thou art come of men of worship, and greatly my conceit faileth me an thou not prove a man of right good worship."

"Sir," said he, "be that as it may; I have asked what I will ask."

"Well," said the King, "ye shall have meat and drink enough. But what is thy name?"

"I cannot tell you," said the young man.

"That is marvel," replied Arthur, "that thou knowest not thy name, and thou art the goodliest man I ever saw."

Then the King betook him to Sir Kay the Steward, and charged him that he should give him all manner of meats and drinks of the best, and also that he had all manner of finding, as he were a lord's son.

"That shall little need," replied Sir Kay, "to do such cost upon him, for I daresay he is a villain born, and never will make man. Had he come of gentlemen he would have asked for a horse and armour. Since he hath no name, I will give him one—Beaumains, for he hath fair hands; and into the kitchen will I bring him; there he shall have fat broth every day, and shall be as fat as a pork hog by the twelvemonth."

So the two attendants departed, and left "Beaumains" with Sir Kay, who scorned and mocked him. But Sir Launcelot and Sir Gawaine were wroth because Sir Kay mocked "Beaumains," and bade the Seneschal leave his mocking, as they were sure Beaumains would prove a man of worship.

"Let be," said Sir Kay; "it may not be, for so he is as he hath asked."

"Beware!" returned Sir Launcelot. "Ye gave the good knight Brewnor, Sir Dinadan's brother, a name, and called him La Cote Male Taile, and that turned you to anger after."

"As for that," replied Sir Kay, "this shall never prove none such, for Sir Brewnor desireth ever worship, and this desireth bread and drink and broth. Upon pain of my life he was fostered up in some abbey, and howsoever it was they failed meat and drink, and so here he has come for his sustenance."

So Sir Kay bade him get a place and sit down to meat, and Beaumains went to the hall door and set himself down among boys and lads, and ate sadly. Then Sir Launcelot after meat bade him come to his chamber, and there he should have meat and drink enough. So did Sir Gawaine; but the young man refused them all, and would do none other but as Sir Kay commanded him. So thus he was put in the kitchen, and lay nightly as all the boys of the kitchen did.

He endured all that twelvemonth, and never displeased man or child, but was always meek and mild. But whenever there was any jousting of knights, he would see it all he might. Sir Launcelot and Sir Gawaine would give him gold to spend, and clothes, for Sir Gawaine knew him; then would Sir Kay say, "How like you my boy of the kitchen?"

Thus it continued to Whitsuntide, and the King held it at Caerleon in the royalest fashion. Then came a squire, who said, "Ye may go, sir, to your meat, for here cometh a damsel with strange adventures."

Then was the King glad, and sat him down.

Right so there came a damsel into the hall, and saluted the King and prayed him of succour.

"For whom?" said the King; "what is the adventure?"

"Sir," she said, "I have a lady of great renown, and she is besieged by a tyrant, so that she may not remove out of her castle."

"What is her name? where dwelleth she? who is she? and what is his name that hath besieged her?" asked the King.

"Sir," said the damsel, "the name of the lady ye shall not know it of me for this time, but I let you wit she is of great worship and hath great lands. The tyrant that besiegeth her is called the Red Knight of the Red Lawns."

"I know him not," said the King.

"Sir," said Sir Gawaine, "I know him well, for he is one of the perilousest knights in the world. Men say he hath seven men's strength, and from him I escaped once full hard with my life."

"Fair damsel," said the King, "there be knights here would do their powers to rescue your lady; but because you will not tell her name, and where she dwelleth, therefore none of my knights that be here now shall go with you by my will."

"Then must I speak further," said the damsel.

Just then came to the King Beaumains, and said, "Sir King, God thank you. I have been these twelvemonths in your kitchen, and have had my full sustenance, and now I will ask thee two gifts that be behind."

"Ask upon my peril," said the King; "I grant it thee."

"Sir, these are my two gifts. First, that ye will grant me the adventure of this damsel, and that ye shall bid Sir Launce- lot du Lake make me knight, for of him will I be made knight, or else of none. And when I am past, let him ride after me, and make me knight when I require him."

"All this shall be done," said the King.

"Fie on you!" said the damsel; "shall I have none but your kitchen page?"

Then was she wroth, and took her horse and departed. With that there came one to Beaumains, and told him that his horse and armour were come; and there was the dwarf, who had provided all in the richest manner. Thereat all the Court had great marvel whence came all that gear. So when Beau- mains was armed, there was but few so goodly as he was.

And right so he came into the hall, and took his leave of King Arthur, and Gawaine, and Launcelot, and prayed Sir Launcelot to hie after him. So he departed and rode after the damsel.

CHAPTER II

AS HE departed many went after him to behold how well he was horsed and trapped in cloth of gold, but he had neither shield nor spear. Then Sir Kay said openly in the hall, "I will ride after my boy of the kitchen, and wit whether he will know me for his better."

So Sir Kay made him ready, and took his horse and his spear, and overtook him as Beaumains had come up with the damsel.

"Beaumains," said Sir Kay, "know ye not me?"

Then he turned his horse, and, seeing Sir Kay, said, "Yea, I know thee for an ungentle knight of the Court, so beware of me."

Therewith Sir Kay put his spear in rest and ran upon him; but Beaumains came fast with his sword in his hand, and put away the spear with his sword, and with a feint thrust him through the side, so that Sir Kay fell down as one dead. All that saw Sir Launcelot and the damsel. Then Beaumains told the dwarf to take Sir Kay's horse, which he did, and by that time Sir Launcelot had come up, and Beaumains proffered Sir Launcelot to joust, and they came together so fiercely that they bore each other to the earth, and sore were they bruised. Then Beaumains threw away his shield, and proffered to fight Sir Launcelot on foot. So they rushed together, and for the space of an hour they fought, tracing, racing, and feinting.

Sir Launcelot marvelled at Beaumains and his strength, for he fought like a giant more than a knight, and his fighting was passing durable and perilous. So Sir Launcelot had much ado not to be ashamed, and said to him, "Beaumains, fight not so sore; your quarrel and mine is not so great but we may leave off."

"That is truth," said Beaumains; "but it doth me good to feel your might, and yet, my lord, I showed you not the utterance I could do."

"Well," said Sir Launcelot, "I promise you I had enough to do to keep myself unshamed from you; therefore have ye no doubt of any earthly knight."

"Hope ye that any time I may stand a proved knight?" said Beaumains.

"Yea," said Sir Launcelot, "do as ye have done, and I will be your warrant."

"Then, I pray you," said Beaumains, "give me the order of knighthood."

"Ye must tell me your name," said Sir Launcelot, "and of what kin ye were born."

"Sir, so that ye will not discover me, I shall."

"Nay," said Sir Launcelot, "that I promise you, by the faith of my body, until it be openly known."

"Then, sir, my name is Gareth, and brother unto Sir Gawaine, of father and mother."

"Ah, sir!" said Sir Launcelot, "I am more glad than ever I was, for ever methought you were of great blood, and that ye came not to the Court for meat nor for drink." And then Sir Launcelot gave him the order of knighthood.

Sir Gareth then requested Sir Launcelot to depart, and let him go; so he did, and came to Sir Kay, whom he had carried home on his shield. He was hard treated with his life, and all men scorned Sir Kay, and in especial Sir Gawaine; and Sir Launcelot said it was not Sir Kay's part to rebuke any young man, for full little knew he of what birth he had come, or for what cause he came to the Court.

Now we will leave Sir Kay, and follow Sir Beaumains.

When he had overtaken the damsel, she said, "What dost thou here? Thou stinkest of the kitchen; thy clothes be foul of the grease and tallow. Weenest thou that I allow ye of the knight thou hast killed? Nay, truly, for thou slewest him unfortunately and cowardly; therefore turn again, foul kitchen-page. I know thee well, for Sir Kay named thee Beaumains: thou art but a tubber, and turner of spits, and a ladle-washer."

"Damsel," said Beaumains, "say what ye will, I will not go from you, whatsoever ye say, for I have undertaken for King Arthur to achieve your adventure, and so I shall finish it or die therefor."

And as they rode on to a wood, there came a man flying towards them with all his might, and said to Beaumains, "O lord, help me, for here in a glade are six thieves, who have taken my lord and bound him, and I fear they will slay him."

"Bring me thither," said Sir Beaumains.

So they rode together till they came to where the knight was bound, and then Sir Beaumains rode unto the thieves, and struck one to death, then another, and then a third, whereat the other three fled. But he rode after, and overtook them, when they turned and assailed him hard; but at the last he slew them, returned and unbound the knight, who thanked him, and prayed them to ride with him to their castle.

"Sir," said Beaumains, "I will have no reward, but God reward me; and also I must follow this damsel."

But when he came nigh her, she bade him ride from her, telling him he smelt all of the kitchen.

"Weenest thou that I have joy of thee?" said she, "for all this deed that I have done is mishap to thee; but thou shalt see a sight that will make thee turn again, and that lightly."

Then the knight who had been rescued of the thieves again asked Sir Beaumains and the damsel to lodge at his castle that night. The damsel consented; but she ceased not to upbraid and chide Sir Beaumains on every occasion.

On the morn the damsel and he took their leave and departed, and came to a ford, where were two knights to stay the passage, whom Beaumains slew; but the damsel gave him no credit for his valour, saying all he did was by misadventure, and not by the prowess of his hands. So he rode with that lady till evensong time, and ever she chid him, and would not rest.

At last they came to a black lawn, where was a black hawthorn, and thereon hung a black banner, and on the other side a black shield. By it stood a great black spear, and a black horse covered with silk.

CHAPTER III

HOW SIR BEAUMAINS FOUGHT WITH THE KNIGHT OF THE
BLACK LAWNS, AND OVERCAME HIM WITH HIS BROTHERS

THERE sat a knight armed in black harness, and his name was the Knight of the Black Lawns. Then the damsel bade Beaumains flee down the valley, for his horse was not saddled.

"Gramercy," said Beaumains, "for always ye would have me a coward."

When they came near the Black Knight, he said, "Damsel, have you brought this knight of King Arthur to be your champion?"

"Nay," she replied, "he is but a kitchen knave that was fed in King Arthur's kitchen for alms."

"Why cometh he," said the knight, "in such array? It is shame he beareth you company."

"Sir, I cannot be delivered of him," she said: "would that ye put him from me, or else to slay him, an ye may, for he is an unhappy knave. Through mishap, I saw him slay two knights at the passage of the water, with other deeds right marvellous, but through unhappiness."

"That marvelleth me," said the Black Knight, "that any man that is of worship will have ado with him."

"They know him not," said the damsel, "and because he rideth with me they think he is of worship born."

"That may be," said the Black Knight; "howbeit, as ye say he is no man of worship, he is a full likely person; but I shall put him down upon one foot; and his horse and his harness he shall leave with me, for it were shame to me to do him any more harm."

When Sir Beaumains heard him say this, he said, "Sir Knight, thou art full liberal of my horse and harness; but whether it liketh thee or not, this lawn I will pass, and horse and harness gettest thou none of me; therefore let see what thou canst do."

"Sayest thou that?" cried the Black Knight. "Now yield thy lady from me, for it beseemeth never a kitchen-page to ride with such a lady."

"Thou liest!" said Beaumains. "I am a gentleman born, and of more high lineage than thou, as I will prove on thy body."

Then in great wrath they departed with their horses, and came together as it had been the thunder. The Black Knight's spear brake, but Beaumains thrust him through both his sides, when his spear brake, and the truncheon left still in the Black Knight's side. Nevertheless, the Black Knight drew his sword, and smote Beaumains full sore; but at the last he fell off his horse in a swoon, and there he died.

Then Beaumains saw him so well horsed and armed that he lighted down, armed him in the knight's armour, took his horse, and made after the damsel. And when she saw him come nigh, she said,—

"Away, kitchen knave! out of the wind! the smell of thy foul clothes agrees not with me. Alas!" she said, "that ever such a knave as thou should by mishap slay so good a knight as thou hast done! But hereby is one shall pay thee all thy payment, therefore I counsel thee flee."

"It may happen me," said Beaumains, "to be beaten or slain; but I will not flee away, or leave your company."

Thus they rode on together, and perceived a knight coming towards them clad all in green, and when he came nigh the damsel he asked her, "Is that my brother, the Black Knight, ye have brought with you?"

"Nay," said she, "this unhappy kitchen knave hath slain your brother through unhappiness."

"Alas!" said the Green Knight, "it is great pity that so noble a knight as he was should be slain by the hand of a knave, as ye say he is. Ah, traitor! thou shalt die for the slaying of my brother."

"I defy thee!" said Beaumains; "for I let thee wit I slew him knightly, and not shamefully."

Then the Green Knight rode unto a horn that was green, and hung upon a thorn-tree. There he blew three deadly notes, and two damsels came and armed him; so he and Beaumains ran together, and either wounded other full ill. At the last, at an over-thwart, Beaumains' horse struck the Green Knight's horse upon the side, and he fell to the earth. The Green Knight avoided his horse lightly, and stood upright, when Sir Beaumains dismounted, and they rushed together like two mighty champions. With that came the damsel, and said, "My lord the Green Knight, why for shame stand ye so long fighting with the kitchen knave?"

Therewith the Green Knight was ashamed, and gave such a great stroke of might, that he clave Beaumains' shield through. He, when he saw his shield cloven, was ashamed of that stroke and the damsel's language, and gave the Green Knight such a buffet on the helm that he fell on his knees, and Beaumains pulled him to the ground grovelling.

Then the Green Knight cried him mercy, which Beaumains would not grant unless the damsel prayed to save his life.

"Fie upon thee, false kitchen knave! I will never pray thee to save his life, for I never will be so much in thy danger."

"Then shall he die," said Beaumains.

"Alas!" said the Green Knight, "suffer me not to die, for a fair word may save me. Fair knight, save my life, and I will forgive thee the death of my brother, will even become thy man, and thirty knights that hold of me shall do you service."

"Sir Knight," said Beaumains, "all this availeth you not but if my damsel speak with thee for my life."

Therewith he made pretence to slay him.

"Let be," said the damsel, "thou foul knave! slay him not, for, an thou do, thou shalt repent it."

"Damsel," replied Beaumains, "your charge is to me a pleasure. At your commandment his life shall be saved, and else not. Sir Knight with the green arms, I release thee quit at this damsel's request, for I will not make her wroth. I will fulfil all that she chargeth me."

Then the Green Knight kneeled down, and did him homage with his sword.

Then said the damsel, "Me repenteth, Green Knight, of your damage, and of your brother's death, for of your help I have great need, as I dread me sore to pass this forest."

"Nay, dread you not," said the Green Knight, "for ye shall lodge with me, and to-morn I shall help you through the forest."

So they took their horses and rode to his manor, which was fast there beside.

All the time the damsel rebuked Beaumains, and would not suffer him to sit at her table; and the Green Knight said to her, "Why do ye rebuke this noble knight? For I warn you, damsel, he is noble, and I know no knight is able to match him. Therefore ye do great wrong to rebuke him, for he shall do you right good service, and prove at the end that he is come of a noble blood and king's lineage."

"Fie, fie!" said the damsel; "it is shame for you to say of him such worship."

"Truly," said the Green Knight, "it were shame for me to say of him any disworship, for he hath proved himself a better knight than I am; yet have I met with many knights, and never have I found knight his match."

Then they went to rest, and the Green Knight commanded thirty men to watch Beaumains, to keep him from all treason.

CHAPTER IV

HOW BEAUMAINS JOUSTED AND DEFEATED THE THIRD BROTHER,
THE RED KNIGHT; AND HOW HE SUFFERED GREAT REBUKES OF
THE DAMSEL

IN THE morn they all arose, and the Green Knight con-
veyed them through the forest, and then he said, "Sir
Beaumains, I and these thirty knights shall be always at your
summons, both early and late, at your calling, and wherever
you will send us."

"It is well said," replied Beaumains; "and when I call
upon you, you must yield you unto King Arthur, and all your
knights."

"Fie, fie!" said the damsel, "that any good knights should
be obedient to a kitchen knave!"

So then departed the Green Knight and the damsel, and
she said unto Beaumains, "Why followest thou me, kitchen
boy? Cast away thy spear and flee away."

"Damsel," said Beaumains, "who is afeard, let him flee, for
it were shame to turn again, having ridden so long with you."

"Well," said the damsel, "ye shall soon whether ye will or
not."

So they went on, and in a while they saw a watch tower
as white as snow, all fenced about and double dyked. Over
the gate hung fifty shields of divers colours; and beneath the
tower was a meadow, wherein were many knights and squires,
for a tournament was to be holden in the morn.

The lord of the tower was within, so, looking out, beheld
a knight, a damsel, and a dwarf, armed at all points.

"By my faith," said the lord, "with that knight will I joust,
for I see he is a knight-errant."

When he was on horseback with his shield and his spear,
they and his armour and trappings were all red; and when he

came nigh to Sir Beaumains, he thought he was his brother, the Black Knight, and cried to him, "Brother, what do ye in these marches?"

"Nay, nay," said the damsel, "it is not he; this is but a kitchen knave, who hath killed thy brother, and his horse and harness was the Black Knight's; also I saw thy brother the Green Knight overcome at his hands. Now may ye be revenged upon him, for I can never be quit of him."

With this either knight departed asunder, and came together with all their might, fighting like two boars for the space of two hours. At the last Sir Beaumains struck the Red Knight to the earth, and he begged for mercy.

"Noble knight," said he, "slay me not, and I shall yield to thee with fifty knights. I will forgive thee all the despite thou hast done to me, and the death of my brother the Black Knight."

"All this availeth not," said Sir Beaumains, "but if my damsel pray thee to save thy life."

So she interceded for him, and the Red Knight asked him to stop at his castle, where they had merry cheer. But the Red Knight marvelled at the words the damsel spoke to Beaumains, and he set threescore knights to watch Beaumains, that he should suffer no villainy.

On the morn the Red Knight proffered his homage and fealty to Beaumains at all times, and agreed to be ready at his summons to come before King Arthur and yield to him. So Sir Beaumains departed with the damsel, and ever she rode, chiding him in the foulest manner.

"Damsel," said Beaumains, "ye are uncourteous to rebuke me as you do, for ever ye threaten me I shall be beaten by knights that we meet, but for all your boast they lie in the dust. Therefore, I pray thee, rebuke me no more."

"Well," said she, "right soon thou shalt meet a knight that shall pay thee all thy wages, for he is the most man of worship of the world, except King Arthur."

Then anon they came near a city rich and fair. Betwixt them and the city, a mile and a half, there was a fair meadow that seemed new mown, wherein were many pavilions fair to behold.

"Lo," said the damsel, "yonder is a lord that owneth yonder city, and his custom is, when the weather is fair, to lie in this meadow to joust and tourney."

"That goodly lord," said Beaumains, "would I fain see."

"Thou shalt see him time enough," said the damsel. "His name is Sir Persant of Inde—the most lordliest knight that ever thou lookedst on."

"Why," said Beaumains, "an he be such a knight as ye make him, he will not set upon me with all his men. An there come no more but one at once, I shall him not fail while life lasteth."

"Fie, fie," said the damsel, "that such a dirty knave should blow such a boast!"

"Ye are to blame," he said, "so to rebuke me, for I had liever do five battles than so to be rebuked. Let him come and do his worst."

"Sir," she said, "I marvel what thou art, of what kin thou art come; boldly thou speakest, and boldly thou hast done, therefore I pray thee save thyself. Here I dread me sore lest I should catch some hurt; but this Sir Persant of Inde is nothing of might or strength unto the knight that laid the siege about my lady."

"Damsel, have ye no doubt but by the grace of God I shall so deal with this knight that within two hours after noon I shall have done with him. Then shall we come to the siege by daylight."

"Ah, mercy! Marvel have I," said the damsel, "what manner of man ye be, for it may never be otherwise but that ye be come of a noble blood, for so foul and shamefully did never woman rule a knight as I have done you, and ever courteously have suffered me: that came never but of gentle blood."

"Damsel," said Beaumains, "a knight may little do that may not suffer a damsel. Whatsoever ye said unto me, I took none heed to your words, but your wrath I wreaked upon them that I had ado withal; therefore all your missaying furthered me in my battle, and caused me to think to prove myself at the end what I was; for though I had meat in King Arthur's kitchen, yet I might have had meat enough in other places; but all that I did to prove my friends. So whether I be a gentleman born or no, fair damsel, I have done you gentleman's service, and peradventure better service yet will I do ere I depart from you."

"Alas!" she said, "fair Beaumains, forgive me all that I have missaid or misdone against you."

"With all my heart," said he, "I forgive it you, for ye did nothing but as ye should do, for all your evil words pleased me. And, damsel, since it liketh you to speak thus fair to me, wit ye well it gladdeth mine heart greatly, and now meseemeth there is no knight living but I am able enough for him."

CHAPTER V

HOW SIR BEAUMAINS FOUGHT WITH SIR PERSANT OF INDE, AND MADE HIM TO BE YIELDEN

SIR PERSANT of Inde spied them as they tarried in the field, and knightly he sent to them to know whether Sir Beaumains came in war or in peace. So Beaumains returned answer that it should be as pleased Sir Persant, who said he would have ado with him.

Then Beaumains made him ready, and they met, breaking their spears together, and gave each other many great blows, so that their harness was all cut to pieces, and they were sore wounded. But at the last Sir Beaumains smote Sir Persant through the body, and he still maintained the battle, until Sir Beaumains smote him on the helm. With that the damsel came and begged his life.

"I will well," said Beaumains; "I would not the noble knight should die."

"Gramercy, gentle knight and damsel," said Sir Persant. "Now I know well ye slew the Black Knight my brother: he was a good knight, and his name was Sir Percard. Also I am ware ye won my other brother, the Green Knight, whose name is Sir Pertolepe. Also ye won the Red Knight, my brother, whose name is Sir Perimones. Now, sir, since ye have won all these knights, ye shall have homage and fealty of me, and a hundred knights shall always be at your command, to go and ride where ye will command us."

So they went unto Sir Persant's pavilion, and there Beaumains drank wine and ate spices; and after supper he had a bed there, where he remained till morning.

On the morn Sir Persant said, "Whither are ye leading away this knight?"

"Sir," replied the damsel, "this knight is going to help my sister, who is besieged in the Castle Dangerous."

"Ah," said Persant, "that is by the Knight of the Red Lawn, which is the most perilous knight that I know now living, a man without mercy, who they say hath seven men's strength. God save you from that knight," he said to Beaumains, "for he doth great wrong to that lady, who is one of the fairest of the world, and meseemeth that your damsel is her sister. Is not your name Linet?" he asked.

"Yea, sir," she replied, "and my lady sister's name is Dame Liones."

"Now shall I tell you," said Sir Persant: "this Red Knight of the Red Lawn hath lain long at the siege, to the intent to have Sir Launcelot du Lake or Sir Tristram or Sir Gawaine to do battle with him. Therefore God speed you well," said he, "for an ye may match the Red Knight, ye shall be called the fourth of the world."

"Sir," said Beaumains, "I would fain be of good fame and knighthood, and so that ye will keep it close, I will tell you of what kin I am."

"We will not discover you," said they both.

"Truly, then," said he, "my name is Gareth of Orkney. King Lot was my father; my mother is King Arthur's sister. Sir Gawaine is my brother, and Sir Agravaine and Sir Gaheris; and I am the youngest of all. Yet wot not King Arthur or Sir Gawaine who I am."

The lady that was besieged had word of her sister's coming by the dwarf, and of the knight with her, and how he had passed all the perilous passages. Then the lady said, "Dwarf, I am glad of these tidings, therefore go thou to a hermitage of mine hereby, and bear with thee wine and bread, with fat venison and dainty fowls. A cup of gold here I deliver thee that is rich and precious; bear all this to thy hermitage, and put it into the hermit's hands. Then go thou to my sister, and greet her well. Commend me also to that gentle knight, and pray him to eat and drink and make him strong, and say ye that I thank him for his courtesy and goodness."

So the dwarf departed, and came to Sir Persant, where he found the damsel Linet and Sir Beaumains; so within a little while they came to the hermitage, and there they drank the wine, and ate the venison and the fowls.

Upon the morn Beaumains and the damsel took their horses and rode through a fair forest. Then they came to a plain, and saw there many pavilions and tents, and a castle where there was much smoke and much noise. When they came near the siege, Sir Beaumains espied upon great trees that there hung full goodly armed knights by the neck, and their shields about their necks, with their swords agirt, spurs upon their heels. Then said Sir Beaumains, "What meaneth this?"

"Fair sir," said the damsel, "abate not your cheer for all this sight. These knights came thither to rescue my sister Dame Liones, and when the Red Knight of the Red Lawns had overcome them, he put them to shameful death without mercy or pity; and in the same wise he will serve you, if ye quit ye not the better."

Then they rode into the ditches and saw them double dyked, and there were lodged many great knights in either walls; and there was great noise of minstrelsy. And the sea rose upon one side of the walls, where were many ships, and the noise of mariners, with "hale and how." Also there was close by a sycamore-tree, and there hung a horn of an elephant's bone. The Knight of the Red Lawns had hanged it there, so that if any knight-errant came he should blow the horn, and then the Red Knight would come and do him battle.

"But, sir, I pray you," said the damsel Linet, "blow ye not the horn till it be to high noon, for now it is about prime, and he increaseth his might till, as men say, he hath the strength of seven."

"Ah, fie, for shame, fair damsel! Say ye never more to me, for I should never fail him in his most might. Either I will win worship worshipfully, or die knightly in the field."

Therewith he spurred his horse straight to the sycamore-tree, and blew the horn so loudly, that the siege and the castle rang thereof. Then the Red Knight of the Red Lawns armed him hastily, and two barons set on his spurs upon his heels; all was blood-red—his spear, his shield, and armour. An earl buckled his helm upon his head, and they brought him a red steed. So he rode into a little vale under the castle, that all that were at the siege and in the castle might behold the battle.

CHAPTER VI

HOW THE KNIGHTS MET; AND OF THEIR LONG FIGHTING; AND HOW SIR BEAUMAINS DEFEATED THE RED KNIGHT, AND MADE HIM YIELD TO KING ARTHUR

SIR," said the damsel Linet unto Sir Beaumains, "yonder is your deadly enemy, and at the window is my sister, Dame Liones."

"Where?" said Beaumains.

"Yonder," replied the damsel, as she pointed to the casement.

"She beseemeth the fairest lady that ever I looked on," said he; "and truly I ask no better quarrel than now to do battle, for truly she shall be my lady, and for her I will fight."

And ever he looked up at the window with glad countenance. Then the Lady Liones made curtsey to him, whereat the Knight of the Red Lawns called to Sir Beaumains, and said,—

"Leave, Sir Knight, thy looking, and behold me, I counsel thee, for I warn you she is my lady, and for her I have done many strong battles."

"If thou hast so done, it seemeth to me but waste labour, for she loveth none of thy fellowship, and thou to love who loves not thee is great folly; for an I understood she were not glad of my coming, I would be advised or I did battle for her. Wilt thou well I love her, and will rescue her, or else die."

"Sayest thou that?" said the Red Knight. "Meseemeth thou ought of reason to beware by yonder knights that thou sawest on yonder trees."

"Fie, for shame," said Beaumains, "that ever thou shouldst do or say so evil, for in that thou shamest thyself and knighthood, and thou mayest be sure no lady will love thee that knoweth thy wicked customs."

"Make thee ready," said the Knight of the Red Lawns, "and talk no longer with me."

Then Sir Beaumains had the damsel go from him and the knights put their spears in rest. Then they came together with such force that their breastplates, horse-girths, and cruppers burst. So they both fell to the earth, and the reins of their bridles in their hands, and thus they lay a great while sore astonied.

All that were in the castle and the siege weened their necks were broken, and then many said the stranger knight was a big man and a noble jouster, for they never saw a knight match the Knight of the Red Lawns.

But after a while the jousters arose, and avoided their horses, and put their shields before them. Then drawing their swords, they buffeted each other so upon the helms that they reeled backwards, and hewed great pieces out of their harness and their shields.

So they fought till it was past noon, and never would stint, until at last they lacked wind both, and then they stood panting and bleeding sore, that all wept for pity. Then they went to battle again, and so on until evensong time, and none could tell which was likely to win the battle. By that time their armour was so hewn that in places men might see their naked bodies; but ever the naked places they did defend.

The Red Knight was a wily man of war, and his wiliness cautioned Sir Beaumains to be wise; but he bought it full sore until he did espy his fighting. At last, by assent of both, they granted each other rest, and sat down on two molehills, while the pages came and unlaced their helms.

When Sir Beaumains' helm was off, he looked up, and saw the fair lady, Dame Liones, and she made him such countenance that his heart waxed light and jolly; and so he bade the Knight of the Red Lawns make ready and do battle to the uttermost.

Then they laced up their helms, and fought freshly. But

the Knight of the Red Lawns awaited Sir Beaumains, and at an over-thwart he smote him within the hand, so that his sword fell from his grasp, and then he gave him another buffet on the helm, that he fell grovelling to the earth; and the Red Knight fell over him to hold him down.

Then cried the maiden Linet on high, "O Sir Beaumains! where is thy courage become? Alas! my lady my sister beholdeth thee, and she sobbeth and weepeth, and maketh my heart heavy."

When Sir Beaumains heard her say so, he started up with great might and gat upon his feet, and gripping his sword, he doubled his pace unto the Red Knight, and smote him so thick that he beat him down upon the earth, and Sir Beaumains fell upon him, and unlaced his helm to have slain him.

Then the Red Knight said, "O knight, I yield to thy mercy."

But Sir Beaumains replied, "I may not with worship save thy life, for the shameful deaths thou hast caused many good knights to die."

"Sir," said the Knight of the Red Lawns, "hold your hand, and ye shall know the cause whereby I put them so to death."

"Say on," said Sir Beaumains.

"Sir, I once loved a lady, and she had her brother slain by Sir Launcelot or by Sir Gawaine, and she prayed me heartily that I would make her a promise, by the faith of my knighthood, to labour daily in arms till I met with one of them, and that I should put all I met unto a shameful death. This is the cause for so I ensured her to do all the villainy unto King Arthur's knights, and take vengeance upon them. And now, sir, I will tell thee that every day my strength increaseth till noon and all this time I have seven men's strength."

Then came many earls and barons and noble knights, and prayed Sir Beaumains to save the life of the Red Knight, promising honour and fealty if he consented, where by his death he had no advantage.

"Fair lords," said Beaumains, "wit you well I am full loth to slay the knight, nevertheless he hath done passing ill and shamefully. But as he did it at a lady's request I blame him the less; so for your sakes I will release him, if he will yield him to the lady, and she will quit and forgive him. And also he must make her amends of all the trespass he hath done; and then must he go to the Court of King Arthur, and there ask Sir Launcelot forgiveness, and Sir Gawaine, for the evil he has done against them."

"Sir," said the Red Knight, "all this will I do as thou dost command, and certain assurance and sureties ye shall have."

So when the assurance was made he made his homage and fealty, and all the earls and barons with him. Then the maiden Linet came unto Sir Beaumains and unarmed him, and searched his wounds; so she did also to the Knight of the Red Lawns. Then they sojourned ten days in their tents, and the Red Knight made all his servants do Sir Beaumains' pleasure. Then, within a while, the Red Knight of the Red Lawns went into the castle, and put him in the Lady Liones' grace. So she received him on sufficient security; and all her hurts were well restored. Then the knight departed unto the Court of King Arthur, and there he put himself openly in the mercy of Sir Launcelot and Sir Gawaine, and told them how and by whom he had been overcome, and all the battles.

"Mercy!" said King Arthur and Sir Gawaine; "we wonder of what blood he be come? He is a noble knight."

"Have ye no marvel," said Sir Launcelot, "for ye shall right well wit that he comes of a full noble blood; for his might and hardiness, there be few living so mighty as he is, and so noble of prowess."

"It seemeth that you know his name," said King Arthur, "and from whence he comes, and of what blood he is?"

"I suppose I do so," replied Sir Launcelot, "or else I would not have given him the order of knighthood; but he gave me such charge at the time that I should never discover him until he required me, or else it be known openly by some other."

CHAPTER VII

HOW SIR BEAUMAINS CAME TO THE LADY, AND FOUND THE CASTLE GATES CLOSED AGAINST HIM

NOW we turn unto Sir Beaumains, who desired of Linet that he might see her sister.

"Sir," said she, "I would fain ye saw her."

Then Sir Beaumains armed him, took his horse and his spear, and rode straight to the castle, where he found the drawbridge pulled up and the port closed. He marvelled why they would not suffer him to enter; but when he looked up to the window, there he saw the fair Liones, who said, "Go thy way, Sir Beaumains, for as yet thou shalt not have wholly my love, until thou be called one of the number of the worthy knights. Therefore go labour in worship this twelvemonth, and then thou shalt hear new tidings."

"Alas, fair lady! I have not deserved ye should show me this strangeness."

"Fair courteous knight," said Dame Liones, "be not displeased nor over-hasty. A twelvemonth will soon be done; and trust me, fair knight, I will be true to you and never betray you, but to my death shall love you and none other."

Therewith she turned from the window, and Sir Beaumains rode away from the castle, making great dole till it was dark night, when he came to a poor man's house, and there he was harboured. He had no rest, and on the morrow he took his horse and armour and rode till noon, when he came to a broad water, whereby was a great lodge. There he alighted to sleep, and commanded his dwarf to watch all night.

Meantime the lady of the castle thought much upon Sir Beaumains, and called Sir Gringamore her brother, and prayed that he would ride after Sir Beaumains. "Wait for him till you may find him sleeping, and then, in the priviest manner ye can, take his dwarf and go your way with him as fast as you may, or Sir Beaumains awake; for my sister telleth me that the dwarf can tell of what kindred his master is come, and what is his right name; and my sister and I will ride unto your castle to await when ye bring with you the dwarf."

"Sister," said Sir Gringamore, "all this shall be done after your intent."

So he rode all the day and night till he found Sir Beaumains lying by the water to sleep. Then Sir Gringamore came quietly behind the dwarf, plucked him fast under his arm, and rode away unto his own castle; but as he rode with the dwarf he cried unto his lord and prayed him of help, and therewith awoke Sir Beaumains, who leapt up lightly and saw where Sir Gringamore rode his way with the dwarf, and so out of his sight.

Then Sir Beaumains armed himself, and came following his dwarf to Sir Gringamore's castle, where Sir Gringamore and the dwarf had come. Anon Dame Liones and Dame Linet her sister asked the dwarf where was his master born, and of what lineage he was come. Then he told her his name was Sir Gareth of Orkney, brother to the good knight Sir Gawaine.

And as they sat talking there came Sir Gareth in at the gate with an angry countenance, and his sword drawn in his hand. He called aloud, saying, "Thou traitor, Sir Gringamore! Deliver me my dwarf again, or by my faith I will do thee all the harm I can."

Then Sir Gringamore looked out at the window, and said, "Sir Gareth of Orkney, leave thy boasting words, for thou gettest not thy dwarf again."

"Thou coward knight!" said Sir Gareth; "bring him with thee, come and do battle with me—win him and take him."

"So will I do," said Sir Gringamore, "an me list; but for all thy great words thou gettest him not."

"Ah, fair brother!" said Dame Liones, "I would he had his dwarf again, for now he hath told me all I desire I want him no longer."

"Well," said Sir Gringamore, "since I know thy will I will obey unto him." Therewithal he went down to Sir Gareth, and said, "Sir, I cry your mercy; and all that I have misdone I will amend it at your will. Therefore I pray you that ye would alight, and take such cheer as I can make you in this castle."

"Shall I have my dwarf?" said Sir Gareth.

"Yea, sir, and all the pleasure I can make you."

Then Sir Gareth alighted, and there came his dwarf and took his horse.

"Oh, my fellow!" said Sir Gareth, "I have had many adventures for thy sake."

Then Sir Gringamore took him by the hand, and led him into the hall where his own wife was.

CHAPTER VIII

HOW AT THE FEAST OF PENTECOST ALL THE KNIGHTS THAT SIR GARETH HAD OVERCOME YIELDED TO KING ARTHUR, AND HOW HE PARDONED THEM

SO LEAVE we Sir Gareth with Sir Gringamore and his sisters, and turn we unto King Arthur, that at the next Feast of Pentecost held his feast; and there came a Green Knight with fifty knights, and yielded them all to King Arthur; also the Red Knight his brother, with threescore, and the Blue Knight, with a hundred knights, and yielded them all. These three brethren told King Arthur how they were overcome by a knight that a damsel had with her, and called him Beaumains, while the King marvelled who he was, and of what lineage he had come.

As the King stood so talking with the three brethren, there came Sir Launcelot du Lake and told the King that there was come a goodly lord with six hundred knights. Then the King went out of Caerleon, where was the feast, and then came to him this lord and saluted him.

"What will ye?" said King Arthur, "and what is your errand?"

"Sir," he said, "my name is the Red Knight of the Red Lawns, called Sir Ironside; and, sir, wit ye well here I am sent to you by a knight called Beaumains, for he won me in plain battle, hand for hand, which did never no knight but one have the better of me, and commanded to yield me to you at your will."

"Ye are welcome," said the King, "for ye have been long a great foe to me and to my Court, and now I trust that ye shall be my friend."

"Sir, both I and these six hundred knights shall always be at your summons to do your service as may lie in our powers."

"Truly," said King Arthur, "I am much beholden unto that knight; and as to thee, I consider, if thou wilt hold of me, I will make thee knight of the Table Round, but then thou must be no more a murderer."

"Sir, as to that, I have promised Sir Beaumains never more to use such customs. Therefore I must go unto Sir Launcelot and Sir Gawaine and ask them forgiveness of the evil will I had unto them, for all that I put to death were only for their love of Sir Launcelot and Sir Gawaine."

Then he kneeled down to Sir Launcelot and Sir Gawaine, and prayed them of forgiveness of his enmity that ever he had against them.

Then they said, all at once, "God forgive you as we do, and pray you that ye will tell us where we may find Sir Beaumains?"

"Fair lord," said Sir Ironside, "I cannot tell you, for all such young knights as ye be never abiding in one place."

And the worship that the Red Knight and Sir Persant and his brothers said of Beaumains was marvellous to hear.

Then the King and they went to meat, and were served in the best manner. While they sat came in the Queen of Orkney, with ladies and knights a great number, and Sir Gawaine, Sir Agravaine, and Gaheris rose and went to her. They saluted her upon their knees, and asked her blessing, for they had not seen her for fifteen years.

Then she spake aloud to her brother King Arthur: "Where have ye done my young son Sir Gareth? He was here amongst you a twelvemonth, and ye made a kitchen knave of him, which is a shame to you all."

"O dear mother," said Sir Gawaine, "I knew him not."

"Nor I," said the King. "That now me repenteth; but thanked be God he is a worshipful knight as any is now living of his years, and I shall never be glad till I may find him."

"Ah, brother," said the Queen to King Arthur and his knights, "ye did yourselves great shame when ye kept my son Gareth in the kitchen, and fed him like a poor hog."

"Fair sister," said King Arthur, "I knew him not, no more

did Sir Gawaine or his brethren. But we must shape a remedy to find him. Also, sister, ye might have done me to wit of his coming; then had I not done well unto him, ye might have blamed me. When he came hither he came leaning on two men's shoulders; and he asked me three gifts, and the first was that I would give him meat enough for a twelvemonth. The other two he asked that day a twelvemonth, and that was that he might have the adventure of the damsel Linet, and that Sir Launcelot should make him a knight. So I granted him all his desire."

"Sir," said the Queen of Orkney, "wit ye well that I sent him to you right well armed and horsed, and worshipfully beseen of his body, with gold and silver in plenty to spend?"

"It may be," said the King, "but thereof saw we none, save that same day as he departed from us, knights told me that there came a dwarf here suddenly, and brought him armour, with a good horse, well and richly beseen, and thereat had we all marvel."

"Brother," said the Queen, "all this I say I believe; but I marvel that Sir Kay did mock and scorn him, and gave him the name Beaumains; yet Sir Kay named him more righteously than he wot of, for I daresay an he be alive he is as fair a handed man as any living."

"Sister," said Arthur, "let this language be still. By the grace of God he shall be found an he be within these seven realms. Let all this pass, and be merry, for he is proved to be a man of worship, and that is my joy."

CHAPTER IX

HOW KING ARTHUR SENT FOR LADY LIONES, AND OF THE GREAT TOURNAMENT HELD AT HER CASTLE

THEN said Sir Gawaine unto King Arthur, "Sir, will ye give us leave to seek our brother?"

"Nay," said Sir Launcelot, "that need ye not, for by our advice the King shall send to Dame Liones a messenger, and pray her to come to the castle with all the haste she may, and doubtless she will come, so then she will give you counsel where ye shall find him."

"That is well said," replied the King.

So goodly letters were written, and the messenger went forth, who travelled night and day, till he came to the Castle Perilous. Then the Lady Liones was sent for, there as she was with Sir Gringamore her brother, and Sir Gareth. And when she had understood the message, she bade the man ride on his way to the King, and she would come after in all goodly haste. So she told the two knights how King Arthur had sent for her.

"That is because of me," said Sir Gareth.

"Now advise me," said Dame Liones, "what shall I say, and in what manner shall I rule me?"

"My lady love," said Sir Gareth, "I pray ye in no manner be ye aknown where I am. Well I wit that my mother is there, and all my brethren, and they will take upon them to seek me. But this I would ye advised the King: that at the Assumption ye do make a call [to a tournament], and the knight that there proveth him best, he shall wed you and all your land. And if he be a wedded man, his wife shall have the degree, and a coronet of gold, beset with stones to the value of a thousand pounds, and a white ger-falcon."

So Dame Liones departed and came to King Arthur, where she was nobly received, but sore questioned of the King and of the Queen of Orkney, but she answered she could not tell where Sir Gareth was. And then she said to Arthur, "Sir, I will cry a tournament that shall be done before my castle, at the Assumption of our Lady, and the cry shall be that you, my Lord Arthur, shall be there with your knights, and my knights shall be against yours; then I am sure we shall hear of Sir Gareth."

"This is well advised," said King Arthur.

So she departed, and great preparations were made for that tournament; and the cry was made in England, Wales, Scotland, Ireland, and Cornwall, in all the out isles, and in Brittany, that at the Feast of the Assumption men should come to this Castle Perilous beside the isle of Avilion, and there all the knights should have choice which party they would join. So there came many good knights that were at large, and held them for the most part against King Arthur and his knights at the Round Table.

But Sir Gareth prayed Dame Liones, and the knights who knew him, that they should in no wise tell his name, for he said, "I will not be known of neither more nor less, neither at the beginning nor at the ending."

Then Dame Liones said to Sir Gareth, "Sir, I will lend you a ring, but I pray you, as you love me heartily, let me have it again when the tournament is done, for that ring increaseth my beauty much more than it is of itself, and whoso beareth the ring shall lose no blood; so for great love I will give you this ring."

Upon the Assumption Day, when mass and matins were done, there were heralds with trumpets commanded to blow to the field. So there came out Epinogrus, the son of the King of Northumberland, and there encountered with him Sir Sagramore le Desirous, and either of them brake their spears to their hands. Then came in Sir Palamides out of the castle, and Gawaine encountered him, so that both the good knights and their horses fell to the earth; and then the knights of either party rescued their knights. After much fighting came in the Red Knight of the Red Lawns, and Sir Gareth from the castle, and there encountered with them Sir Bors de Ganis and Sir Bleoberis. The Red Knight and Sir Bors smote each other so hard that their spears burst, and their horses fell grovelling to the earth. Then Sir Bleoberis brake his spear upon Sir Gareth; but of that stroke Sir Bleoberis fell to the earth. When Sir Galihodin saw that, he bade Sir Gareth keep him, but Sir Gareth smote him to the earth, and in the same way he overcame Sir Galihud and Sir Dinadan, with his brother La Cote Male Taile, Sir Sagramore le Desirous and Sir Dodinas le Savage. Likewise he smote many knights and kings, but the enchantment of the ring made him change his colour every course he rode, so neither king nor knight had any cognizance of him.

"Truly," said King Arthur, "the knight of many colours is a good knight."

And King Arthur had marvel who he was, for the King saw by his hair he was the same knight.

"Now go," said King Arthur to his heralds, "and espy what manner of knight he is, for I have asked many this day, and they all say they knew him not."

So a herald rode nigh Sir Gareth, and saw written about his helm in gold, "This helm is Sir Gareth's of Orkney," and they all cried his name. When Sir Gareth espied that he was discovered, he doubled his strokes, and smote down Sir Sagramore and his brother Sir Gawaine.

"Oh, brother," said Sir Gawaine, "I weened ye would not have stricken me."

When Sir Gareth heard say so, with great pain he gat him out of the press, and by means of his ring he hid his body, so they wist not what had become of him.

Sir Gawaine had in a manner espied where Sir Gareth rode, and he followed him with all his might. But when he was passed, Sir Gareth asked the dwarf his counsel, who advised him to send back Lady Liones her ring.

"It is well advised," said Sir Gareth. "Bear it to her, and

say I will come when I may, and that I pray her to be true and faithful to me as I will be to her."

So the dwarf did his errand unto the lady, who, with her brother Sir Gringamore and forty knights, came to King Arthur's Court, where she had all the cheer that might be done both of the King and of many other kings and queens.

CHAPTER X

HOW SIR GARETH AND DAME LIONES ACKNOWLEDGED THAT THEY LOVED EACH OTHER, AND OF THEIR GREAT WEDDING FEAST

IT CAME to pass that after many adventures Sir Gareth met with his brother Sir Gawaine, and fought with him, when the damsel Linet discovered them to each other. They then embraced, and when their wounds were healed, all three departed to King Arthur's Court. Among all the ladies there, Dame Liones was named the fairest and peerless. Then when Sir Gareth saw her, there was many a goodly look and goodly words, so that all men of worship had joy to behold them.

Then came King Arthur with many other kings, and Dame Guenever with the Queen of Orkney. The King asked his nephew whether he would have the lady for his wife.

"My lord," said Sir Gareth, "wit you well that I love her above all ladies living."

"Now, fair lady," said King Arthur, "what say ye?"

"Most noble King," said Dame Liones, "wit you well that I would rather hold Sir Gareth as my husband than any king or prince; and if I may not have him, I promise you I will have none. He is my first love, and he shall be my last; and if ye will suffer him to have his will and free choice, I daresay he will have me."

"That is truth," said Sir Gareth: "an I hold you not for my wife there shall never lady or gentlewoman rejoice me."

"What, nephew," said the King, "is the wind in that door? I would not for the loss of my crown to be causer to withdraw your hearts, so ye shall have my love and my lordship in the uttermost wise that shall lie in my power."

In the same wise said Sir Gareth's mother.

Then was there made a provision for the day of marriage,

and by the King's advice it was provided that it should be at the Michaelmas following, at Kinkenadon, by the seaside, for there is a plentiful country. So it was cried in all places in the realm.

Sir Gareth sent his summons unto all those knights and ladies that he had won in battle, that they should be at his day of marriage, at Kinkenadon, by the sands; and Dame Liones and Linet, with Sir Gringamore, rode to their castle, where a goodly and rich ring she gave to Sir Gareth, and he gave her another. King Arthur gave her a rich bangle of gold, and he and his fellowship rode towards Kinkenadon, where he was joined by Sir Gareth.

Oh, the great cheer that Sir Launcelot made of Sir Gareth, and he of him! for there was never knight that Sir Gareth loved so well as he did Sir Launcelot, and ever he would be in his company, for he withdrew himself from his brother Sir Gawaine's fellowship, for he was vengeable, and where he hated would be avenged with murder; and he hated Sir Gareth.

So it drew fast to Michaelmas, and thither came Dame Liones and her sister and brother, who were lodged at the device of King Arthur. On Michaelmas Day the Bishop of Canterbury made the wedding betwixt Sir Gareth and Dame Liones with great solemnity. At the same time Sir Gaheris wedded Dame Linet, and Sir Agravaine Dame Liones' niece, Laurel.

When this solemnization was done, the Green Knight, Sir Pertolepe, came with his thirty knights and did homage unto Sir Gareth. Sir Pertolepe also begged that he might be Sir Gareth's chamberlain, and it was granted.

Then came in the Red Knight, with his threescore followers, and did Sir Gareth homage and fealty for evermore; and Sir Perimones prayed Sir Gareth to grant him to be his chief butler at that high feast.

"I will well," said Sir Gareth, "that ye have this office, and that it were better."

Then came in Sir Persant of Inde with a hundred knights,

and did homage and fealty to Sir Gareth, and he prayed him to make him his server chief at the feast.

Then came the Duke de la Rowse with a hundred knights, and there he did homage and fealty unto Sir Gareth, and to hold their lands of him for ever, as the others had done. He required Sir Gareth that he might serve him of the wine that day at the feast.

"I will well," said Sir Gareth, "and that it were better."

Then came in the Red Knight of the Red Lawns, Sir Ironside, and he brought with him three hundred knights, who did homage, and held their lands of him for ever. Sir Ironside asked to be his carver.

"I will well," said Sir Gareth, "an it please you."

Then came into the Court thirty ladies, who all seemed widows, and brought with them many fair gentlewomen. These all kneeled down at once unto King Arthur and Sir Gareth, and told the King how the knight had delivered them from the Dolorous Tower; therefore they and their heirs for evermore would do homage unto Sir Gareth of Orkney.

So the kings and queens, princes, earls, barons, and many knights went unto meat, and there was all manner of it plenteously, with revels and games and minstrelsy of those days. Also there were great jousts three days. But the King would not suffer Sir Gareth to joust, because of his new bride, for it is said that Dame Liones desired the King that none of the wedded should joust at that feast.

On the first day jousted Sir Lamorak de Galis, who overthrew thirty knights, and did passing marvellous deeds of arms. And then King Arthur made Sir Persant of Inde and his two brethren knights of the Round Table, and gave them great lands.

On the second day there jousted Tristram the best; he overthrew forty knights, and did marvellous deeds of arms. King Arthur made Sir Ironside, the Red Knight of the Red Lawns, a knight of the Table Round unto his life's end, and gave him great lands.

The third day jousted Sir Launcelot du Lake. He overthrew fifty knights, and did such marvellous deeds of arms that all men wondered of him; and then King Arthur made the Duke de la Rowse a knight of the Table Round, and gave him great lands to spend.

As soon as these jousts were done, Sir Lamorak and Sir Tristram departed suddenly, and they would not be known, at which King Arthur and all his Court were sore displeased. But they held Court forty days with great solemnity. And this Sir Gareth was a noble knight, well ruled, and fair languaged. Great and mighty lands, with great riches, gave King Arthur to him, and Dame Liones, with the others who wedded, that royally they might all live unto their lives' ends.

CHAPTER I

HOW SIR TRISTRAM DE LIONES WAS BORN; HOW HE WAS NAMED TRISTRAM, AND WAS NEARLY POISONED BY HIS STEPMOTHER

THERE was a King called Meliodas, who ruled the country of Liones (or Lionesse). He married the sister of King Mark of Cornwall, whose name was Elizabeth, a fair lady and a good. At that time King Arthur reigned over England, Wales, and Scotland, and many other realms.

It fell out that one day, while King Meliodas was hunting —for he was a great chaser—that he followed a hart alone till he came to an old castle, where by enchantment he was taken prisoner. When the Queen Elizabeth missed her lord she was nearly out of her mind, and, taking a gentlewoman with her, she ran into the forest to seek her lord. And in this search she took such great cold, that death came upon her; she felt she needs must die, and depart out of this world. So when this Queen Elizabeth saw there was no hope for her, she made great dole, and said to her attendant, "When ye see my lord Meliodas, recommend me unto him, and tell him what I have endured here for his love in default of help; and I charge thee that thou beseech him that when our little child is christened, he be called Tristram—that is to say, the Sorrowful One." Therewith the Queen gave up the ghost and died. Then the gentlewoman laid her under the shadow of a great tree, and proceeded to do as the Queen had commanded her.

On the morn after the Queen died, Merlin delivered King Meliodas out of prison; but the sorrow he made for his Queen no tongue might tell. But he called the child Tristram, as his wife had commanded before her death.

But after seven years it befell that King Meliodas wedded the daughter of King Howell of Britanny, and when she had children, she was wroth that they should not enjoy the country of Liones, wherefore she ordained to poison young Tristram. So she let poison be put into a vessel of silver in the chamber where Tristram and her children were together, so that when he was thirsty he might take that drink.

It so fell upon a day that the Queen's own son espied the cup with poison, and he weened it had been good drink. He took the cup and drank freely, and therewithal fell down and died suddenly. When the Queen wist of the death of her son she was very sad; but notwithstanding she would not leave this, but continued the poison in the cup. By fortune the King found the cup, and would have drunken; but the Queen perceiving it, pulled the cup from him suddenly. The King marvelled why she did so, but at once remembered him how her son had suddenly died of poison.

"Thou false traitress!" said he, "thou shalt tell me what manner of drink this is, or I will slay thee."

"Ah! mercy, my lord," said she, "and I will tell thee all."

Then she told him why she had done it.

"Well," said King Meliodas, "and therefore shall ye have the law."

So she was condemned by the assent of the barons to be burnt, and then was a great fire made. But as she was at the fire to take her execution, young Tristram kneeled before the King, and besought of him a boon. "Give me the life of thy Queen my stepmother," said he.

"That is unrightfully asked," said King Meliodas, "for thou ought to hate her, as she would have slain thee with that poison."

"Sir," said Tristram, "I beseech you of your mercy that you will forgive it her, as I do, and so much it liked your highness to grant me my boon, for God's love I require you hold your promise."

"Since it is so," said the King, "I will that she have her life. Go ye to the fire, take her, and do ye with her what ye will."

So Sir Tristram delivered her from death. But after that King Meliodas would never see her again, until by the good means of Tristram he made the King and her accorded, when Meliodas would not suffer his son to abide longer at the Court.

CHAPTER II

HOW TRISTRAM WAS SENT INTO FRANCE, AND LEARNED TO HAWK AND TO HUNT; HOW HE ENTERPRISED THE BATTLE FOR THE TRUAGE OF CORNWALL, AND WAS MADE KNIGHT

SO KING MELIODAS put young Tristram under the care of a gentleman well taught and learned, whose name was Gouvernail, and sent him into France to learn the language and nurture and deeds of arms. There was Tristram more than seven years; and when he had learned all that he might be taught in that country, he came home to his father, King Meliodas, again.

So Tristram learnt to be a harper passing all other; and after he was grown in might and strength, he laboured ever in hunting and in hawking, so that never gentleman knew more that ever we heard tell of. And, as the book saith, he began good measures of blowing of beasts of venery and of beasts of chase, and all these terms we have yet of hawking and hunting. Therefore the book of venery, of hawking and hunting, is called the Book of Sir Tristram.

Thus Sir Tristram endured in Cornwall until he was big and strong, of the age of nineteen years, and King Meliodas, and the Queen his wife, had great joy of Sir Tristram, for as Sir Tristram had saved her from the fire she loved him ever after, and gave him many great gifts, for every estate loved him where that he went.

But it happened that King Anguish of Ireland sent to King Mark of Cornwall for the truage that Cornwall had paid many winters, but King Mark was behind of the tribute for seven years; and he and his barons said they would none pay, but sent a message to King Anguish, that if he would have truage he should send a trusty knight of his hand who would fight for his right, "and we will find another to defend our right."

When King Anguish heard this answer he was very wroth, and called Sir Marhaus, the good knight, that was nobly proved, being a knight of the Table Round. This Sir Marhaus was brother to the Queen of Ireland, and he right gladly undertook the journey, and arrived in Cornwall by the castle of Tintagel.

When King Mark understood that he had arrived there to fight for Ireland he was sorry, for they knew no knight that durst take ado with him. But Sir Marhaus abode in the sea, and every day sent to King Mark to pay the truage that was behind, and the barons counselled King Mark to send to the Court of King Arthur to seek Sir Launcelot du Lake, and cries were made in every place that what knight would fight to save the truage of Cornwall, he should be rewarded, so that he should fare the better the term of his life.

Meanwhile came the language and the noise unto King Meliodas, how Sir Marhaus abode battle fast by Tintagel, and how King Mark could find no manner of knight to fight for him. When young Tristram heard of this he was wroth, and went unto his father to ask him what was best to do for to recover from Cornwall truage; "For as me seemeth," said Sir Tristram, "it were shame that Sir Marhaus, the Queen's brother of Ireland, should go away, unless that he were fought with."

"As for that," said King Meliodas, "wit ye well, son Tristram, that Sir Marhaus is called one of the best knights of the world, and I know no knight in this country who is able to match with him."

"Alas," said Sir Tristram, "that I am not made knight! and if Sir Marhaus should thus depart into Ireland, may I never have worship an I were made knight I should match him. Sir," he continued, "I pray you give me leave to ride to King Mark, and so ye be not displeased, of him will I be made knight."

"I will well," said King Meliodas, "that ye be ruled as your courage will rule you."

So this young Sir Tristram rode unto his uncle, to King Mark of Cornwall, and said, "Sir, if ye will give me the order of knighthood I will do battle with Sir Marhaus."

"What are ye?" said the King, "and from whence are ye come?"

"Sir," said Tristram, "I come from King Meliodas, that wedded your sister, and a gentleman wit ye well I am."

King Mark beheld Sir Tristram, but saw he was a young man, though passingly well made and big. Then he inquired his name and where he was born.

"Sir, my name is Tristram, and in the country of Liones was I born."

Then King Mark made him knight, and sent a messenger unto Sir Marhaus to say that he had found a young knight ready to take the battle to the uttermost.

"It may well be," said Sir Marhaus, "but tell King Mark that I will fight with no knight but if he be of blood royal."

Then King Mark sent unto Sir Marhaus, and told him that a better born man than he was himself should fight with him, his name Sir Tristram de Liones, the son of King Meliodas, and King Mark's sister. Sir Marhaus was glad and blithe that he should fight with such a gentleman, and so it was arranged that they should fight on an island nigh Sir Marhaus' ships.

So was Sir Tristram, and all that belonged to him, put into a vessel; but when King Mark and his barons beheld how young Sir Tristram departed to fight for the right of Cornwall, there was neither man nor woman of worship but wept to see and understand so young a knight to jeopard himself for their right.

CHAPTER III

HOW SIR TRISTRAM ARRIVED ON THE ISLAND AND FOUGHT WITH SIR MARHAUS, WHO DIED OF HIS WOUNDS IN IRELAND

WHEN Sir Tristram arrived within the island, he commanded his servant Gouvernail to bring his horse to the land; and when he was in the saddle, well apparelled, he asked Gouvernail, "Where is the knight that I shall have ado withal?"

"Sir," said Gouvernail, "see ye him not? I weened ye had seen him. Yonder he hovereth, under the shadow of his ships, upon horseback, his spear in his hand and his shield upon his shoulder."

"That is truth," said Sir Tristram; "now I see him well enough."

Then he commanded his servant Gouvernail, and said, "Go, commend me unto my uncle King Mark, and pray him, if that I be slain in this battle, to inter my body as to him seemeth best. As for me, let him wit that I will never run for cowardice; and if I be slain and flee not, then have they lost no truage for me. But if it so be that I flee or yield me as recreant, bid my uncle never bury me in Christian burial; and upon thy life come thou not nigh this island till thou see me overcome or slain, or else that I win yonder knight."

So either departed from the other sore weeping. Then Sir Marhaus perceived Sir Tristram, and said, "Young knight, what doest thou here? Me sore repenteth of thy courage, for wit thou well the best knights of this land have been assayed of my hands, and I have matched the best knights of the world; therefore, by my counsel, return again to thy vessel."

"Fair knight, and well proved knight," said Sir Tristram, "thou shalt well wit I may not forsake thee in this quarrel.

I am a King's son, and such promise I have made that I shall fight with thee to the uttermost, and deliver Cornwall from the old truage. And also wit ye well, Sir Marhaus, that this is the greatest cause that thou couragest me to have ado with you, for thou art called one of the most renowned knights of the world, and I am well pleased to have ado with such a good knight as thou art."

"Fair knight," replied Sir Marhaus, "since it is so that thou castest to win worship on me, I let thee wit thou mayest lose no worship if thou stand me three strokes; for I tell you, for my noble deeds proved and seen, King Arthur made me knight of the Table Round."

Then they placed their spears in rest, and met so fiercely together, that they smote each other down, both horse and all; but Sir Marhaus smote Sir Tristram a great wound in the side with his spear. Then they avoided their horses, pulled out their swords, and lashed together as men that were wild and courageous.

When they had stricken so together long, they left their strokes and feinted at each other's visors, and when they saw they might not prevail, they hurtled together like rams to bear each other down. Thus they fought more than half a day, and either was wounded passing sore that the blood ran down freshly from them upon the ground.

By that time Sir Tristram waxed fresher than Sir Marhaus, and being better winded and bigger, with a mighty stroke he smote Sir Marhaus upon the helm such a buffet that it pierced it through the coil of steel and through the brain-pan. The sword stuck so fast in the helm and in the brain-pan that Sir Tristram pulled thrice at his sword or ever he might pull it out from the head of Sir Marhaus, who fell down on his knees, the edge of the sword being still in his brain-pan.

Suddenly Sir Marhaus rose grovelling, threw his sword and shield from him, and ran away to his ships; so Sir Tristram had ever his shield and his sword. When Sir Tristram saw him go, he said, "Ah, Sir Knight of the Round Table, why withdrawest thou? thou doest thyself and thy kin great shame, for I am but a young knight; yet rather than I should withdraw from thee, I would be hewn in a hundred pieces."

Sir Marhaus answered no word, but went his way, sore groaning.

"Well, Sir Knight," said Tristram, "I promise thee thy sword and thy shield shall be mine; thy shield shall I wear in all places where I ride on my adventures, and in the sight of King Arthur and all the Round Table."

Anon Sir Marhaus and his fellowship departed into Ireland; and when his head was searched a piece of Sir Tristram's sword was found therein, and might never be had out of his head. So he died of Sir Tristram's sword, and that piece of it the Queen his sister kept for ever with her, for she thought to be revenged an she might.

CHAPTER IV

OF SIR TRISTRAM WOUNDED, AND HOW HE WAS PUT TO THE KEEPING OF LA BELLE ISOLDE FOR TO BE HEALED

NOW we turn to Sir Tristram, who was sore wounded, and full sore bled, that he might not within a little while scarcely stir him of his limbs when he had taken cold. Then he sat him down softly upon a little hill, and bled fast.

Then anon came Gouvernail his man with his vessel, and the King and his barons came in procession. When he was come to the land, King Mark took Sir Tristram in his arms, and he and Sir Dinas the seneschal led him into the castle of Tintagel; and when King Mark saw his wounds he wept heartily, and so did all his lords.

"So God me help," said King Mark, "I would not for all my lands that my nephew died."

So Sir Tristram lay there a month and more, and was like to die of the stroke that Sir Marhaus smote him first with the spear; for as the French book saith, the spear's head was envenomed, so that Sir Tristram might not be whole. Then the King and his barons were passing heavy, for they deemed Sir Tristram should not recover, and the King sent after all manner of leeches and surgeons, both men and women.

Then came there a lady, and she said plainly to Sir Tristram that he should never be whole unless he went to the same country that the venom came from, and in that country he would recover, or else never.

When King Mark understood that, he had a vessel well victualled, and therein was put Sir Tristram and Sir Gouvernail; and Sir Tristram took his harp. So he was sent to Ireland, and by good fortune he arrived even fast by a castle where the King and Queen were. At his arrival he sat and harped in his bed a merry lay; such a one never they heard in Ireland before that time.

When it was told the King and the Queen that there was a knight such a harper, anon the King sent for him, and had his wounds searched. Then he asked his name, and Sir Tristram told him he was of the country of Liones, and his name was Tramtrist, who had been wounded in a battle for a lady's right.

"Truly," replied King Anguish, "ye shall have all the help in this land that ye may have here. But I let you wit that in Cornwall I had as great loss as ever king had, for there I lost my best knight of the world, Sir Marhaus." And then he told Sir Tristram how Sir Marhaus was slain, and the knight made semblance to be very sorry, but better knew he how it was than the King.

Then King Anguish for great favour put Tramtrist under the care of his daughter, who was a noble surgeon. When she had searched him she found poison at the bottom of his wound, and healed him within a while. Therefore Tramtrist felt a great love for La Belle Isolde, who was at that time the fairest lady of the world. He taught her to harp, and she began to have a great fancy for Tramtrist.

At that time Sir Palamides was at the Court, and high in favour of the King and Queen. And every day he offered La Belle Isolde gifts, for he loved her passing well. Sir Tramtrist espied all this, and knew that Sir Palamides was a mighty man. So there was much jealousy between them. Then it came to pass that a great tournament was cried for a lady called the Lady of the Laundes, a cousin to the King, and what man should win her might wed her and have all her lands.

Now it happened that La Belle Isolde came one day and told Sir Tramtrist of this tournament, and he answered and said, "Fair lady, I am but a feeble knight, and but lately I had been dead had not your ladyship been here. Now what would ye that I do in this matter? Well ye wot that I may not joust."

"Ah, Tramtrist!" said she, "why will ye not have ado at

this tournament? Well I wot Sir Palamides will be there to do what he may, and therefore I pray you to be there, else he is likely to win the degree."

"Madam," said Sir Tramtrist, "it may well be so, for he is a proved knight, and I am but a young knight, late made; and the first battle I did it went hard with me, and I was sore wounded. But, an I wit ye would be my better lady at the tournament, I will be there, so that ye keep my counsel and let no one know that I shall joust: my poor person I will jeopard for your sake, that peradventure Sir Palamides shall know whence I come."

"Thereto do your best," said La Belle Isolde, "and I will purvey you horse and armour at my devise."

"As ye will, so be it," replied Tramtrist. "I am at your commandment."

So at the day of the jousts there came Sir Palamides with a black shield, and he overthrew many knights, so that all the people had marvel at him. For he put to the worse Sir Gaheris, Sir Gawaine, Sir Agravaine, Sir Bagdemagus, Sir Kay, and many other; and these all he struck down on the first day. So all the knights were adread of Sir Palamides, and many called him the Knight with the Black Shield. Thus he had great worship.

Then came King Anguish unto Sir Tramtrist, and asked him why he did not joust.

"Sir," he replied, "I was but lately hurt, and dare not venture."

Soon afterwards a squire came up and recognized Sir Tramtrist, and fell flat on his face at the knight's feet. But Sir Tramtrist charged him not to tell his name, and he consented; but La Belle Isolde thought that Sir Tramtrist was some man of worship proved, and therewith she comforted herself, and loved him more than ever she had done.

CHAPTER V

HOW SIR TRISTRAM WON THE DEGREE AT THE TOURNAMENT, AND MADE SIR PALAMIDES TO BEAR NO HARNESS FOR A YEAR

SO IN the morn Sir Palamides made ready to come into the field as he did on the first day, and he smote down the King of the Hundred Knights and the King of Scotland. La Belle Isolde had well arrayed Sir Tramtrist in white harness, with a white horse; and then she let him out of a private postern, so he came to the field as it were a bright angel.

Anon Sir Palamides espied him, and encountered him; but Sir Tramtrist smote down Sir Palamides to the earth. And there was a great disturbance, but the Belle Isolde was passing glad. Sir Gawaine and his fellow, all had marvel what knight he was who had overthrown Palamides. And none would joust with Sir Tramtrist, but all forsook him.

And when Sir Palamides had recovered from his fall he was sore ashamed, and withdrew from the field as privily as he might. All this perceived Sir Tramtrist, and lightly he rode after Sir Palamides, and bade him turn, for better he would assay him ere he departed. Then Sir Palamides turned him, and they lashed at one another with their swords; but at the first stroke Tramtrist smote Sir Palamides, and felled him to the earth.

Sir Tramtrist then bade him do his commandment, else he would slay him; and when Sir Palamides beheld his countenance, he so dreaded his buffets that he did all his asking.

"Well," said Sir Tristram unto him, "this shall be your charge. First, that upon pain of your life ye forsake my lady Isolde, and in no manner approach her; also this twelvemonth and a day ye must bear no armour nor none harness of war. Now, promise me this, or else thou shalt die."

"Alas!" said Sir Palamides, "for ever am I ashamed."

Then he sware as Sir Tristram had commanded him, and for despite and rage he cut off his harness, and threw it all away. So Sir Tristram turned again to the castle where was the Belle Isolde; and by the way he met with a damsel, who asked after Sir Launcelot. And she inquired of Sir Tristram who he was, for he told her that he had smitten Sir Palamides, who had vanquished King Arthur's ten knights. The damsel prayed him to tell her who he was, and whether he was Sir Launcelot du Lake, for she deemed there was no knight in the world, save Sir Launcelot, who might do such deeds of arms.

"Fair damsel," said Sir Tristram, "wit ye well that I am not Sir Launcelot, for I was never of such prowess; but in God is all, and He may make me as good a knight as Sir Launcelot."

"Now, gentle knight," said she, "put up thy visor."

When she beheld his features, she thought she had never seen a better man's visage, nor a better faring knight. So when she thus knew certainly that he was not Sir Launcelot, then she took her leave and departed from him.

Then Sir Tristram rode on, and came privily to the postern, where La Belle Isolde met him, and bade him good cheer, and thanked God for his good speed. Anon within a while the King and Queen understood that it was Sir "Tramtrist," who had smitten down Sir Palamides, and the young knight was made of more worship than he had been before.

CHAPTER VI

HOW THE QUEEN ESPIED WHO SIR TRAMTRIST WAS, AND HIS
JEOPARDY; AND HOW HE FOUGHT WITH KING MARK HIS UNCLE

THEN was Sir "Tramtrist" much cherished of King Anguish and his Queen and La Belle Isolde. But it fell out one day, while the knight was at the bath, that the Queen and the Belle Isolde entered his chamber, and by chance beheld his sword as it lay upon his bed. The Queen drew it out, and beheld it for a long while, thinking it was a passing fair sword, until she noticed that within a foot and a half of the point there was a great piece broken out of it. And when the Queen saw this, she remembered the piece of the sword that had been in Sir Marhaus' brain-pan.

"Alas!" she said unto her daughter, "this is the same traitor knight that slew my brother thine uncle."

When Isolde heard her say that, she was abashed, for well she loved Sir Tristram, and full well she knew the cruelness of her mother the Queen. Anon, therefore, the Queen went into her own chamber, and sought her coffer, whence she took out the piece of the sword that had been taken from the head of Sir Marhaus after he was dead. Then she ran to Sir "Tramtrist's" chamber with the piece of iron, and found it fitted to the sword that lay upon the bed as if it had been only new broken.

Then the Queen hurried to the bath, gripping the sword in her hand, and there would have roved Sir Tramtrist through as he sat, had not Sir Hebes, who attended him, caught the Queen in his arms, and pulled the sword from her. Then, when she was prevented of her evil will, she ran to the King, and said, kneeling,—

"O my lord, here have ye in your house the traitor knight that slew my brother and your servant, Sir Marhaus."

"Who is that?" inquired the King.

"It is Sir Tramtrist, the same knight my daughter healed."

"Alas!" said the King, "now am I right heavy. He is as noble knight as ever I saw in the field. I charge you not to have to do with this knight. Let me deal with him."

Then the King went into the knight's chamber, and found him fully armed and ready to mount his horse. When the King found him all ready armed, he said to him, "Nay, Tramtrist, it will not avail to compare against me. But this will I do for my worship and for thy love. Insomuch as thou art within my Court, it were no worship for me to slay thee. Therefore on this condition I will give thee leave to depart in safety, so thou wilt tell me who was thy father, what is thy name, and whether thou slew Sir Marhaus my brother."

"Sir," replied Sir Tramtrist, "I will tell thee all the truth. My father's name is Meliodas, King of Liones; my mother's name was Elizabeth, sister unto King Mark of Cornwall. My mother died in the forest after I was born, and she commanded that I should be called Tristram. But because I should not be known in this country, I turned my name and called me 'Tramtrist.' For the truage of Cornwall I fought for mine uncle's sake, and for the right of Cornwall, that ye had possessed many years. I did the battle only for the love of mine uncle King Mark, for the love of the country of Cornwall, and for my own honour. For on that same day that I fought Sir Marhaus I was made knight, and I fought Sir Marhaus, who went from me alive, but left his shield and his sword behind."

"Truly," said the King, "I may not say but ye did it as a knight should, and as it was your part to do, to increase your worship as a knight; howbeit I may not contain you in this country with my worship without displeasing my barons, my wife, and her kin."

"Sir," said Tristram, "I thank you for your goodness I have had with you here, and the great kindness my lady your daughter hath showed me; and therefore it may happen that ye shall win more by my life than by my death, for it may be I shall do you service at some season that ye shall be glad ye ever showed me your good lordship. With more I promise you, as I am true knight, that in all places I shall be my lady your daughter's servant and knight. I beseech your good grace that I may take leave of her and the barons and knights."

The King consented, and Sir Tristram went and took leave of La Belle Isolde. He told her all; how he changed his name, and how he never could have been made whole till he came to this country, where the poison was made.

"O gentle knight," said La Belle Isolde, "full woe am I of thy departing, for I saw never man I owed so good will to."

Then Sir Tristram gave her a ring, and she gave him another. Thus he departed from her, leaving her making great dole and lamentation. Then he went into the Court among all the barons, and said, "Fair lords, now it is that I must depart: if there be any here that I have offended, or any be with me grieved, let him complain here before me, and I shall amend it unto my power. If there be any that shall proffer me wrong or say of me wrong behind my back, say it now or never, and here is my body to make it good."

But there was not one of them to say a word, though were there some knights that were of the Queen's blood and Sir Marhaus' blood; yet they would not meddle with him. So Sir Tristram departed and arrived at Tintagel, whereof King Mark was passing glad, and so were all the barons. Then Sir Tristram rode to his father King Meliodas, and there he had all the cheer the King and Queen could make him. Afterwards he returned to the Court of King Mark, and lived in great joy, until at last there fell a jealousy and an unkindness between the King and Sir Tristram.

So after awhile it came to pass that King Mark determined to await Sir Tristram as he rode, and a knight called Segwarides rode out after him one day, and after awhile overtook him, and calling upon as a false traitor, bade him turn against him. So Sir Tristram turned, and therewithal Segwarides smote him with a spear that broke to pieces, and then swinging out his sword, he smote fast at him again.

"Sir Knight," said Sir Tristram, "I counsel ye that ye smite no more. I will forbear you as long as I may."

"Nay," said Segwarides, "that shall not be, for either thou shalt die, or I."

Then Sir Tristram drew out his sword, and hurtled his horse unto him fiercely; then through the waist he smote Sir Segwarides, that he fell to the earth in a swoon. So Sir Tristram departed and left him, and rode into Tintagel. He wist not that it had been King Mark that had sent to meet with him; but as long as he lived he loved never Sir Tristram after that, though there was fair speech, but love there was none; and King Mark cast always in his heart how he might destroy him.

With this view he imagined to send Sir Tristram into Ireland for La Belle Isolde, for Sir Tristram had so praised her beauty and her goodness that King Mark said he would wed her, whereupon he prayed Sir Tristram to take his way into Ireland for him on message. But all this was done with the intent to slay Sir Tristram, so he departed and took the sea, with all his fellowship. Anon, as he was in the broad sea, a tempest overtook him, and drove the ship back unto the coast of England, and there they arrived fast by Camelot. When they were landed, Sir Tristram set up his pavilion on the land of Camelot, and there he hung his shield.

CHAPTER VII

HOW KING ANGUISH OF IRELAND WAS SUMMONED TO KING ARTHUR'S COURT FOR TREASON, AND HOW SIR TRISTRAM FOUGHT FOR HIM AND OVERCAME HIS ADVERSARY

IT FELL out about that time that Sir Bleoberis and Sir Blamor de Ganis, who were brethren, had summoned King Anguish of Ireland to come to Arthur's Court on pain of forfeiture of the King's good grace, and if he came not at the day assigned, King Anguish would lose his lands; so when the Kings were at Camelot, King Anguish was come to know his accusers. Then was there Blamor de Ganis, and appelled the King of Ireland of treason, and he knew full well there was none other remedy but to answer him knightly. So when King Anguish understood his accusing he was passing heavy, but the judges gave him respite to the third day to give his answer. So the King departed unto his lodging.

Meanwhile, when Sir Tristram was in his pavilion, his man came and told him how King Anguish of Ireland was come thither, and was in great distress, being appelled of murder.

"Truly," said Sir Tristram, "these be the best tidings that ever came to me this seven year, for now shall this King of Ireland have need of my help. I will take the battle upon me; therefore, Gouvernail, I pray thee bring me, I charge thee, to the King."

And when Sir Tristram saw the King, he said, "My gracious lord, gramercy of your great goodness showed me in your marches and lands. At that time I promised you to do my service an ever it lay in my power."

"Now, gentle knight," said the King, "I have great need of you; never had I so great need of a knight's help."

Then he told him how Sir Blamor de Ganis had summoned him to fight, or to find a knight in his stead.

"Sir," said Sir Tristram, "I will take the battle for you upon this condition: that ye grant me two things—the one is, ye shall swear to me ye are in the right and that ye were never consenting to any knight's death; and when I have done this battle, if God give me grace that I speed, ye shall give me a reward what thing reasonable that I will ask of you."

"Truly," said the King, "ye shall have whatsoever ye will ask."

"It is well said," replied Sir Tristram.

So King Anguish departed unto King Carados and the other judges, and told them he had found hi champion ready. So when they had taken the charge, Sir Blamor and Sir Tristram made them ready for battle. They put their spears in rest, and came together as it had been thunder, and Sir Tristram through great might smote down Sir Blamor and his horse to the earth. Anon Sir Blamor avoided his horse and pulled out his sword, bidding Sir Tristram alight. Sir Tristram alighted, and dressed him unto battle, and there they lashed together strongly as racing and tracing, foining and dashing many sad strokes, so that there were never knights seen fight more fiercely than they did. But at last Sir Tristram smote Sir Blamor such a buffet upon the helm that he fell down upon his side, and Sir Tristram stood and beheld him.

When Sir Blamor could speak he said, "Sir Tristram, I require thee as a noble knight that thou wilt slay me out of hand, for I had liever die with worship than live with shame; therefore, if thou dare slay me, slay me, I require thee."

When Sir Tristram heard him speak so knightly, he wist not what to do with him, but he besought the judges to take the matter into their hands; and the Kings who were judges asked Sir Bleoberis for his advice.

"My lords," said Bleoberis, "though my brother be beaten, I thank God he is not shamed this day; and rather that he should be shamed, let Sir Tristram slay him out."

"It shall not be so," said the Kings, "for his part-adversary, both the King and the champion, have pity of Sir Blamore's knighthood."

Then by all their advices Sir Tristram and Sir Bleoberis took up Sir Blamor, and the two brethren were accorded with King Anguish, kissed, and made friends for ever. The brethren also made oath with Sir Tristram that none of them should ever fight the other, and for that gentle battle Sir Launcelot loved Tristram for ever.

Then King Anguish and Sir Tristram took their leave and sailed into Ireland, where the King made known throughout all the land what Sir Tristram had done for him. But the joy that La Belle Isolde made of Sir Tristram might no tongue tell, for of all men earthly she loved him the most.

CHAPTER VIII

HOW SIR TRISTRAM DEMANDED LA BELLE ISOLDE FOR KING MARK, AND OF THEIR WEDDING; OF BRAGWAINE, HER MAID, AND SIR PALAMIDES

ON A day King Anguish asked Sir Tristram why he had not demanded his boon, for he should have it without fail.

"Sir," said Sir Tristram, "this is all I desire, that ye will give me La Belle Isolde, your daughter, not for myself, but for my uncle King Mark to wife, for so have I promised him."

"Alas!" said the King, "I would liever than all my land that ye would wed her yourself."

"Sir, an I did, then were I shamed for ever in this world, and false of my promise. Therefore, I pray you, hold your promise, for this is my desire, that ye will give me La Belle Isolde to be wedded to King Mark my uncle."

"As for that," said King Anguish, "ye shall have her with you to do as it please you—that is to say, if ye wish to wed her yourself, I would rather; but if ye will, give her unto King Mark—that is in your choice."

And anon Sir Tristram took the sea, and La Belle Isolde, and came into Cornwall, and there all the barons met them. Then after a time King Mark and La Belle Isolde were richly wedded, and there were great jousts and tourneyings where Sir Tristram was most praised of all. Thus dured the feast long; and after the feast was done—within a little while after, by the assent of two ladies who were with Queen Isolde —they ordained, for hate and envy, to destroy Dame Bragwaine, that was maiden and lady unto La Belle Isolde. So she was sent into the forest to fetch herbs, where she was met, and bound hands and feet to a tree for three days.

By fortune Sir Palamides found Dame Bragwaine, and there he delivered her from death, and brought her to a nunnery beside to be recovered. But when Isolde missed her maiden, wit ye well she was right heavy, for of all earthly women she loved her best, because she came with her out of her country. So upon a day the Queen walked in the forest to put away her thoughts, and suddenly there came Sir Palamides to her, who had heard all her complaint, and said,—

"Madame Isolde, if ye will grant me my boon, I shall bring to you Dame Bragwaine safe and sound."

The Queen was glad of his proffer, that she granted all his asking, and Palamides promised that if she would abide half an hour, he would bring the maiden to her.

"Now, madam," said Sir Palamides, when he had brought the gentlewoman again to the Queen, "remember your promise, for I have fulfilled mine."

Therewith the Queen departed, and rode home to the King, and Sir Palamides after her. And when he came before the King, he said,—

"Sir, I promised your Queen Isolde to bring again Dame Bragwaine that she had lost, upon this covenant, that she should grant me a boon, which she did. Now," said Sir Palamides, "I will that ye let her ride with me, to lead her where I list."

And the King answered hastily, "Take her, with the adventures that shall fall of it; for I suppose thou wilt not keep her no while."

And so, to make short tale, Sir Palamides took her by the hand, and said, "Madame, grudge not to go with me, for I desire nothing but your own promise."

"As for that," said the Queen, "I fear not greatly to go with thee; howbeit thou hast me at advantage with my promise, but I doubt not that I shall be doubtfully worshipfully rescued from thee."

So Queen Isolde was set behind Palamides, and rode his way. But when Sir Tristram wist that La Belle Isolde was gone, he was wroth out of measure, and he hasted after Sir

Palamides, and rode till he came nigh to a castle, and inquired for the Queen.

"Where is my lady?" said Sir Tristram.

"Sir," said the knight, "she is sure enough within my castle, and she can hold her within it."

So Sir Tristram rode on till he came nigh to that castle, and found Sir Palamides at the gate sleeping, and his horse pastured fast before him. When Sir Tristram bade him arise, he got up stilly without words, and gat his horse and saddled him. So they encountered, and Sir Tristram smote Sir Palamides over his horse's tail. Then there began a strong battle on both parts, for they fought for the lady, who beheld them from the castle, and well-nigh swooned for dole and sorrow.

"It were great pity," she said, "that I should see Sir Palamides slain, because he is not christened; and I would be loth he should die a Saracen."

Therewithal she came down and besought Sir Tristram to fight no more.

"I will not your dishonour," said La Belle Isolde; "but I would that ye will for my sake spare this unhappy Saracen Palamides."

"Madame," said Sir Tristram, "I will leave fighting for this time for your sake."

Then she said to Sir Palamides, "This shall be your charge: that thou shalt go out of this country while I am within it."

Then Sir Tristram took the Queen, and brought her again to King Mark; and there was great joy of her home-coming.

CHAPTER IX

HOW SIR TRISTRAM WENT TO BRITTANY AND WEDDED; OF HIS RETURN, AND HIS ADVENTURES IN WALES

IT FELL out that Sir Tristram and Gouvernail left King Mark's Court and sailed unto Brittany, and there was about that time one Knight Grip, and this earl made war upon King Hud of Brittany, and put him to the worse. On a time Sir Kehydius, son of King Howell, as he made a sally, was sore wounded, and nigh to the death. Then Gouvernail went unto the King, and said, "Sir, I counsel you to send Sir Tristram as in your need to help you." The King agreed, and Sir Tristram issued out of the town where they were besieged, and did such deeds that all Brittany heard of him, and at the last he slew Earl Grip with his own hands, and more than one hundred knights. Then King Howell embraced Sir Tristram, and by means of the King and his son there grew up a great affection between Isolde La Blanche Main and Sir Tristram; and because he had such cheer and riches, Sir Tristram agreed to wed her, for she was the King's daughter, and good and fair. So they were wedded, and solemnly held their marriage.

But it happened one day that Sir Tristram and his wife took a little barge, with Sir Kehydius his brother, to play them on the coast. And when they were from the land, there was a wind drove them unto the coast of Wales upon the isle of Servage, where the barge all torove [was wrecked]. The Dame Isolde was hurt.

[Meantime, a knight named Suppinabiles came over the sea into England, and to the Court of King Arthur, and told of the marriage of Sir Tristram to Isolde La Blanche Main; but La Belle Isolde was grieved when she heard that Sir Tristram was wed.]

Sir Tristram and his wife remained a little time on the

island, and he encountered Sir Nabon, the lord thereof, and slew him, and advanced Sir Segwarides in his stead, who proclaimed it in all Cornwall; so it was openly known. But Sir Tristram and his wife found a vessel, and sailed with Kehydius to Brittany unto King Howell, where he was welcome.

. . . .

When La Belle Isolde understood that Sir Tristram was wedded, she sent unto him letters by her maiden Bragwaine to come to the Court, and bring with him Isolde La Blanche Main, and they should be kept as well as herself. Then Sir Tristram asked Sir Kehydius whether he would go with him into Cornwall secretly. He answered that he was ready. Then he privily ordained a vessel, and therein they went—Sir Tristram, Kehydius, Dame Bragwaine, and Gouvernail, Sir Tristram's squire. But a contrary wind blew them on the coast of North Wales nigh the Castle Perilous.

As it came to pass that in a wood there Sir Tristram helped King Arthur, who was, by enchantment, set upon by two knights; but Sir Tristram slew his enemies. He refused to tell the King his name, saying he was only a poor knight adventurous. So then he departed to the ship, and sailed unto Cornwall, where he went to the Court of King Mark. The Queen was full joyful to see him again, yet Sir Tristram did not long tarry in Tintagel Castle, but rode away, followed by his squire, for he could not remain and not let his love for Isolde be seen. Then, by the advice of the barons, Sir Tristram was banished out of the country for ten years, because he had returned without leave; and he departed from Cornwall, bitterly saying, "Greet well Sir Mark and all mine enemies, and tell them I will come again when I may." And therewith he took the sea.

But as he went towards the ship, a knight of King Arthur's, named Sir Dinadan, sought him, and said to him, "Fair knight, ere you pass out of this country I pray you joust with me."

"With a good will," he said. So they ran together, and Sir Tristram lightly smote Sir Dinadan from his horse; anon he begged him to bear him company, and Sir Dinadan consented, and they rode together towards the ship.

After a while the vessel stopped at a landing on the coast of Wales, and there met with Sir Tristram and Sir Dinadan, Sir Ector de Maris and Sir Bors de Ganis. Sir Ector jousted with Sir Dinadan, and smote him and his horse down; Sir Tristram would have jousted with Sir Bors, but he refused, saying Cornish knights were not men of worship. Presently there met them Sir Bleoberis and Sir Driant; and the former offered to joust with Sir Tristram, and he smote Sir Bleoberis down. At that Sir Bors said he wist not that any Cornish knight could do so valiantly.

After this Sir Tristram and Sir Dinadan departed, and rode away through a forest, where met them a damsel, who was seeking some to help Sir Launcelot, who was threatened by the Queen Morgan le Fay; for she had ordered thirty knights to lie in ambush for him as he passed, with intent to kill him—for she hated him. The damsel therefore prayed Sir Tristram and his fellow to rescue Sir Launcelot.

"Fair damsel," said Sir Tristram, "bring us to the place where the men should meet Sir Launcelot."

But Sir Dinadan said he would never go to match fifteen knights himself, when Sir Tristram called shame upon him, and told him to do his part.

"Nay," said Sir Dinadan, "I will not thereof, but if ye will lend me your shield, for ye bear a shield of Cornwall, and for the cowardice of those knights they are not much set upon."

"Nay," said Sir Tristram, "I will never yield my shield. But if thou wilt not promise to abide with me here, I shall slay thee, for I desire of thee no more but to answer for one knight. If thy heart will not so serve thee, then stand by, and look upon me and them."

"Sir," said Sir Dinadan, "I promise to look on, and to do

what I may to save myself; but I would I had not met with you."

Anon came the thirty knights, and Sir Tristram cried, "Lo, here is a knight against you, for the love of Sir Launcelot!" And then he slew two with one spear, and ten with his sword. Then came in Sir Dinadan, and he did passing well. So of the thirty knights there went but ten away, and they fled. This battle saw Sir Bors and his fellows, and they rode unto Sir Tristram and praised his good deeds; but he would not tell them his name, and so they parted.

Sir Tristram and Sir Dinadan then rode on till nightfall, until they met with some shepherds and herdsmen, and asked for lodging. "Forsooth, lords," said one, "hereby is good lodging in a castle; but there is a custom that no knight shall be harboured unless he joust with two knights; and as soon as ye be within ye shall find your match."

"There is shrewd harbour," said Sir Dinadan; "lodge where ye may, I will not go there."

"Fie, for shame!" said Sir Tristram. "Are ye a knight of the Table Round? Wherefore ye may not with your worship refuse."

Then Sir Tristram required him of his knighthood to go with him, and so they rode thither. And it happed that they smote down the knights of the castle, and had good cheer. Then, when they had unarmed, there came to the castle Sir Palamides and Sir Gaheris, and desired the custom of the castle; and Sir Tristram said to his fellow, "We must needs defend it."

"I would much rather rest than fight," said Sir Dinadan.

"That may not be," said Sir Tristram, "for we must make ready."

So Sir Gaheris encountered Sir Tristram, and Sir Palamides overthrew Sir Dinadan; but Gaheris got a fall. Then they would have fought on foot, but Sir Dinadan would not, saying he was sore bruised and hurt at the encounter he had had with the thirty knights; and he said to Tristram, "Ye fare like a man out of his mind that would cast himself away, and I curse the hour that ever I saw you. In all this world I ne'er saw two such knights as you and Sir Launcelot, for one I fell into his fellowship, and he set me to work that kept me three months in my bed."

Then said Sir Tristram, "I will fight with them both."

So he bade both the knights come forth, and they three encountered; but Sir Palamides said it was not fair, so he bade Sir Gaheris stand aside. Then Sir Tristram and Sir Palamides fought long, until by one consent the others parted them, and they would have lodged in the castle, but Sir Dinadan would not; so he took his horse and harness and departed, and lodged in a priory that night.

On the morrow came Sir Tristram to find him, and seeing him so weary he left him, for he could not ride.

CHAPTER X

OF SIR TRISTRAM AND SIR PELLINORE, AND OF THE JOUSTING WHERE SIR TRISTRAM GOT THE PRIZE

AT THE same priory with Sir Dinadan was Sir Pellinore lodged, and he desired to know the name of Sir Tristram; but Sir Dinadan would not tell him. Then he said, "I will ride after him, and make him tell his name, or he shall die therefor."

"Beware, Sir Knight," said Dinadan; "ye will repent it."

But he rode after Sir Tristram, and required him to joust, and Sir Tristram smote him down, wounding him on the shoulder, and he passed on his way. On the day after Sir Tristram met a herald, who told him of a great tournament to be holden at the Castle of Maidens between King Carados of Scotland and the King of North Wales. So Sir Tristram thought to be at the jousts. And as he rode, he met with Sir Kay, who offered to engage him; but he declined, desiring to keep himself fresh for the tournament.

Then Sir Kay called him recreant, which incensed Sir Tristram, so that he set his spear in rest and assailed him, whereupon Sir Kay refused, and Sir Tristram called him "coward," when he came on for shame, and Sir Tristram lightly smote him down, and rode away. But Sir Sagramore also required him to joust, and he turned him, and smote the knight from his horse.

The same day he met with a damsel, who told him where he might meet with much worship. So he turned aside with her, and met Sir Gawaine, who knew the damsel as a maiden of Queen Morgan le Fay, who would have evil plots against Sir Tristram for helping Launcelot. So Sir Gawaine courteously inquired of Sir Tristram, and told him of his danger. Then said Sir Gawaine to the damsel, as he drew his sword,

"Tell me whither thou leadest this knight, else thou shalt die, for I know thy lady's treason."

"Mercy, Sir Gawaine," said the damsel, "and I will tell thee all. Sir," she continued, "Queen Morgan le Fay has ordained thirty damsels to seek and espy after Sir Launcelot, or Sir Tristram, and by their wiles persuade them to her castle, where she has thirty knights to slay them."

"Fie, for shame," said Sir Gawaine, "that ever such false treason should be wrought by a Queen and a King's sister!" Then said he to Sir Tristram, "Will ye stand by me and prove the malice of these knights?"

"I will not fail you," said Sir Tristram, "for but few days ago I had to do with thirty knights of that same Queen, and God now speed us to win worship as lightly."

So they rode on together towards the castle of Morgan le Fay, and when they came to it Sir Gawaine cried aloud, "Queen Morgan le Fay, send out thy knights that thou hast laid in a watch for Sir Launcelot and Sir Tristram. I know your false treason, and where I ride men shall know of it."

Then the Queen urged her knights to go forth, but they would not come out of the castle for fear of Sir Tristram; so he and Sir Gawaine went on their way. And as they rode they saw a knight called Sir Brewse Sans Pité chasing a lady to slay her.

"Hold you all still," said Sir Gawaine, "and see me reward yonder false knight." So saying, he rode betwixt Sir Brewse and the lady, and said, "False knight, leave her and have ado with me."

When Sir Brewse saw no more but Sir Gawaine, he put his spear in rest and attacked him; and Sir Gawaine was overthrown. Then Sir Brewse rode over and across him twenty times to destroy him. When Sir Tristram saw him do so villainous a deed, he hurtled out against him; but Sir Brewse saw the shield of Cornwall, and knowing Sir Tristram bore it, he fled. But Sir Brewse was so well horsed that he got away, and after a long chase Sir Tristram was fain to rest.

Anon Sir Tristram and Sir Gawaine arrived at the Castle

of Maidens, and were lodged with an old knight, Sir Pellounes, and he told them of the great tournament to be at the castle. And as they were talking Sir Tristram was aware of a knight riding upon a black horse, and with a black-covered shield.

"What knight is that?" said Sir Tristram.

"He is one of the best knights in the world," said Sir Persides, the son of Pellounes.

"Is he Sir Launcelot?" asked Sir Tristram.

"Nay," said Persides, "it is Sir Palamides, that is yet unchristened."

They saw much people saluting him as they rode, and shortly there came a messenger to the lord of the castle that a knight with a black shield had smitten down thirteen knights. When they heard this the friends armed themselves, and went to see the tournament. When Sir Palamides saw Sir Persides he required him to joust with him, and Sir Persides made him ready, but when he encountered he was overthrown. Then Sir Tristram dressed him against Sir Palamides, who was ready, but Sir Tristram was not; so Palamides took him at advantage when he had no spear in rest, and threw him over his horse's tail. Then was Sir Tristram wroth and sore ashamed, so he started up and sent a squire to Sir Palamides to joust again. But he would not, and said to the squire,—

"Tell thy master to revenge himself to-morrow at the Maidens' Castle, where he may see me."

On the morrow Sir Tristram commanded Gouvernail his servant to ordain him a black shield with no remembrance thereon, and departed from their host towards the tournament, and took the side of King Carados of Scotland. Anon knights began the field on the part of the King of North Galis and of Carados, and the party of the King of North Wales was beaten back.

But Sir Bleoberis and Sir Gaheris came with them of North Galis, and smote down Sir Persides and almost slew him. When Sir Tristram beheld them, and saw them do great

deeds of arms, he marvelled who they were; also thinking it
shame that Sir Persides was so treated, he gat a great spear
in his hand and smote down Sir Gaheris from his horse. Then
was Sir Bleoberis wroth, and rode against Sir Tristram, who
smote him from his horse. But the King with the hundred
knights re-horsed them, and with Sir Dinadan came against
Sir Tristram, who gave them all such buffets that he wounded
them sore. And then King Arthur blew to lodging. For King
Arthur was there as judge with Sir Launcelot, who jousted
not on the first day. And they gave Sir Tristram the prize,
but they knew him not, so they named him the Knight with
the Black Shield.

Sir Palamides was on the side of the King of North Galis,
and knew not where Sir Tristram was, who, when he heard
that Sir Palamides had changed and gone over to King
Carados and King Arthur, who were akin, changed his side
to the King of North Galis; for he said,—

"I am the knight Sir Palamides smote down yesterday,
and whatever side he taketh I will take the opposite, else I
will be on my lord King Arthur's."

CHAPTER XI

HOW SIR TRISTRAM FARED AT THE TOURNAMENT, AND JOUSTED WITH KING ARTHUR; AND OF MANY OTHER FEATS

WHEN King Arthur came into the field the trumpets blew unto the tourney, so there began a great party, and there was hurling and rushing. Then the King of North Galis's knights were beaten back; but when Sir Tristram came in none could withstand him, and he endured long.

"Since I bare arms," said King Arthur, "I never saw knight do such marvellous deeds."

Sir Tristram meanwhile smote right and left, so that all lords and ladies spoke of him; but at the last he would have had the worst, had not the King and a hundred knights rescued him. And Sir Launcelot thought to meet with Sir Tristram, and rode to meet him sword in hand; but when he saw him hard beset, he refrained, and put up his sword.

Then the King of the Hundred Knights, and those of North Wales, set upon twenty knights who were of Sir Launcelot's kin, who fought all together, and none would fail the other. When Sir Tristram beheld the noblesse of these twenty knights, he thought shame to see two hundred knights battering upon twenty. Then he rode unto the King with the Hundred Knights, and said, "Sir, leave your fighting with those twenty knights, for ye win no worship of them—ye be so many and they so few—else I will ride and help them with all my might and power."

"Nay," said the King, "ye shall not do so. I will withdraw my knights for your pleasure, as evermore a good knight will favour another, and like will draw to like." So he withdrew his knights.

All this while, and long before, Sir Launcelot had watched Sir Tristram, intending to make fellowship with him; but suddenly Sir Tristram, with his squire and Sir Dinadan, rode into the forest, that no man perceived where they went. So then King Arthur gave the prize to the King of North Galis, because Sir Tristram was upon his side. Sir Launcelot rode here and there to find Sir Tristram, and all the lords and ladies cried "The Knight of the Black Shield hath won the field."

"Alas!" said King Arthur, "where is that knight? It is a shame to let him escape. With courtesy ye might have brought him to me to the Castle of Maidens."

Then the noble King Arthur comforted his knights, and bade them not be dismayed, though they had lost the field that day.

"My fellows," said the King, "look that ye be of good cheer. To-morrow I will be in the field with you, and revenge you of your enemies."

So that night King Arthur and his men reposed themselves, and on the morrow the heralds blew unto the field for the third day's jousting. So the King of North Galis, and the King with the Hundred Knights, encountered with King Carados and the King of Ireland, and overthrew them. Then came in King Arthur and did great deeds of arms, for he put the King of North Galis and the King with the Hundred Knights to the worst.

With this came Sir Tristram, bearing his black shield, and anon he jousted with Sir Palamides, and smote him over his horse's croup. Then came King Arthur, and cried, "Knight with the black shield, make thee ready to me." But Sir Tristram smote him also.

Sir Palamides and King Arthur were soon horsed again, and the King with eager heart smote Sir Tristram over his horse, when Sir Palamides came upon him to have overriden him; but Sir Tristram was ware of him, and stooping down, pulled him from his horse. So they engaged, and dashed together mightily, so that all stood and beheld them. At the last Sir Tristram smote Sir Palamides upon the helm three mighty strokes, and at every stroke he said, "Have this for

Sir Tristram's sake!" With that Sir Palamides fell to the earth grovelling.

Soon the King with the hundred knights came and horsed Sir Tristram, and Sir Palamides was also put on horseback, and with great ire jousted upon Sir Tristram; but he avoided his spear, and gat his enemy by the neck with both hands, pulled him clean out of the saddle, and after bearing him along the length of ten spears, he let him fall at his adventure. At this moment came King Arthur, with a naked sword in his hand, and Sir Tristram ran upon him with a spear; but King Arthur boldly abode him, and with his sword shore his spear in two. Therewithal Sir Tristram was astonished, and drawing his sword, assailed King Arthur hard. After a while they were separated in the press; but Sir Tristram rode here and there, doing great deeds, till all estates marvelled of his prowess, and cried upon the knight with the black shield.

Then the cry was so loud that Sir Launcelot heard it, and he gat a great spear, and came towards the field, crying, "Knight with the black shield, make ready to joust with me." When Sir Tristram heard him say so, he got his spear in his hand, and either abashed down his head and came together as thunder, and Sir Tristram's spear broke in pieces, while Sir Launcelot by evil fortune struck Sir Tristram on the side a deep wound nigh to death; but Sir Tristram avoided not his saddle, and so the spear brake. Therewithal Sir Tristram got out his sword, and rushed to Sir Launcelot, and gave him three great strokes on the helm that the fire sprang out, and Sir Launcelot abashed his head slowly towards his saddle-bow.

Then Sir Tristram departed from the field, for he felt so wounded he thought he should have died; but Sir Dinadan espied him, and followed him into the forest. So when Sir Tristram was departed by the forest-side, he alighted, and unlaced his harness and refreshed his wound; and afterwards Sir Tristram and Sir Dinadan rode to an old knight's place to lodge them.

When Sir Tristram had departed into the forest, Sir

Launcelot held the fight, and when King Arthur saw Sir Launcelot do such marvellous deeds, he and many of his knights armed and came to help him. On this account the King of North Galis and the King of the Hundred Knights were put to the worst; so the prize was given to Sir Launcelot, because he was last in the field. But he would not have it, and cried out that Sir Tristram had won the field, for he began first, and last he had endured; so had he done the first day, the second, and the third day.

All the estates, high and low, said great worship of Sir Launcelot for the honour he did unto Sir Tristram, and he was more renowned than if he had overthrown five hundred knights. But the King and all were dismayed that Sir Tristram had thus departed from them, and many knights set out in his quest.

"As for me," said Sir Launcelot, "for all the lands that ever my father left me I would not have hurt Sir Tristram, had I known him at the time, for late he did as much for me as ever knight did." So Sir Launcelot said all the worship that might be said of Sir Tristram.

Then King Arthur made a great feast to all that would come, and spoke to Sir Launcelot concerning the departure of Sir Tristram; but the knight brought forth a book, and said, "Here are we ten knights that will swear upon a book never to rest one night where we rest another this twelvemonth, until that we find Sir Tristram."

And the names of the ten knights that had undertaken this quest were these following:—Sir Launcelot, Sir Ector de Maris, Sir Bors de Ganis, Sir Bleoberis, Sir Blamor de Ganis, and Lucan the Butler, Sir Uwaine, Sir Galahad, Sir Lionel, and Galiodin.

So these ten noble knights departed from the Court of King Arthur, and they rode upon their quest together till they came to a cross, where departed four highways; and there separated the fellowship in four to seek Sir Tristram.

CHAPTER I

AFTER many adventures Sir Tristram came to a castle to ask lodging wherein was Queen Morgan le Fay, who made him promise to bear a shield that she would deliver unto him at the Castle of the Hard Rock, where King Arthur had cried a great tournament.

"There I pray you that you will be," said she, "and do for me as much deeds of arms as you may do."

So the shield was brought forth, and it was goldish, with a king and a queen therein painted, and a knight standing above them, with one foot upon the king's head and the other upon the queen's. So Sir Tristram bore away the shield, and did many great deeds before King Arthur, who marvelled greatly to what intent the shield was made. So anon King Arthur and Sir Uwaine dressed them before Sir Tristram, and required him to tell them where he had that shield.

"Sirs," he said, "I had it of Queen Morgan le Fay, sister of King Arthur. I cannot describe these arms, for it is no point of my charge."

"Truly," said King Arthur, "ye ought to bear none arms but if ye wist what ye bear. But I pray you tell me your name."

"Sir, ye shall not wit as at this time," said Sir Tristram.

"Then shall ye and I do battle together," said King Arthur.

Therewithal King Arthur dressed his shield and his spear, and Sir Tristram against him; and they came so eagerly together that King Arthur brake his spear upon Sir Tristram's shield, but Sir Tristram hit him so that horse and man fell to the earth, and the King was sorely wounded in the left side. When Sir Uwaine saw his Lord Arthur lie sore wounded, he called upon Sir Tristram to defend himself, and they engaged, but Sir Tristram smote him harder and stronger. Then he said,—

"Fair knights, I had no need to joust with you, for I have had enough to do with you this day."

Then arose Arthur and went to Sir Uwaine, and said, "We have as we deserved, for through our pride we demanded battle."

Then Sir Tristram departed, and in every place he asked after Sir Launcelot, and continued straight unto Camelot until he reached the tomb of Sir Lanceor, that was the King's son of Ireland, slain by Balin; and in the same place was the fair Lady Colombe slain, who killed herself after his death. At this place Merlin prophesied that the two best knights of King Arthur's days should fight.

So when Sir Tristram came to the tomb he was aware of a seemly knight all in white with a covered shield, who Sir Tristram thought was Sir Palamides, and he said,—

"Ye be welcome, Sir Knight: well and truly have ye holden your promise."

Then they dressed their shields and spears, and came together so fiercely that both knights and horses fell to the earth. Then they fought on foot, and wounded each other wonderly sore for the space of four hours, and the squires stood and wept when they saw the bright swords covered with blood. Then at the last spake Sir Launcelot, and said,—

"Knight, thou fightest wonderly well as ever I saw, therefore an it please you tell me your name."

"Sir," said Sir Tristram, "I am very loth to tell any man my name."

"An I were required," said Sir Launcelot, "I was never loth to tell my name."

"It is well," quoth Sir Tristram; "then I require you to tell me your name."

"Fair knight," he said, "my name is Sir Launcelot du Lake."

"Alas!" said Sir Tristram, "what have I done? for ye are

the man in the world that I love best. My name is Sir Tristram de Liones."

Therewith Sir Launcelot kneeled down and yielded up his sword, and Sir Tristram kneeled down and yielded up his sword, and anon after they took their helms, and rode to Camelot. There they met with Sir Gawaine and with Sir Gaheris, who had made promise to Arthur never to come again to the Court till they had brought Sir Tristram with them.

Then they all proceeded to Arthur's Court, and the King took Sir Tristram by the hand, and went to the Table Round. Then came Queen Guenever, and many ladies with her, and all the ladies said at once, "Welcome, Sir Tristram!" "Welcome!" said the damsels. "Welcome!" said the knights.

"Welcome!" said Arthur, "for one of the best knights and the gentlest of the world, and the man of most worship. Therefore are ye right heartily welcome to this Court, and I also pray ye grant me a boon."

"It shall be at your commandment," said Sir Tristram.

"Well," said King Arthur, "I pray ye to abide at my Court."

"Sir," said Sir Tristram, "thereto am I loth, as I have much to do in many countries. But I will as ye will."

Then went King Arthur unto the sieges about the Round Table, and looked in every siege that was void, that lacked knights. And the King saw in the siege of Sir Marhaus letters that said, "This is the siege of the noblest knight, Sir Tristram."

Then King Arthur made Sir Tristram knight of the Round Table with great nobleness and feasting. At that time King Mark heard of the honour done to Sir Tristram, and came from Cornwall in jealousy to kill him. But King Mark was disguised on his journey, of which, when his two knights knew the object, they refused to have part in it, and King Mark slew one of them in his wrath, and the other departed from him. So the King rode on, and met six knights of the

Round Table, who dressed up Dagonet, the King's Fool, in Sir Mordred's gear, and sent him against King Mark.

But when the King perceived him he ran away, fearing it was Sir Launcelot, and the Fool pursued him, while the knights laughed aloud, and followed after to see the end of the jest. So it happened that King Mark in his flight met a knight, who stood by him, and, in turn, discomfited all the knights, except Sir Dinadan and Sir Mordred, who were behind or unarmed. Then the knight and King Mark rode on to a castle, where the knight, who was Sir Palamides, let King Mark sleep, and rode away; but King Mark afterwards arrived at Camelot, and at King Arthur's Court.

After a certain day said Arthur unto King Mark, "I pray you give me a gift that I shall ask you."

"Sir," said King Mark, "I will give ye whatsoever ye desire, if it be in my power."

"Gramercy!" said Arthur; "this I will ask you: that ye will be a good lord unto Sir Tristram, for he is a man of great honour; and that ye will take him into Cornwall with you, and cherish him for my sake."

Then Sir Mark promised he would do so, and he and Arthur swore upon the book together. So afterwards Sir Tristram made him ready to ride away with King Mark, whereat all the knights were heavy, for they well knew King Mark would do all he could to slay or destroy Sir Tristram. But it was Sir Tristram's own desire to go.

Then Sir Launcelot went to King Mark, and said, "Beware, I counsel thee, of treason! By the faith of God and my knighthood, I will slay thee with my own hands if thou mischief that knight by any treason or falsehood! It is well known that ye came only into this country to slay Sir Tristram."

So with great dole the King and Sir Tristram departed, and proceeded together to Tintagel, where Tristram was warned by letters of King Mark's treachery by Sir Launcelot. As Sir Tristram was at joust it happed that he was sore hurt, and went to a castle to dwell with a knight, Sir Dinas the

Seneschal. Meantime King Mark's enemies entered into his lands, and the council demanded the return of Sir Tristram to save them, and he came, still unable to bear arms; so King Mark said, "Repose ye for eight days, and I will go and meet the Sessoins with my host." So he went unto Tintagel, where, after much fighting, he was beset, and sent messengers to Sir Tristram to tell him; then, he being whole, got ten good knights of King Arthur, and came to the rescue, and cut his way by night into the castle with his following.

On the morrow Elias, the captain of the Sessoins, bade King Mark come out and do battle. But Sir Tristram took the battle upon himself to rule it, and so he divided his men. On the same night he burned all the enemy's ships to the water's edge, which made Elias desperate; and when the fight began it wavered long, until at length it reached night, and each party drew to their rest. King Mark lost one hundred, and the enemy two hundred, besides wounded, so either party was loth to fight more.

Then Elias, being wroth at the death of his men, proposed a single combat to fight a knight body for body, and if he vanquished King Mark's champion he was to have the tribute of Cornwall yearly. But none save Sir Tristram would encounter Elias, and deliver Cornwall from the truage on the morrow.

At the appointed time the armies were drawn up, and Sir Elias and Sir Tristram ran together in the space betwixt them, and at once both horses and men went to the earth. Then the knights rose and engaged with force, and traced, traversed, and hewed at each other, cutting away the cantels of their shields, so that both were wounded sore. After an hour Sir Tristram waxed faint and gave back, and Sir Elias seeing this pressed on more freely and wounded him in many places. Then was there laughing of the Sessoins party, but great dole in King Mark's, for Sir Tristram never had been so matched save by Sir Launcelot.

Then as they stood Sir Tristram remembered him of Isolde La Blanche Main, and he was likely never to see her again.

So he pulled up his shield, met Elias, and gave him many grievous blows, twenty against one, and broke his shield and hauberk, so the blood ran down to the earth. Then King Mark and his Cornishmen began to laugh, and the other party to weep. And Sir Tristram called upon Elias to yield, for when he saw him so staggering on the ground he was sorry for such a good knight. But Elias suddenly fell down and died.

Then his party fled, but many were made prisoners, while some were sent to ransom their fellows. Sir Tristram was taken and healed of his wounds, yet for all that King Mark still hated him as much as ever, and would fain have slain him. Nevertheless, Sir Tristram took no heed, and would never beware of his treason.

We turn now to another matter that befell King Mark and his brother, the good Prince Sir Baudwin, who, when the Saracens came after the departure of the Sessoins, took three of his own ships, and setting them on fire, sent them amongst the enemy's vessels, and did great damage. Then with his men he attacked and slew forty thousand, and left none alive of the Saracens.

Now, when King Mark heard this he was very angry that his brother should win such worship, and he thought to slay him. Thus hastily, as a man out of his wit, he sent for King Baudwin and Anglides his wife, bidding them bring their young son that he might see him, but with the intent to slay the child and the father. So when the good Prince came with his wife and child, he made them fair semblance till after dinner, when he said that the Prince ought to have sent him word, that he might as King have had the honour also. The Prince replied,—

"Had I tarried until you came, I had destroyed my country."

"Thou liest, false traitor!" cried King Mark, "for thou art ever about for to win worship from me, and to put me to dishonour."

Then, with a dagger, he smote him a sudden blow to the

heart, that he never spake a word again. Then the Lady
Anglides swooned when her lord was slain before her face,
but the Queen sent her word privily, and so she gat her
horse and her husband's doublet, and his shirt she carried
away, with her child, hastily and in fear, with such poor men
as would ride with her.

The Prince was buried, and the knights made great dole
for him, for he was well beloved. But King Mark was not
satisfied, and searched from chamber to chamber to find the
lad Alisander, to slay him; and when he could not be found,
King Mark sent Sir Sadok, a good man, to fetch Anglides and
her son. So Sir Sadok found her, and he let her go only on
the condition that when her son grew up he should avenge
the murder of his father. This gladly she agreed to, and
Anglides came to the castle of Magouns in Sussex [now
Arundel], where she was received by Bellangere the constable, for the castle was hers by inheritance. There lived the
Princess and her son, who grew up to man's estate, big and
strong, and was knighted. When Sir Tristram heard that he
was made knight, he sent him a letter, and desired him to go
to the Court of King Arthur. But King Mark sent to Morgan
le Fay, and other ladies who were sorceresses, to enchant
Alisander, so that he should either be taken or slain. This he
did with intent to destroy him, for when Alisander had been
made knight he had sworn to be avenged of King Mark.

When Sir Alisander departed from home, he carried with
him the bloody shirt of his father, to think always upon his
murder. As he went he engaged in a tournament, and won a
prize, but got him into the power of Morgan le Fay, who
detained him in her castle and would not let him depart. But
in that castle was a damsel, who offered to release him if he
would hold the ground against all comers for a year; so
Alisander agreed, and the damsel wrote to her father and
bade him come and burn it, which he had long desired. Then
he came, and the damsel saved Alisander by a private postern
when the castle burned, and the spot of ground he came to
he held against all knights.

It happened that his deeds were cried abroad, and many of King Arthur's knights would assay him for love of Alice la Belle Pilgrim, who had promised to wed the knight who overcame Sir Alisander. But when he had overcome Sir Hugon, whom he smote sore, she desired to see him, and fell in love with the young knight, and he with her. So at the twelve months, and after he had vanquished many knights, he departed with Alice and married her. They then lived in the country of Benoye in great joy.

CHAPTER II

HOW KING MARK TRIED TO KILL SIR TRISTRAM WITH TREASON, AND WHAT HAPPENED TO HIM

THERE was cried a great tournament by the coasts of Cornwall, and it was done by Sir Galahault, the haut-prince, with intent to slay Sir Launcelot. Then King Mark bethought him that he would have Sir Tristram brought into the tournament, and disguised as Sir Launcelot, so that he might be slain.

So at the jousts came in Sir Tristram, and they all weened it were Sir Launcelot, and King Mark said so plainly. Then they set upon him, and it was a wonder Sir Tristram ever endured the pain. Notwithstanding all, Sir Tristram won his degree at the tournament, and hurt many knights. So when the jousts were done, they knew he was Sir Tristram.

Then came King Mark, and said to him, "Fair nephew, I am sorry for your hurts"; and he made him to be put on a horse-bier as a sign of love, and would be his leech himself. But at night he gave him a strong drink, which made him sleep, and while Sir Tristram slept, he had him carried to a castle where was a strong prison, and there he was a great while, so that no creature knew what had become of him.

But Queen Isolde sent Sir Sadok to find out the prison of Sir Tristram. And when Sir Sadok discovered that he had been put in prison by King Mark and his four nephews, he made an ambush by Tintagel. When the King and his nephews came riding by there, Sir Sadok attacked them, and killed the four nephews of King Mark, who himself rode away. Then Sir Sadok rode away, and found out the treachery and treason of the King at a castle called Liones, the people of which rode with him to the castle Arbray, and so stirred up the people against King Mark.

Meanwhile the King, hearing of these things, wished himself rid of Sir Tristram, and he caused letters to be written as from the Pope, commanding King Mark to go to Jerusalem, and make war upon the Saracens. These letters the King sent to Sir Tristram, with a message that he should be released an he would go and fight in the Holy Land. But Sir Tristram replied, saying,—

"Tell King Mark that since the Apostle Pope hath sent for him, bid him go thither himself, for at the command of that traitor King I will not come out of prison."

The messenger then returned, and the King said, "Well, yet he shall be beguiled."

So he counterfeited letters from the Pope, commanding Sir Tristram himself to go and fight the Saracens. But the knight perceived the counterfeiting, and said,—

"False hast thou ever been, King Mark, and false shalt thou be to the end."

But after a while Sir Percivale by knightly means delivered Sir Tristram out of prison. Then went he and told the King what he had done, and said, "If Sir Tristram makes war upon ye, ye may not abide it."

"That is true," said King Mark; "but I may not love Sir Tristram, because he loveth my Queen and my wife."

"Fie, for shame!" said Sir Percivale; "are ye not his uncle, and he your nephew? Do you think such a noble knight would do such a villainy? He may love your Queen sinless, because she is one of the fairest ladies of the world."

Then King Mark made more treason, but was taken by the insurgent knights under Sir Dinas, and put in prison to be slain. So when after a while Sir Tristram heard it, he made ready, and so devised, when the King had been put away with, that he and La Belle Isolde took ship, and she came to England with her nephew.

After that Sir Launcelot met him at a tournament, and brought him and La Belle Isolde to his castle, Joyous Gard, with honour.

CHAPTER III

HOW SIR TRISTRAM HUNTED, AND MET SIR DINADAN; HOW HE VANQUISHED TWO KNIGHTS, AND MADE A GAME OF SIR DINADAN AFTER

EVERY day Sir Tristram would go riding and hunting, for the books say, of him came all the terms of venery and hunting, and of all the sizes and measures of the blowing of horns, the terms of hawking, and all blasts that belong to games; so that all gentlemen have cause to the world's end to praise Sir Tristram and to bless his soul.

One day, as he was hunting, he met with Sir Dinadan, who had come into that country, and told his name; but Sir Tristram would not tell *his* name, at which Sir Dinadan was wroth.

"Such a foolish knight I saw to-day lying by a well. Now tell me your name, else I shall do battle with you."

"As for that," said Tristram, "it is no reason to fight with me but I tell you my name. Yet at this time ye shall not know it!"

"Fie!" said Sir Dinadan; "are ye a knight, and feared to tell your name? I will fight with thee."

"If I do battle, ye are not able to withstand me," replied Sir Tristram.

"Fie on thee, coward!" said the other.

But then they disputed, until there came riding another knight.

"Lo," said Sir Tristram, "yonder knight will joust with thee."

Anon Sir Tristram saw that it was the knight he had seen sleeping by the well.

"I know him," said Sir Tristram; "he is the son of the

King of Northumberland, and called Epinagris, and loveth
the daughter of the King of Wales—a full fair lady."

"Now," said Sir Dinadan, "ye will see what I shall do."
Therewith he cried out, "Make thee ready to joust, Sir
Knight, for it is the custom of knights-errant to do so."

"Sir," said Sir Epinagris, "is it a rule of your knights-
errant to joust will he or nill?"

"As for that," said Sir Dinadan, "make thee ready, for here
is at thee."

Therewithal they spurred their horses, and Sir Epinagris
smote down Dinadan. Then Sir Tristram said to the fallen
knight, "How now? It seemeth me the lover hath well sped."

"Fie on thee, coward!" said Sir Dinadan. "If thou be good
knight, avenge my shame."

"Nay, rather let us go hence," said Tristram.

"God defend me from your company," said Sir Dinadan.
"I never sped since I met thee."

"Peradventure I could tell thee of Sir Tristram," said he.

"Defend me from thy friendship," said Sir Dinadan. "Sir
Tristram were mickle the worse for thy company."

"Sir," said Sir Tristram, "it may happen we shall meet in
other places."

Then rode Sir Tristram into Joyous Gard, and he heard a
great noise and cry; so he asked what it meant.

"Sir," they said, "here is a knight who has been slain by
two knights for no other cause than he said Sir Launcelot was
better than Sir Gawaine."

"That were a simple cause to slay a good knight, because
he spake well of his master," said Sir Tristram.

"That were little remedy for us. Had Sir Launcelot been
here we should have been revenged upon those false knights."

When Sir Tristram heard them say this, incontinent he sent
for his shield and his spear, and soon overtook those knights,
bidding them turn again, and "amend what they had done."

"What amends wouldst thou have?" said one of them; and
immediately he dressed himself at Sir Tristram, who bore
him from his saddle. Then the other attacked, and was served

in the same manner. They then rose and drew their swords; but Sir Tristram inquired their names. They told him they were Sir Agravaine and Sir Gaheris, nephews of King Arthur.

"It is shame," said Sir Tristram, "ye are destroyers of such good knights, for it is but now I heard say ye and Sir Gawaine slew between ye a better knight than ever ye were— Sir Lamorak de Galis. However, for King Arthur's sake I will let you pass. Had it pleased God I would have been by Sir Lamorak at his death."

"Then shouldest thou have gone the same way," said Sir Gaheris.

"Fair knight," replied Sir Tristram, "there must have been many more knights than ye are."

Then he departed from them and came to Joyous Gard; but they took their horses, and one said to the other, "We will overtake him, and be revenged upon him in the despite of Sir Lamorak."

So when they had overtaken him, Sir Agravaine said, "Turn, traitor knight."

"That is evil said," replied Sir Tristram; so he pulled out his sword and smote Sir Agravaine such a buffet that he fell off his horse in a swoon, and he had a grievous wound. After he turned to Sir Gaheris and smote him out of his saddle. Then Sir Tristram rode on into Joyous Gard, and told La Belle Isolde of his adventures.

As he was telling her of them, there came a varlet and announced an errant knight with colours on his shield.

"That is Sir Dinadan," said Tristram. "Send for him, my Lady Isolde, and I will not be seen, and he will make you good cheer, for he is the maddest and merriest talker."

Anon Isolde sent into the town and bade Sir Dinadan to the castle. And she asked him whence he was.

"Madam," said he, "I am Dinadan, of King Arthur's Round Table."

"What do ye in this country?" said La Belle Isolde.

SIR TRISTAM AND LA BELLE ISOLDE TOOK SHIP AND
CAME TO ENGLAND

"Madam, I seek the noble knight Sir Tristram, for it was told me he was here."

"It may well be," replied the Queen. "And, sir, now I pray ye, will ye fight for my love with three knights that did me great wrong?"

Then Sir Dinadan said, "I shall tell you that ye are as fair a lady as ever I saw, and much fairer than Queen Guenever, but wit ye well I will not fight with three knights for you."

Then Isolde laughed and had good game at him. So he had all the cheer she could make him, and stayed there that night. On the morning early Sir Tristram armed him, and he promised Isolde he would meet Sir Dinadan and they would ride unto the tournament at Lonazep. Then departed Sir Tristram, with two squires bearing his shield and his spears, great and long.

CHAPTER IV

HOW SIR DINADAN MET AGAIN WITH SIR TRISTRAM, AND
WHEN JOUSTING WITH SIR PALAMIDES HE KNEW HIM

AFTER that Sir Dinadan departed, and riding, he overtook Sir Tristram. When he had overtaken him he hated his fellowship above all other knights.

"Ah," said he, "art thou that coward knight that I met with yesterday? Keep there, for thou shalt joust with me."

"Well," said Sir Tristram, "but I am loth to joust."

But they let their horses run, and Sir Tristram missed Sir Dinadan on purpose, but let him break a spear upon him; and therewith Sir Dinadan dressed him to draw out his sword.

"Not so," said Sir Tristram. "Why are ye so wroth? I will not fight."

"Fie on thee, coward!" said Sir Dinadan, "thou shamest all knights."

"I care not," said Sir Tristram. "I will wait upon you and be under your protection, for as ye are so good a knight ye may save me."

"Devil deliver me out of thee!" said Dinadan. "Thou art a goodly man of arms and person, but the most coward that I ever saw. What wilt thou do with the great spears thou carriest with thee?"

"I shall give them to some good knight," replied Sir Tristram, "when I come to the tournament. If I see you do your best I will give them to you."

So thus as they rode talking they came to an errant knight, who desired them to joust.

"Lo!" said Sir Tristram, "yonder is one who will joust; dress thyself unto him."

"A shame betide thee!" said Sir Dinadan.

"Not so," replied Tristram, "that knight seemeth a shrew."

"Then shall I," said Sir Dinadan. And he encountered, when he was smitten from his horse.

"Lo!" said Sir Tristram, "it had been better had ye left."

"Fie upon thee, coward!" said Sir Dinadan. And he gat up and seized his sword to do battle on foot.

"Whether in love or in wrath?" asked the other knight.

"Let us do battle in love," said Dinadan.

"Tell me your name," said the other.

"My name is Dinadan," said he.

And the other told his name—Sir Gareth, youngest brother unto Sir Gawaine. Then either made great joy of other, for Sir Gareth was the best knight of all the brethren, and he proved a full good knight. After the encounter they took their horses and spoke of Sir Tristram, who laughed them to scorn. Then were they ware of a knight well horsed and armed.

"Fair knights," said Sir Tristram, "look ye, who shall joust with yonder knight, for I warn you I will not have to do with him."

"Then shall I," said Sir Gareth.

So they encountered together, and the knight smote Sir Gareth over his horse's crupper.

"How now?" said Sir Tristram unto Sir Dinadan; "dress thee now, and revenge the good knight Sir Gareth."

"That shall I not, for he hath stricken down a bigger knight than I am."

"Ah, Sir Dinadan, I see thy heart hath failed thee, therefore ye shall see what I can do."

So Sir Tristram hurled into the knight, and smote him from his horse. And when Sir Dinadan saw it he marvelled greatly, and deemed his companion was Sir Tristram. Then the knight on foot drew out his sword to do battle.

"What is your name?" said Sir Tristram.

"My name is Sir Palamides," he said.

"What knight hate ye most?" asked Tristram.

"I hate Sir Tristram to the death," replied the other knight, "and when I meet him one of us shall die."

"Ye say well, and wit ye that I am Sir Tristram de Liones, so now do your worst."

When Sir Palamides heard this he was astonished, and said, "I pray you, Sir Tristram, forgive me all my evil will, and if I live I will do you service; and as I have owed you evil, it me sore repenteth. Therefore, as no other good knight should hate you, I require you to take no displeasure at my words."

"Sir Palamides," replied Sir Tristram, "ye say well, and I wot ye are a good knight; but if ye have any evil will to me, now may ye right it, for I am ready at your hand."

"Not so, my lord; I will do you knightly service in all things as you command."

"So will I take you," said Sir Tristram.

Then they rode on their ways, and Sir Dinadan came up, and said, "Oh, my lord Sir Tristram, foul have ye mocked me. Truly I came into this country for your sake, by the advice of my lord Sir Launcelot; yet would not he tell me the place I should find you."

"Truly Sir Launcelot wist well where I was," replied Tristram, "for I was abiding within his own castle."

As they went along they discoursed concerning the death of Sir Lamorak, and Sir Tristram declared that had not the knights that slew him been cousins of King Arthur they should have died for that deed.

"Sir Gawaine and his three brethren set on him in a retired spot, and having slain his horse, they fought with him on foot more than three hours, and Sir Mordred gave him his death-wound behind his back, and hewed him in pieces; for one of his squires told me who saw it," said Sir Palamides. "But speak we of other things, and see how we shall do at this tournament. By my advice we shall hold all four together against all that will come."

"Not by my counsel," said Sir Tristram, "for I see that

there will be four hundred knights and many good knights; so be a man ever so fair and good, he may be overmatched."

So they rode on until they came to the Humber bank, where they heard a cry and a doleful voice. Then were they ware of a vessel covered with red silk, and this vessel landed fast by them.

CHAPTER V

HOW THEY FOUND A SHIP WITH THE BODY OF KING HERMANCE; AND HOW SIR TRISTRAM AND HIS FELLOWS FOUGHT WITH A HOST; AND OF OTHER MATTERS

THEN Sir Tristram and his fellows alighted and entered into the vessel; and when he came within he saw a fair bed, richly covered, and thereon lay a seemly knight, all armed save the head, which was bloody.

"How may it be that the knight is thus slain?" said Sir Tristram. Then he was aware of a letter in the knight's hand. "Master mariners," said Tristram, "what meaneth this letter?"

"Sir," they answered, "in this letter ye shall know how he was slain, and for what cause, and what was his name; but, sir, wit ye well that no man must take that letter unless he be a good knight, and that he will faithfully promise to revenge his death."

"Some of us may avenge his death as well as others," replied Tristram, taking the letter from the knight's hand.

And he read it thus: "Hermance, King and Lord of the Red City—I send to all knights-errant recommendation, and unto you, noble knights of King Arthur's Court, I beseech you to find one knight who for my sake will fight with two brethren who have traitorously slain me: whereof I beseech one good knight to revenge my death, and he that doeth so shall have my Red City and all my castles."

"Sir," said the mariners, "wit ye well that this King and knight that here lieth was a worshipful man, and of full great prowess, and well he loved all manner of knights-errant."

"Truly," said Sir Tristram, "it is a piteous case, and were it not that I must be at the great tournament I would take it on me, for I wot that King Arthur for my sake in especial has made these jousts. Therefore I fear to take this enterprise upon me, that I come not betimes to these jousts."

"Sir," said Palamides, "I pray you give me this enterprise, and ye shall see me achieve it worshipfully, or else I shall die in the quarrel."

"Well," said Sir Tristram, "this enterprise I give you, with this, that ye be with me at the tournament that shall be this day seven night."

"Sir," said Palamides, "I promise you I will be with you by that day if I be unslain or unmaimed."

Then departed Sir Tristram, Sir Gareth, and Dinadan, leaving Sir Palamides in the vessel, and beheld the mariners sailing over the Humber. And when Sir Palamides was out of sight they were aware of a knight, who came to them unarmed save his sword, and asked them to lodge in his castle. But when they had come in, and were seated at the board the knight knew Sir Tristram, and waxed wroth with him; and he said, "What cheer make ye?"

"I fare much the worse for thee," said the knight. "I know thee well, Tristram of Liones: thou slewest my brother, and therefore I give thee summons I will slay thee."

"Sir Knight, I am not advised that ever I slew any brother of yours, and if ye say that I did it, I will make you any amends."

"I will none of your amends; but keep ye from me."

So when he had dined, Sir Tristram asked his arms, and departed. But within a little while they perceived a knight coming, well armed and horsed, but without a shield.

"Here is your host," said Sir Dinadan, "coming to have to do with you."

"Let him come," said Sir Tristram. "I shall abide him as well as I may."

Anon, when he came nigh, he cried to Sir Tristram to defend himself, and they rushed together. Sir Tristram bore him over his horse's croup; but he rose again, and smote Sir Tristram twice sore upon the helm.

"I pray you leave off," said Sir Tristram, "for I will be loth to deal with you as I might choose, as I have your meat and drink within my body."

Yet, as he would not leave off, Sir Tristram gave him such a buffet upon his helm that the blood spurted out from his helmet, and he lay like dead. And Tristram repented he had smitten him so sore. But they left him, and went their way, when, ere they had gone far, they met two goodly knights, with servants attending on them. One was Sir Berrant le Apres, and the other Sir Segwarides. At that time Sir Dinadan was bearing Sir Tristram's helm, which the Queen of North Galis had given to Isolde, and she to Sir Tristram. Then Berrant, who was the King with the Hundred Knights, said,—

"Sir Knight, where gat ye that helm? I will have ado with thee for the sake of her who gave it thee; therefore keep thee."

So they came together, and the King of the Hundred Knights smote Sir Dinadan down, horse and all, and then commanded his servant to take the helm.

"What wilt thou do?" said Sir Tristram. "That helm shall not depart from me unless it be dearer bought."

"Then make you ready," said the other; and Sir Tristram smote him over the horse's tail. But the knight arose, and strake fiercely at Sir Tristram again, and he at length gave Sir Berrant a stroke that he fell over his horse sore stunned.

"Then," said Sir Segwarides, "who will joust with me?"

"Let me have this joust, I pray ye," said Sir Gareth to Sir Dinadan; and he suffered him, saying he would not do it. So Sir Gareth attacked, and he was smitten to the ground by Sir Segwarides.

"Now," said Sir Tristram to Sir Dinadan, "joust with yonder knight."

"I will not thereof," said he.

"Then will I," said Sir Tristram, and he ran to him and gave him a fall.

So they left the two knights on foot and rode unto Joyous

Gard, when Sir Gareth would not have gone into the castle, had not Sir Tristram constrained him. Then they entered and had great cheer; but Dinadan, when he came before La Belle Isolde, cursed the time he bare Sir Tristram's helm; and he told her how Tristram had mocked him.

Then they were all very merry, laughing and jesting at Sir Dinadan, so that they wist not what to do with him.

CHAPTER VI

HOW PALAMIDES WENT TO FIGHT WITH TWO BRETHREN FOR THE DEATH OF KING HERMANCE, AND HOW HE PROSPERED IN HIS QUEST

WE MUST now speak of Sir Palamides, who continued to sail down the Humber to the sea-coast, where was a fair castle. Early in the morning the mariners went unto him and called him to arise and enter the castle; then he blew the horn which the mariners had given him, and when those in the castle had heard the sound, many knights came and stood upon the walls, crying, "Welcome be ye to this castle."

At daylight Sir Palamides entered the castle and heard much lamentation.

"What may this mean?" said he. "I love not to hear such sorrow."

Then there came before him one Sir Ebel, who said, "Wit ye well, Sir Knight, this dole and sorrow is made every day; for we had a King called Hermance of the Red City, a noble knight, large and liberal. He loved nothing so much as the errant knights of Arthur's Court, and all manner of knightly games; so kind a King had never the rule of poor people; and because of his goodness and gentleness we bemoan him, and ever shall."

"Tell me," said Palamides, "in what manner and by whom was your lord slain?"

"Sir," said Sir Ebel, "our King brought up of children two men that now are perilous knights, and these our King had so in charity that he trusted none other that was about him. By these two knights our King was governed, and so they ruled him peaceably, for he was so free and so gentle, and they so false and deceivable, which espied the lords of our King's blood, who departed from him. When these two traitors understood they had driven all the lords of his blood from him, they thought to have more power, as in the old saw: 'Give a churl rule, and thereby he will not be sufficed, for whatsoever he be that is ruled by a villain born, and the lord of the soil to be a gentleman born, the same villain shall destroy all the gentlemen about him.'

"By the advice of these false traitors our lord rode into the forest and chased the red deer. When he alighted, and drank at a well, one of the traitors, called Helius, suddenly smote our King through the body with a spear, and left him there. After they departed, by fortune I came to the well and found him wounded to the death. When I heard his complaint, I brought him to the water's side, and in that ship I put him alive, and while he was in that vessel he required me by my faith to write a letter, which ye have seen. This letter I was to put fast in his hand when he died, and he told me to put the vessel down Humber, and the mariners were never to stint till they came to Logris, where all the noble knights assemble at this time."

"Truly," said Sir Palamides, "it grieveth my heart to hear you tell this doleful tale. I saw that same letter, and one of the best knights on the earth read it to me. By his commandment I came hither to revenge your King's death; therefore let me wit where I shall find those traitors, for I shall never be at ease in my heart till I be in hands with them."

"Sir," said Sir Ebel, "you must then take your ship again, and sail to the Delectable Isle, fast by the Red City. We shall pray for you, and abide your returning, for this same castle must be yours an ye speed well; but we keep it with a strong hand."

"Whatsoever come of me, look ye keep well this castle," said Sir Palamides; "for if it misfortune me to be slain in this quest, I am sure there will come one of the best knights in the world to revenge my death, that is Sir Tristram de Liones or Sir Launcelot du Lake."

Then Sir Palamides departed from the castle, and as he came nigh the city, there came out of a ship a goodly knight, armed, against him, and said, "Sir Knight, what seek ye here? Leave this quest, for it is mine, and mine it was ere ever it was yours; therefore I will have it."

"Sir Knight," said Palamides, "it may well be this quest was yours ere it was mine; but when the letter was taken out of the dead King's hands, no knight had undertaken to revenge the death of King Hermance, and as I promised to revenge his death, so I shall, else I am ashamed."

"Ye say well," said the knight; "but I will fight with you, and let the better of us both take the battle upon hand."

"I assent me," said Sir Palamides.

Then they dressed their shields and pulled out their swords, and lashed together more than an hour; but at last Sir Palamides waxed big and smote the other knight upon his knees. So he said, "Gentle knight, hold thy hand; thou art better worthy to have this battle than I. I require thee of knighthood tell me thy name."

"Sir, my name is Palamides, a knight of King Arthur and of the Table Round; hither I came to revenge the death of this dead King."

"Well be ye found," said the knight, "for of all alive, except three, I had lievest have you. I am brother unto King Hermance that is dead, and my name is Sir Hermind."

"Ye say well," said Sir Palamides, "and ye shall see how I speed. If I be slain, go to my lord Sir Launcelot or Sir Tristram; as for Sir Lamorak, him shall ye never see in this world—he was slain by Sir Gawaine and his brethren."

So when Sir Palamides had told Hermind all the manner of Sir Lamorak's death by treason, he took ship, and arrived at the Delectable Isle; meanwhile Sir Hermind went up to the Red City, and told how there was come a knight of King Arthur's to avenge King Hermance's death; and all the city made great joy.

So they sent a messenger unto the two brethren and bade them make ready, for a knight was come, by name Sir Palamides, to fight with them both; and they appointed to be at the city within two days. Within the third day the two

brethren came to the city—one called Helius, the other
Helake—men of great prowess, but false and full of treason,
and, though poor men born, were noble knights of their
hands. With them they brought forty knights, with great
boasting and pride, for they had put the Red City in fear and
damage.

When they were brought to the lists, Sir Palamides came to
the place and said, "Be ye the two brethren that slew your
King and lord Sir Hermance by felony and treason, for whom
that I am come hither to revenge his death?"

"Wit thou well," said Sir Helius and Sir Helake, "that we
are the same knights that slew King Hermance; and also wit
thou well, Palamides, Saracen, that we shall handle thee so
ere ye depart that thou shalt wish thou wert christened."

"It may well be," said Sir Palamides; "yet so am I not
afeard of you. But I trust to God that I shall die a better
Christian man than any of you both; and doubt you not, either
ye or I shall be left dead in this place."

Then they parted, and the two brethren came against Sir
Palamides, and he against them, as fast as their horses might
run. By fortune Sir Palamides smote Helake through his
shield and his breast more than a fathom. All this while Sir
Helius held up his spear, and would not for pride smite Sir
Palamides; but when he saw his brother lie upon the earth, he
said unto the knight, "Help thyself," and therewith he came
hurtling unto Sir Palamides, and smote him quite from his
saddle.

Then Sir Helius rode over Sir Palamides twice or thrice,
so he got his enemy's horse by the bridle, and it reared, and
with the rider fell to the earth. Anon Sir Helius leaped up
lightly and smote Sir Palamides down upon his knee. Then
they lashed together many sad strokes, and traced and
traversed, now backward, now sidelong, till they fell both
grovelling to the earth.

Thus they fought without any reposing for two hours, and
then Sir Palamides waxed faint and weary, but Sir Helius
waxed passing strong. He drove Sir Palamides all the length

of the field; and they of the city, when they saw him in this case, made great dole that such a noble knight should be slain for their King's sake; but the other party made as great joy.

While they were thus weeping and crying, Sir Palamides beheld how they wept, and therewith he bare up his shield, and looking Sir Helius in the visage, smote him a great stroke upon the helm, and after that another and another. Again he smote him with such might that he fell to the earth, and Sir Palamides, tearing his helm off, separated his head from his body. So Sir Helius died.

Then were the people of the city the joyfullest that might be, and they brought their champion to his lodging with great solemnity, and all the people became his men. But Sir Palamides prayed them to take care of all the lordship of King Hermance, for he was obliged to join King Arthur at the castle of Lonazep, which he had promised.

But the people were heavy at his departing, and offered him the third part of their goods so that he would abide with them; but he could not. So he departed, and came to the castle where Sir Ebel was, and when they wist how Sir Palamides had sped, there was a joyful company. Still he went on, and came to Lonazep; but as Sir Tristram was not there, he followed him to Joyous Gard. When he arrived, Sir Dinadan went unto him, and they made of each other much joy. On the morning early came Sir Tristram and Sir Gareth, and found them in their beds. So they arose, and brake their fast.

CHAPTER VII

OF THE TOURNAMENT OF LONAZEP; AND HOW SIR TRISTRAM
AND HIS FELLOWS JOUSTED, AND ALL THEIR NOBLE FEATS

SIR TRISTRAM and his fellows, with La Belle Isolde
and her maidens, soon went up to the tournament at
Lonazep, and they talked concerning which party they should
favour.

"Sirs," said Palamides, "ye shall have my advice to be
against King Arthur to-morn, for on his side will be Sir
Launcelot and many good knights of his blood with him.
And the more men of worship there be the more honour we
shall win."

"That is full knightly spoken," said Sir Tristram, "and so
will we do."

On the morn when it was day, they all arrayed themselves,
and came into the field, riding straight to the party of the
King of Scots.

When King Arthur beheld this, he asked Sir Launcelot
what knights they were.

"Sir," said he, "if Palamides or Tristram be in this country, they be yonder."

And when Sir Kay had told what knights were lacking
from the Table Round, King Arthur said, "Some, I dare
undertake, are this day against us."

Then two knights, cousins of Sir Gawaine, named Sir
Edward and Sir Sadok, came to King Arthur and begged to
have the first jousts.

"I am pleased," said King Arthur.

Then Sir Edward encountered with the King of Scots and
smote him from his horse; and Sir Sadok smote the King of
North Wales, and his fall made Sir Palamides passing wroth,
so he met with Edward and Sadok and smote them both

down. Then King Arthur marvelled at him; but, as he looked, Sir Tristram came in, and smote down four knights of Orkney of the kin of Sir Gawaine, while Sir Gareth and Sir Dinadan also struck down knights. But Tristram and Palamides rushed in and did so wonderfully that all men marvelled; and King Arthur likened Sir Tristram to a lion, and Sir Palamides to a leopard, Sir Gareth and Sir Dinadan were like wolves; so the deeds of Sir Tristram were so great that they of Orkney waxed weary of him, and they withdrew to Lonazep.

"Now," said King Arthur unto Sir Launcelot, "which knight will ye encounter?"

"Sir," he replied, "I will meet the Green Knight upon the black horse"—which was Sir Tristram—"and my cousin will meet the Green Knight upon the white horse"—Sir Palamides—"and my brother Sir Ector shall match the other Green Knight"—Sir Gareth.

"Then," said King Arthur, "must I have ado with the Green Knight upon the grisled horse"—Sir Dinadan.

"Now every man take heed to his fellow," said Sir Launcelot. So they trotted on together, and Sir Launcelot encountered Sir Tristram, and smote him so sore upon the shield that he bare horse and man to the earth; but Sir Launcelot thought it had been Sir Palamides, and passed on. Then Sir Bleoberis encountered Sir Palamides, and smote him so hard upon his shield that he and his white horse hustled to the earth; and Sir Ector struck down Sir Gareth, while King Arthur smote Sir Dinadan from his saddle. So the cry for a time was about the Green Knights who had been stricken down.

When the King of North Galis saw Sir Tristram smitten, he remembered all his brave deeds, and, knowing the custom of taking prisoners, he collected men and rode to deliver Sir Tristram; then, lighting down, he proffered his horse, saying he was more worthy of it than himself, and Tristram mounted. Espied he then King Arthur, and, assailing him, he gave him such a buffet that the King could not keep his saddle, and the knight gave the King of North Galis King Arthur's horse. Then was great pressure to horse the King again, but Sir Palamides would not suffer it, and smote right and left.

Sir Tristram then hewed his way through the thickest of the press, and soon reached his pavilion, leaving Sir Palamides on foot. Then Sir Tristram changed his horse, and disguised himself all in red, horse and harness.

When the Queen La Belle Isolde saw that Sir Tristram was unhorsed, she was greatly moved; but he came dashing into the field when he was ready, and did great deeds of arms. Then Sir Launcelot saw it was Sir Tristram, and repented him that he had smitten him down; and he came into the press, but they knew him not, for he had changed into red armour.

Sir Palamides wished that he might have ado with Sir Tristram, and fought like a lion, so that no man might withstand him. And Sir Tristram beheld him, and said, "Alas that Sir Palamides is not christened!" And so said King Arthur, and all those that beheld him.

At this time came into the field Sir Launcelot du Lake, and saw and heard a noise and great worship that Sir Palamides had. So he dressed him against the knight, and thought to smite him down; but Sir Palamides came upon him fast, and, with his sword, smote Sir Launcelot's horse, and his rider fell to the earth. But many knights held that it was unknightly done in a tournament to kill a horse wilfully.

Then Sir Launcelot came straight upon Sir Palamides, and said fiercely, "Wit thou well thou hast done me this day the greatest despite that ever any worshipful knight did to me in tournament or in jousts; therefore I will be avenged upon thee."

"Ah, mercy, noble knight!" said Palamides, "and forgive me mine unkindly deeds, for I have no power or might to withstand thee; and I have done so much this day, I require thee to spare me, and I promise I shall ever be thy knight while I live."

Therewithal Sir Launcelot suffered Sir Palamides to depart, and then began a great meddle, wherein many knights were smitten down on both parties; but Sir Launcelot and Sir Tristram spared each other, nor would Sir Palamides meddle with Sir Launcelot.

After much fighting the King commanded to blow "to lodging," and because Sir Palamides began first, and was longest enduring, King Arthur and all the Kings gave him the honour for that day, and all knights had wonder at his deeds.

CHAPTER VIII

WHAT HAPPENED ON THE SECOND DAY OF THE TOURNAMENT

THEN there was a cry unto all knights, that when they heard a horn blow they should make jousts as they did the first day. Like as the brethren Sir Edward and Sir Sadok began the jousts the first day, Sir Uwaine and Sir Lucanere de Buttelere began on the second day. Then came in Sir Tristram de Liones and smote them both down, and Sir Palamides smote down other two knights, and Sir Gareth did likewise.

Then said King Arthur unto Sir Launcelot, "See yonder three knights, they do passing well, and namely the first that jousted."

"Sir," said Launcelot, "that knight began not yet, but ye shall see him this day do marvellously."

Sir Palamides rode by himself and did great deeds, so that none there might stand him a stroke. When Sir Tristram saw him do so he said to himself, "He is weary of my company"; and Sir Gareth added, "Let me know this day what ye be, and wonder ye not upon Sir Palamides, for he enforceth himself to win all the honour from you."

"I may well believe it," said Sir Tristram; "and since I understand his evil will, ye shall see that if I enforce myself, whether the praise shall be left that is now upon him."

So Sir Tristram rode into the thickest of the press, and did so marvellously that all men said his deeds did double what Sir Palamides had done. Then the noise went from Sir Palamides, and all the people cried upon Sir Tristram, which, when Sir Palamides perceived, he wept for despite, as he well knew that when Sir Tristram put forth his strength he himself would get but little worship.

Then came King Arthur and his knight into the field—with Sir Launcelot—who soon won praise. Meantime Sir Tristram rode out of the press to his pavilions, and found Sir Dinadan in his bed asleep.

"Awake," said he; "ye ought to be ashamed so to sleep when knights have ado in the field!"

Then Sir Dinadan rose lightly, and said, "What will ye that I should do?"

"Make you ready," said Sir Tristram, "to ride with me into the field."

When Sir Dinadan was armed, and saw so many strokes upon Sir Tristram's helm and shield, he said, "In good time was I thus asleep. I see well now by those strokes that I should have been truly beaten, as I was yesterday."

"Leave your jests," said Sir Tristram, "and come into the field again."

When Sir Dinadan saw that Sir Tristram was arrayed in black harness, he said, "What aileth ye? Meseemeth ye be wilder than ye were yesterday."

Then Sir Tristram smiled, and replied, "Wait well upon me, and I shall make you ready way."

So they took their horses and rode into the field.

But when Sir Palamides saw that Sir Tristram was disguised, he thought to do him a shame; so he rode to a knight that was wounded, and asked him for a loan of his armour and shield, which he granted. Then Sir Palamides rode back, and no one knew him as he attacked Sir Tristram, who marvelled who he was. But after a long encounter Sir Launcelot rode betwixt them, and said to Palamides,—

"Sir Knight, let me have the battle, for ye need repose."

So he suffered Sir Launcelot to fight with Sir Tristram, who was disguised. And so Sir Launcelot gave Sir Tristram many sad strokes, and they fought long together, though Sir Launcelot knew not Sir Tristram. But Sir Dinadan told Sir Gareth who Sir Tristram was, and forthwith Sir Gareth rushed upon Sir Launcelot, while Sir Dinadan attacked him with a spear and brought him to the ground, horse and all. On that came Sir Palamides and smote down Sir Dinadan, and Sir Launcelot also assailed him. But well understood Sir

Tristram that Sir Dinadan might not endure Sir Launcelot, but he could not help him because Sir Palamides was encountering him. When, however, Sir Tristram saw him come, he hurtled unto him and pulled him down underneath, and went to the assistance of Dinadan, who cried out, that Sir Launcelot might hear it,—

"My lord Sir Tristram, take your horse."

When Sir Launcelot heard this, he said, "Alas! what have I done? I am dishonoured. Why are ye thus disguised? Ye have put yourself in great peril this day; but I pray you, noble knight, to pardon me, for had I known you, we had not done this battle."

"Sir," said Sir Tristram, "this is not the first kindness ye showed me."

So they were both horsed again. Then the people on one side gave Sir Launcelot the honour, and on the other side Sir Tristram; but Sir Launcelot said he was not worthy to have it, for Sir Tristram had been longer in the field and had smitten down more knights than he. So he gave his voice for Sir Tristram, who was that day proved the best knight.

Then all returned to lodging, and Queen Isolde was wroth with Sir Palamides, for she saw his treason. When the tournament was done, she rode to her pavilions with Tristram, Gareth, and Dinadan, while Sir Palamides accompanied them in his disguise; but when Sir Tristram espied him, knowing that he was the same knight that had held him so hot that day, he prayed him to depart, but Sir Palamides replied as though he had not known Sir Tristram, nevertheless by his answer he discovered himself.

"Ah, Sir Palamides!" said Sir Tristram, "are ye such a knight? Ye have been named wrong a gentle knight, for this day ye have showed me great ungentleness, and almost brought me to my death."

"Alas!" said Sir Palamides; "are ye my lord Sir Tristram?"

"Yea, sir; and that ye knew well enough."

"By my knighthood, I knew ye not! I weened ye had been

the King of Ireland by your arms, and had turned upon Sir Launcelot's party, which caused me to turn."

"Ye say well," said Sir Tristram, "so I take you and forgive you."

But Queen Isolde told Sir Tristram of the treachery, and how Sir Palamides had changed his armour, and wilfully did battle with Sir Tristram.

"Sir Palamides," said Sir Tristram, "I will take your excuse; all is pardoned on my part."

CHAPTER IX

HOW SIR TRISTRAM AND PALAMIDES DID NEXT DAY; HOW KING ARTHUR FARED; AND HOW PALAMIDES AND SIR SAFERE WERE ASSAILED

ON THE morn Sir Tristram, Gareth, and Dinadan went into Sir Palamides' chamber while he was asleep, for he had been wakeful all the night with weeping, and sorrowful concerning the rebukes of Tristram and of La Belle Isolde. But Sir Tristram awaked Sir Palamides, and bade him make him ready for the field. So they set out; Sir Palamides and Kainus le Strange being the first knights ready, and they encountered. But Palamides smote Sir Kainus quite over his horse's croup, and then overcame another knight, whereat the people cried for him, and King Arthur remarked how he had already begun to play his pageant.

Then Sir Tristram appearing, he did deeds more wonderful, smiting Sir Kay and three knights more so deftly, that the cry was for him, and not for Palamides. Sir Gareth and Dinadan also had great worship, and did great things, so that Arthur spake of them; and Tristram's side did well and knightly.

Then King Arthur and Sir Launcelot dressed them, and got into the thickest of the meddle, where Sir Tristram unknowing smote down King Arthur. Sir Launcelot would have rescued him, but he was so sore beset that he was pulled down from his horse. So the Kings of Ireland and Scotland, seeing the King and Launcelot so pressed, did all they might to take them prisoners; but Sir Launcelot hearing of their intention, laid about him like a hungry lion, and no knight durst abide him. Meanwhile the battle raged, and Sir Ector engaged with Palamides, whom he pulled from his horse; but as Sir

Ector de Maris was bringing Sir Launcelot a horse, Sir Palamides arose and leaped upon it before him.

"Gramercy," said Launcelot, "thou art worthier of that horse than I am." Then he gat another horse.

King Arthur that day, with Sir Launcelot and some of his knights, did most marvellous deeds, and Sir Launcelot alone, as the book showeth, pulled down thirty knights. Notwithstanding, King Arthur and his men were overmatched, but Sir Tristram marvelled at the wonderful deeds they did, and particularly of Sir Launcelot's.

Sir Tristram then called his friends Palamides, Dinadan, and Gareth, and said, "My fair fellows, wit ye well that I will turn unto King Arthur's party, for I never saw so few knights do better, and it will be shame to us of the Table Round to see our lord King Arthur and that noble knight Sir Launcelot dishonoured."

"It will be well done," said Sir Gareth and Sir Dinadan.

But Sir Palamides would not change, and he departed from them, while the others united with Sir Launcelot, and they smote down the Kings of Scots, of Ireland, and of Wales. King Arthur also made for Sir Palamides, and smote him from his horse, and then Sir Tristram bore down all he met. So all the parties began to flee.

"Alas!" said Palamides, "that ever I should see this day, for now have I lost all the worship that I won."

So he went away wailing, and withdrew till he came to a well, where he put off his armour and wept and bewailed himself sorely.

After the tournament many knights would have given the prize to Sir Launcelot and many to Sir Tristram, who gave his voice for Sir Launcelot, and wished him to have the prize; but Sir Launcelot would not have it, so it was given between them both. And then every man went to his lodging.

As Sir Palamides remained by the well wailing and weeping, there came by him fleeing the Kings of Wales and of Scotland, and found him in his rage; but they mounted him and made him go with them. And when they came near Sir

Tristram's pavilion Sir Palamides halted and called for him, saying aloud,—

"Where art thou, Sir Tristram de Liones?"

"Sir," said Dinadan, who heard him, "there is Sir Palamides. Will ye not come in among us?" he added to the knight.

"Fie on thee, traitor!" cried Palamides. "Were it but daylight I would slay thee with mine own hands; thou shalt die for this day's deed!"

"Sir Palamides," replied Tristram, "ye blame me with wrong. Had ye done as I did ye would have worship; but since ye give me such large warning, I will beware of you."

"Fie on you, traitor!" repeated Sir Palamides, and then he departed.

Next day Sir Tristram and all his party went by water and by land until they came to Joyous Gard, while King Arthur and his knights withdrew to Camelot, and Sir Palamides rode with the two Kings, and ever made the greatest dole that any man could ever think, for he remembered the kind and gentle fellowship of Sir Tristram, and could never be merry. Nor did he long remain in the company of the two Kings, though they each pressed him to abide with them; so he departed and sought adventures.

It came to pass that in a forest, by a well, Sir Palamides encountered a wounded knight, whose horse was bound by him; and the knight made the greatest dole, sighing as if his heart would burst. Then Sir Palamides rode to him, and said, "Fair knight, why wail ye so? Let me wail with you, for doubtless I am much heavier than ye are. My sorrow I daresay is a hundredfold more than yours; therefore let us complain to each other."

"First," said the wounded knight, "tell me your name; for an thou be none of the knights of the Round Table thou shalt never know my name, whatever come of me."

"Fair knight," said Palamides, "such as I am I am, were it better or worse; my name is Sir Palamides, son and heir unto King Astlabor, and Sir Safere and Sir Segwarides are my two brothers; wit thou well as for myself I never was christened, but my brethren are."

"Oh, noble knight!" said the other, "well is me that I have met with you. Wit ye well my name is Epinogris, the son of the King of Northumberland."

Then they sat down, and Sir Palamides began his complaint concerning the rebukes he had had from La Belle Isolde and Sir Tristram, which he confessed he had deserved. But he had lost her regard and Sir Tristram's fellowship, so was miserable at having lost them and all the worship and prowess he had in the company of Sir Tristram.

"Nay," said Sir Epinogris, "your sorrow is but a jest to my sorrow, for I rejoiced my lady, and won her with my hands; but lost her the next day. She was an earl's daughter, and I won her as she came from the tournament; and next day there came a knight called Sir Helior le Preuse, a hardy knight, and he challenged me to fight for my lady. But he wounded me, and left me for dead; so took my lady with him. So my sorrow is more than yours."

"That is truth," said Sir Palamides; "but if I can, I will get your lady again, or else Sir Helior shall beat me."

So Sir Palamides walked away under the leaves, and at last he met a knight with a green shield, and thereon a white lion, leading a lady upon a palfrey, and Sir Palamides bade him defend his lady. So they ran together, and fought more than an hour. Then Sir Palamides had marvel what knight he had ado with, and he required his name.

"Wit thou well I dare tell thee my name an thou wilt tell me thine."

"I will," said Palamides.

"Truly," said the knight, "my name is Safere, son of King Astlabor. Sir Palamides and Sir Segwarides are my brethren."

"Now wit thee well that my name is Palamides," said he.

Then Sir Safere kneeled down upon his knees, and prayed of him mercy; and unlacing their helms, they kissed each other, weeping. So Sir Palamides took the lady, and brought her to Sir Epinogris, when both swooned for joy at the meeting. Afterwards they rode on all together unto Sir Epinogris' castle, where Sir Palamides and his brother remained the night. On the next day they departed, and were set upon by the fellows of a knight whom Sir Palamides had slain at the tournament, and taken prisoners unto a castle called Pelownes. But as they were thus riding, a knight came by who knew Sir Palamides, and marvelled to see him in such condition.

"Ah," said Palamides, "I ride towards my death for the slaying of a knight at a tournament at Lonazep, and if I had not left my lord Sir Tristram, now might I have been sure of my life. But I pray you ride to my lord, and tell him, and unto Queen Isolde, and say if I ever trespassed, I ask their forgiveness; and also I pray you recommend me to King Arthur and all the fellowship of the Table Round."

Then the knight wept for pity, and rode away as fast as he might to Joyous Gard, where he went at once unto Sir Tristram, and told him all, and ever the knight wept as he had been mad.

CHAPTER X

HOW SIR TRISTRAM PREPARED TO RESCUE PALAMIDES, BUT SIR
LAUNCELOT DID SO ERE HE CAME; AND HOW THEY ALL CAME
TO JOYOUS GARD, WHERE THEY ENCOUNTERED

WHEN Sir Tristram heard concerning Sir Palamides he
was heavy, and, notwithstanding his wrath at him,
would not suffer him to die, for he was a noble knight. So
Sir Tristram armed himself, and with his two squires rode at
a great pace to the castle of Pelownes.

Meanwhile the knights that were leading Sir Palamides
passed by a well where Sir Launcelot was, and Sir Launcelot,
putting on his helm, let them pass. Then was he aware of Sir
Palamides bounden and led to death.

"Forsooth," said he, "it were shame for me to suffer this
noble knight so to die an I might help him, therefore I will
help him or die for his sake."

So he mounted and rode after the twelve knights who led
Sir Palamides, and inquired why they led him away and
bounden.

Then the knights turned their horses, and said, "Fair
knight, we counsel you not to meddle with this matter, for
the knight hath deserved death, and unto death he is judged."

"It me repenteth in that I cannot ransom him with fairness," replied Launcelot, "for he is over good a knight to die a
shameful death; wherefore keep you as well as ye can, for I
will rescue that knight or die for it."

Then they began to dress their spears, and Sir Launcelot
smote the foremost down, horse and man, and likewise three
more. Then he struck on right hand and left, so within a
while none of the twelve were left, the most part being sore
wounded on the ground. So Sir Launcelot took the best horse
and gave him to Palamides, and carried him to Joyous Gard.

As they proceeded they met Tristram riding, but he knew
not Sir Launcelot, who made ready to joust with Sir Tristram.
But Palamides called out to Tristram,—

"O my lord, joust not with this knight, for he hath saved
my life."

When Sir Tristram heard that, he came trotting towards
them, and Sir Palamides thanked him for his goodness in
coming to his rescue, notwithstanding he had offended him.
Then Palamides told how he had been rescued, and Sir Tristram turning to Sir Launcelot, inquired who he was.

"I am a knight-errant," replied he, "that rideth to seek adventures."

"What is your name?" inquired Tristram.

"Sir," replied Sir Launcelot, "at this time I will not tell
you; but now that ye are met together I will depart from
you."

"Not so," replied Sir Tristram; "I pray you to ride with
me unto my castle."

And he persuaded him at length; so they rode on together
to Joyous Gard, where they unarmed. When Sir Launcelot
was unhelmed they at once knew him and embraced him,
while Palamides went down upon his knees to thank him;
but Sir Launcelot raised him up, saying he was only glad to
rescue such a noble knight. So they remained for a while.

At length Sir Launcelot departed, and a cause of quarrel
arose between Sir Palamides and Sir Tristram, concerning
La Belle Isolde, which they agreed to fight to the uttermost.
Fifteen days thereafter was the time appointed, in the
meadow under Joyous Gard. So Palamides departed unto
King Arthur's Court, and there he gat him four knights and
four sergeants-at-arms; so he returned towards Joyous Gard.

Meanwhile Sir Tristram was hunting and chasing; but one
day—three days before the meeting—an archer shot an arrow,
and smote Sir Tristram through the thigh, and slew his horse.
Then was he passing heavy, and bled sore; yet was he more
heavy because of his inability to meet Sir Palamides than for

the wound, which would not permit him to do battle on the day set.

But no one thought that Sir Palamides would ever hurt Sir Tristram, when he came with the knights and sergeants-at-arms to bear witness of the battle. So Palamides came into the field at the time appointed, and waited two hours. Then he sent a squire unto Sir Tristram, and desired him to come into the field; so the squire was permitted to come to Sir Tristram's bed with his message, where he was shown the wound, six inches deep, that prevented the knight keeping his saddle.

When the squire returned and told Palamides, he was glad, because he knew he should have had hard handling of Sir Tristram, and very likely the worst of it; so he then departed where fortune led him, and within a month Sir Tristram was whole of his hurt. Then he took horse and rode from country to country, and always inquired for Sir Palamides; but all that quarter of summer he could not meet with him. During that time also Sir Tristram did many great deeds, so that his fame increased mightily, and Sir Launcelot's decreased. For this cause Sir Launcelot's friends sought to slay Tristram, because of his fame.

But when Sir Launcelot knew this, he said openly that he would himself slay any who did Sir Tristram evil or shame with treason. So his fame extended, and great joy was made in Liones, whither great gifts were made to his estate. Ever Sir Tristram loved La Belle Isolde, and often resorted to Joyous Gard, where she was.

From her Tristram heard concerning Sir Launcelot, who had been missing for two years: how he had been holpen of the Holy Vessel the Sangreal, and how he was now restored to the Court. So Sir Tristram determined to go up to the Feast of Pentecost. As he rode unarmed, he met Sir Palamides, who called him to battle, "For," said he, "we must redress our old scores."

"As for that," said Tristram, "there was never a Christian man might make his boast that ever I fled from him, and wit ye well, Sir Palamides, thou art a Saracen, that shalt never make thy boast that Sir Tristram de Liones fled from thee."

Therewith Sir Tristram made his horse to run, and with all his might he came upon Sir Palamides, and brake his spear upon him into a hundred pieces. Then he drew his sword, and turning his horse, he struck Palamides six great strokes upon the helm, while the other stood still, thinking whether he should slay Sir Tristram or not with his spear.

"Thou coward knight!" cried Tristram, "what castest thou to do? Why wilt thou not do battle with me? for no doubt I shall endure all thy malice."

"Ah, Sir Tristram! well thou wottest I cannot fight with thee for shame, for thou art here naked, and I am armed. So if I slay thee, the dishonour will be mine."

So they conversed, and meanwhile they became aware of a wounded knight, whose armour Sir Tristram borrowed, and then fairly met Sir Palamides. So they fought like wild boars for more than two hours. Sir Tristram brought Sir Palamides upon his knees; but he in turn wounded Tristram. And at the last Sir Tristram doubled his strokes, and smote Sir Palamides' sword out of his hand. Then Palamides stood still, and beheld his sword with a sorrowful heart.

"How now!" said Tristram; "I have thee at advantage, but it shall never be said that Sir Tristram did ever slay a knight that is weaponless; so take thou thy sword, and let us make an end of the battle."

But Sir Palamides replied that, though he was in no wise afraid, yet had he no desire to fight more, for his quarrel was only for a feeling as to La Belle Isolde.

"Wherefore," he said, "forgive me all I have offended you. Take me to the next church and have me clean confessed, and after that I will be baptized; then will we ride unto King Arthur's Court, and be there at the High Feast."

"Take your horse," said Sir Tristram, "we will do as ye say, and all your evil may God forgive as I do; here within a mile is the Suffragan of Carlisle, that shall baptize you."

So Palamides rode on with Sir Tristram and was baptized.

Then came they to the Court, and the King and all were glad that Sir Palamides had been christened. At the same feast came in Sir Galahad, and sat in the Siege Perilous.

Therewithal severed and departed all the knights of the Table Round, and Sir Tristram returned to Joyous Gard, while Sir Palamides followed the Questing Beast.

BOOK THE NINTH: OF SIR LAUNCELOT AND HIS SON SIR GALAHAD

CHAPTER I

HOW SIR LAUNCELOT SUCCOURED A LADY AND FOUGHT WITH A DRAGON; AND HOW HE WEDDED ELAINE, KING PELLES' DAUGHTER

WE NOW leave Sir Tristram de Liones, to speak for a brief time concerning Sir Launcelot, and Sir Galahad his son. Before Sir Galahad was born there came a hermit unto King Arthur, upon Whit Sunday, as the knights sat at the Table Round. When the hermit saw the Siege Perilous he asked why it was there, and why it was void. So they told him that no one save one should ever seat himself there and not be destroyed. Then asked the hermit if they knew who he should be, and they could not tell who or what the knight would be who would sit upon the Siege Perilous.

"Then wot I," said the hermit, "that he is yet unborn, and this same year he shall be born that shall sit in the Siege Perilous and win the Sangreal."

When the hermit had said this he departed from the Court of King Arthur. After this Sir Launcelot rode on until he came to ride over the bridge of Corbin, and there he saw a passing fair tower, with a number of people, who all cried,—

"Welcome, Launcelot du Lake, the flower of all knighthood, for by thee we shall be delivered out of all dangers."

"What mean ye?" replied Sir Launcelot.

"Ah, fair knight! here is within this tower a dolorous lady that hath been in great pain many winters, for she boileth in scalding water; and but lately Sir Gawaine was here, but he might not help her, so he left her in pain. But we know well that thou shalt deliver her, Sir Launcelot."

"Well," said he, "show me what I must do."

Then they brought him into the tower where was the lady,

and he penetrated the chamber, which was as hot as any stew; and there he took the fairest lady he ever saw by the hand, who had been put there by Morgan le Fay and the Queen of North Galis, because she was called the fairest in the country. And there she had been five years, and never would have been freed, had not the best knight in the world taken her by the hand. And when she was arrayed, Sir Launcelot thought she was the fairest he had ever seen, save Queen Guenever.

After they had been to the chapel to return thanks to God for her with all the people, they said, "Sir Knight, since ye have delivered this lady, ye shall deliver us from a serpent that is here in a tomb."

Then Sir Launcelot took his shield, and said, "Bring me thither, and what I may do unto the pleasure of God and you I will do."

So when Sir Launcelot came thither, he saw written upon the tomb letters of gold that said thus: "Here shall come a leopard of King's blood, and he shall slay this serpent; and this leopard shall engender a lion in this foreign country, the which lion shall pass all other knights."

So then Sir Launcelot lifted up the tomb, and there came out a horrible and fiendly dragon, spitting fire out of his mouth. Then Sir Launcelot drew out his sword and fought with the dragon long, and at last, with great pain, he slew it. Therewithal came King Pelles, the good and noble knight, and saluted Sir Launcelot, and he him again.

"Fair knight," said the King, "what is your name? I require you of your knighthood tell me."

"Sir," said Launcelot, "my name is Sir Launcelot du Lake."

Then the King told him what his name was, and how he was cousin unto Joseph of Arimathæa. Then either made much of the other, and went into the castle to take their repast. Anon there came in a dove at a window, and in her mouth there seemed a little censer of gold, and therewithal there was such a savour as all the spicery of the world had been there. Forthwith there was upon the table all manners of meats and drinks; so came in a damsel, passing fair and young, and she bare a vessel of gold between her hands, and there, too, the King kneeled devoutly and said his prayers, and so did all that were there.

"What may this mean?" said Sir Launcelot.

"This is," said the King, "the richest thing that any man hath living; an when this thing goeth about, the Round Table shall be broken. Wit thou well," he continued, "this is the Holy Sangreal that ye have seen."

So the King and Sir Launcelot led their life the most part of that day together. King Pelles would fain have had Launcelot marry his daughter, for he knew it had been said that such marriage would take place, and that the fair Elaine's son should be Sir Galahad the Good Knight, by whom all the foreign countries should be brought out of danger, and the Holy Grail achieved.

So after a while the marriage was arranged, and the maid Elaine was wed to Sir Launcelot at the castle of Case, and Sir Galahad was born. He was so named because Sir Launcelot was so called at the fountain's stone, and after that the Lady of the Lake confirmed him Sir Launcelot du Lake.

About this time came Sir Bors unto King Pelles' Court, and when the King and Elaine his daughter knew he was nephew unto Sir Launcelot, they made him great cheer, and inquired where Sir Launcelot was, for he had some time before departed from the castle of Corbin.

"Marvel not," replied Sir Bors; "he is with Morgan le Fay, King Arthur's sister." And then he beheld the child in Elaine's arms, and it was passing like Sir Launcelot his father, and he prayed to God that Galahad might be as good a knight as Launcelot. Then there came in a white dove, and she bare a little censer of gold in her mouth, and a maiden carried that Sangreal, and she said openly,—

"Wit you well, Sir Bors, that this child is Galahad, that shall sit at the Siege Perilous and achieve the Sangreal. He shall be much better than ever was Sir Launcelot du Lake his father."

And when the dove took her flight, the maiden vanished with the Sangreal as she came.

Then said Sir Bors unto King Pelles, "This castle may be named the Castle Adventurous, for here have been many strange adventures."

"That is so," said the King; "and I let you wit here shall no knight win worship save he be of worship himself, and good living, one that loveth and dreadeth God."

"This is a wonderful thing," said Sir Bors. "What ye mean I wot not, and therefore I will lie in this castle this night."

"Ye shall not do so," said King Pelles, "by my counsel, for it is hard that ye escape without a shame."

"I shall take the adventure that shall befall me," said Sir Bors. So he was confessed clean, and led unto bed in a fair large chamber with many doors about it.

When Sir Bors espied all these doors, he avoided all the people; but in no wise would he unarm him. So he laid him down upon the bed, and there came a light into the room, so that he could see a great spear come straight upon him, and it seemed as if the head of the spear was burning like a taper. Anon the spear smote him in the shoulder, and wounded him sore.

As soon as he had lain down again for pain, there came a knight armed, and he bade Sir Bors arise and fight with him, which, though he was sore hurt, he did not fail to do. He at last overcame him, and smote him down, and the knight, who was named Bedivere of the Straight Marches, yielded him. So Sir Bors made him to swear to be at the Court of King Arthur a prisoner at the Whit Sunday next coming.

After that Sir Bors lay down again, and a great noise was heard of arrows, which fell so thick upon him that he marvelled, for many fell upon him and hurt him. He was then aware of a hideous lion, which bereft him of his shield; but with his sword Sir Bors smote off the lion's head. Right so he saw a dragon in the court passing horrible, and there seemed letters of gold written on his forehead, and Sir Bors thought the letters made a signification of King Arthur. Then there came a horrible leopard and an old, and this and the dragon did battle together.

At the last the dragon spit out of its mouth as it had been a hundred dragons, and all these small ones devoured the old dragon. Anon there came an old man into the hall, and there seemed to be two adders round his neck. This man had a harp, and he sang an old song, "How Joseph of Arimathæa come into this land," and when he had sung, he said unto Sir Bors,—

"Go from hence, for here ye shall have no more adventures; worshipfully have ye done, and better shall ye do hereafter."

Then Sir Bors saw the white dove with the censer in her mouth, and at once all the tumult ceased, and the court was full of good savours. Also there came four children bearing tapers, and the old man in the midst of the children with a censer in his one hand and a spear in the other; and the spear was called the Spear of Vengeance.

CHAPTER II

HOW SIR LAUNCELOT WENT MAD; AND HOW HE WAS SOUGHT
AND FOUND OF SIR PERCIVALE AND SIR ECTOR DE MARIS

IN THOSE days did Sir Launcelot go out of his mind and become mad, being, with his wife Elaine, banished from the Court by Queen Guenever, for an enchantment had been worked against him. So when he had quite quitted the Court he departed into the woods, and endured pain and want with many privations, but no man knew what had become of him.

Then the news concerning Sir Launcelot came to the Court of King Arthur, and the fellowship of the Table Round. So Sir Gawaine, Sir Uwaine, Sir Sagramore le Desirous, Sir Aglovale, and Sir Percivale de Galis, took upon them, by the great desire of King Arthur, to search throughout England, Wales, and Scotland, to find Sir Launcelot. And with them rode eighteen knights to bear them fellowship.

Thus these noble knights rode together by two, by three, by four, by five, and they assigned where they should meet. Sir Aglovale and Sir Percivale rode together unto their mother, who besought them to abide at home with her; but they could not. They continued their journey into many countries, ever inquiring after Sir Launcelot; but never could they hear of him. At the last they came to a castle called Cardican, and about midnight Sir Percivale came to his brother squire, and said, "Arise, make ready, for ye and I will ride away secretly."

"Sir," said the squire, "I would full fain ride with you, but an my lord your brother take me he will slay me."

"As for that, care thou not, for I shall be thy warrant," said Sir Percivale.

So he rode away till the afternoon, and then came upon a bridge of stone, where he found a knight bounden fast about the waist unto a pillar. This knight's name was Persides, of the Table Round, who came by adventure that way, and had been set upon and chained, and if some knight did not break his bands he would die.

"Be of good cheer," said Sir Percivale; "and because ye are a knight of the Round Table I trust to break your bands."

Therewith he drew out his sword, and struck at the chain with such force that he cut it in twain, and through Sir Persides' hauberk, and hurt him a little.

"Truly," said the knight, "that was a mighty stroke; had not the chain been, ye had slain me."

Therewithal came a knight rushing from the castle, to encounter Sir Percivale, who met him in the centre of the bridge, and bestowed on him such a buffet that he was smitten over, and had it not been for a boat in the water he would have been drowned. Then Sir Percivale took the knight's horse and made Sir Persides ride thereon to the castle, where all his servants were delivered unto him. Then Persides brought Sir Percivale to his own castle, where they made great cheer.

On the morn Sir Percivale bade Sir Persides to ride unto King Arthur, and to tell him how he had been rescued; and to say to his brother not to come in search of him, for he was in quest of Sir Launcelot du Lake. Sir Persides did as he was told, and went unto King Arthur.

Meanwhile Sir Percivale rode along, and in a forest he met a knight with a broken shield and a broken helm; and as soon as either saw the other they made them ready to joust. They met together so hard that Sir Percivale was smitten to the earth; so they fought on foot, and wounded each other full sore. At last Sir Percivale said,—

"Sir Knight, hold thy hand a while, for we have foughten for a simple matter over-long; therefore I require thee tell me thy name, for I was never till now matched."

"Truly," replied the other, "never was there knight that wounded me so sore as thou hast done, and I am a knight of the Table Round; my name is Ector de Maris, brother to the good knight Sir Launcelot du Lake."

"Alas!" said Sir Percivale; "my name is Sir Percivale de Galis, that hath my quest to seek Sir Launcelot. Now I am sure that I shall never finish it, for ye have slain me with your hands."

Then they both made great dole out of measure.

"This will not avail," said Sir Percivale.

So he kneeled down and made his prayers devoutly, for the faith stood high in him. So there came by the Holy Vessel of the Sangreal, with all manner of sweetness and savour; but they could not readily see who bore that vessel, but Sir Percivale had a glimmering of it and of the maiden that bore it, for he was a pure knight. Forthwith they were both as whole of limb as ever they were, and they gave great thankings to God.

"What may this mean?" said Sir Percivale; "just now we were on the point of dying, and now we be healed."

"I wot full well," said Sir Ector, "what it is. It is a Holy Vessel borne by a maiden, and therein is a part of the holy blood of our Lord Jesus Christ—blessed may He be; but it may not be seen save by a perfect man."

"Truly," said Sir Percivale, "I saw a damsel, as me thought, all in white, with a vessel in both her hands, and forthwith I was whole."

Then they amended their harness, mounted their horses, and rode away, telling each other of their adventures.

It came to pass after that there was a great cry made unto the Joyous Isle for a tournament, which drew knights to the number of five hundred, and Sir Percivale, with Sir Ector de Maris, came to that castle called Joyous Isle. There the people told him of a great knight, calling himself Le Chevaler Mal Fet, the mightiest man living, who had come into the country as a madman, but had been healed by the Sangreal.

When he heard this, Sir Percivale passed over the water to the castle, and demanded to joust with the good knight Mal Fet. Said the porter to him, "Good Sir, ride within the castle to the jousting-place, where the lords and ladies may see you."

So anon as the Chevaler had warning, he came, and encountered Sir Percivale, and had a desperate fight for two hours, until Le Chevaler Mal Fet inquired who his adversary was, and when he heard Sir Percivale's name, he said,—

"Alas! what have I done to fight with you, a knight of the Table Round, I that sometime was your fellow!"

At that Sir Percivale kneeled down, and besought the Chevaler to tell his name, and he then declared himself to be Launcelot du Lake, whom they had so long been seeking. Then Sir Ector was informed, and came running, and the two brothers wept upon each other, till all had pity who beheld them. And Dame Elaine was there also.

After a while, upon a certain day, Sir Percivale asked Sir Launcelot whether he would not venture to the Court of King Arthur. But Sir Launcelot refused, saying that they had so ill treated him and his wife that he would not go thither again. But his brother persuaded him. So they took leave of Dame Elaine and King Pelles, who made great sorrow.

"My lord Sir Launcelot," said Elaine, "at this same Feast of Pentecost shall your son and mine be made knight—he is now fully fifteen winters old."

"God give him grace to prove a good knight," replied Sir Launcelot.

Then they departed, and within five days' journey they came to Camelot, and great joy was made about Sir Launcelot by all the lords and ladies of the Court. Then Sir Percivale told his adventures; but Sir Launcelot said little. Howbeit, they were all glad, and made great feasting.

BOOK THE TENTH: THE TALE OF THE SAN-GREAL, OR HOLY GRAIL

CHAPTER I

HOW SIR LAUNCELOT WAS CALLED TO DUB A KNIGHT; HOW THE LETTERS WERE FOUND WRITTEN IN THE SIEGE PERILOUS; AND OF THE MARVELLOUS ADVENTURE OF THE SWORD IN THE STONE

AT THE Feast of Pentecost, when all the fellowship of the Table Round had come to Camelot, and when all the tables were laid, there came to the Court a gentlewoman who had ridden fast, and, kneeling down, she saluted the King.

"Sir," said she, "I pray you say me where Sir Launcelot is."

"Yonder is he," replied the King.

Then she went unto Launcelot, and said, "I salute you on King Pelles' behalf, and I require ye to come with me into the forest."

And he consented. So he went, with the King's leave, and came with the damsel to an abbey of nuns, where they unarmed him; and in a chamber he found Sir Bors and Sir Lionel, who received him with great joy.

As they stood talking together, there came twelve nuns, who brought with them a youth [Galahad] who was passing fair and well made, so that in all the world was not his match.

"Sir," said the nuns, "we bring you this child, whom we have nourished; and we pray you to make him a knight, for of more worthier hands he could not receive the honour of knighthood."

"Cometh this desire of himself?" said Sir Launcelot, when he had admired the youth.

He and they all answered, "Yea."

"Then shall he receive it," said Launcelot, "to-morrow at the High Feast."

That night Sir Launcelot had passing good cheer, and in

the morn, at the hour of prime, at Galahad's desire, he made him a knight; and Launcelot said, "God make thee a good man, for beauty faileth you not as any that liveth! Now, fair sir, will ye come with me unto the Court of King Arthur?"

"Nay," said he, "I will not go with you at this time."

Then Launcelot departed with his two cousins, and came to Camelot by the hour of undorne [nine in the morning] of Whit Sunday. By this time the King and Queen had gone to the minster to hear the service; but when they returned they welcomed the knights.

At the feast-time the barons and knights all espied letters written upon the seats, as to who should occupy them; and so they went round until they arrived at the Siege Perilous, whereon they found this in letters of gold:—

"Four hundred winters and fifty-four accomplished after the Passion of our Lord Jesus Christ ought this Siege to be filled."

Then all the barons said, "This is a marvellous thing!"

"In the name of God," said Sir Launcelot, "it seemeth to me that the siege ought to be filled this same day, for this is the Feast of Pentecost after the four hundred and fifty-fourth year; and if it would please all parties, I would none of these letters were seen until he be come who would achieve this adventure."

So they covered the Siege Perilous, and the King bade them hasten dinner.

"Sir," said Sir Kay, "if ye go now to your meat you will break your old custom, for ye were not used to sit down till ye had some adventure."

"Ye say sooth," replied the King; "but I was so full of joy for Sir Launcelot and his cousins, that I did not think of the old custom."

As they were speaking, there suddenly entered an attendant, who said, "Sir, I bring you marvellous tidings."

"What be they?" inquired the King.

"Sir," said the squire, "here at the river is a great stone, which I saw floating on the water, and sticking in it was a sword."

"I will see that marvel," said the King.

So he and all his knights hurried down to the river, and found the stone floating. It was of red marble, and therein was a fair and rich sword embedded. On the pommel of the sword were precious stones wrought with letters of gold on this wise:—

"Never shall man take me hence but only he by whom I ought to hang, and he shall be the best knight in the world."

"Fair sir," said the King to Launcelot, "the sword ought to be yours, for I am sure you are the best knight in the world."

"Certes, sir," replied Launcelot, "this is not my sword; also I have no hardiness to set my hand unto it, for it belongeth not to my side; also who assayeth to take it and faileth, shall receive a wound of that sword. So I wit that on this day the adventures of the Sangreal—the Holy Vessel—will begin."

Then Sir Gawaine, at the King's desire, attempted to draw the sword from the stone, but he could not stir it.

"I thank you well," said the King.

"My lord Gawaine," said Launcelot, "now wit ye well that this sword shall touch ye so sore, that ye shall wish ye had never put your hand unto it for the best castle of the realm."

When the King heard this he was much troubled, and repented; nevertheless he asked Sir Percivale if he would try for his love. He said, "Gladly." Therewith he set his hand on the sword and pulled it strongly, but he could not move it; and more tried, but none succeeded.

"Now may ye go to your dinner," said Sir Kay to the King, "for ye have seen a marvellous adventure."

So the King and all went into the Court, and every knight knew his own place to set him therein; and young men, who were knights, served them as they feasted.

CHAPTER II

HOW THE OLD MAN BROUGHT SIR GALAHAD TO THE SIEGE PERIL-
OUS, AND HOW HE DREW THE SWORD OUT OF THE STONE IN
THE WATER. THE VOW OF THE QUEST OF THE HOLY GRAIL

WHEN all the seats save the Siege Perilous were filled,
and all the knights were served, a marvellous thing
happened. All the doors and windows of the palace closed
of themselves, and in the gloominess there advanced into the
hall an ancient man, clothed all in white; and none knew
whence he came. With him came a young knight on foot
in red armour, without sword or shield, a scabbard only hanging by his side; and he said,—

"Peace be to you, fair lords."

Then said the old man to King Arthur, "I bring to you a
young knight of kingly lineage, and of the kindred of Joseph
of Arimathæa, whereby the marvels of this Court and of
strange realms shall be fully accomplished."

The King felt right glad at this, and said to the old man,
"Sir, ye be right welcome, and the young knight with you."

Then the young knight was unarmed, and he bare a mantle
of fur upon his shoulders. So the old man made him follow
him to the Siege Perilous, which was beside Sir Launcelot.
Anon he lifted up the cloth which covered the seat, and
therein were found letters written, which said, "This is the
Siege of Galahad, the Haut Prince."

"Sir," said the old man, "this place is yours."

Then Sir Galahad sat him down securely in that place, and
said to the old man, "Ye may now go your way, for ye have
done that ye were commanded to do. Recommend me to my
grandsire King Pelles, and say I will come as soon as I may."

Then the old man departed with his company, while all
the knights of the Table Round marvelled greatly of Sir

Galahad that he dared to sit in the Siege Perilous, so tender of age as he was. They knew not whence he came but only through God's grace, and said to one another that he it was by whom the Sangreal should be achieved.

Sir Launcelot beholding his son had great joy of him, and Sir Bors declared that the young knight would come to great worship. Many also remarked how like he was to Sir Launcelot, and the Queen said he was the son of that knight and King Pelles' daughter.

So when the feasting was done and the King had risen, he went unto the Siege Perilous, and saw the name of Galahad written, and he pointed it out to Sir Gawaine. So Galahad was received, and the King said to him,—

"Sir, ye be welcome, for ye shall move many knights to the quest of the Sangreal, and ye shall achieve what many knights could not bring to an end."

Then the King took him down to the river to see the marvel of the sword in the stone.

The Queen also heard thereof, and went down to see it, and the King said unto Sir Galahad, "Here is as great marvel as ever I saw, and many good knights have assayed and failed."

"That is no marvel," replied Sir Galahad, "for this adventure is mine, not theirs; for the certainty of this sword brought I none with me, for here by my side hangeth the scabbard." Anon he laid his hand on the sword in the stone and drew it out with ease. Then, putting it into the scabbard, he said, "Now it goeth better than it did aforehand."

"God shall send you a shield," said the King.

"Now," continued Galahad, "have I the sword of the noble knight Balin le Savage. With this he slew his brother Balan, and either slew the other through a dolorous stroke that Balan gave unto my grandsire, King Pelles, who is not yet whole, nor will be till I heal him."

At that time they all perceived a lady riding down by the river on a white palfrey, and she, saluting the King and Queen, inquired for Sir Launcelot, and when he came she said to him, weeping, "How your great doings have changed since this day in the morn!"

"Damsel, why say ye so?" replied Launcelot.

"I tell ye truth," she answered. "Ye were this day the best knight of the world, but now there is one better than ye are, as is well proved by the adventure of the sword, whereto ye durst not set your hand; so henceforth ye are not the best knight in the world."

"As for that," replied Sir Launcelot, "I never was the best."

"Yes," said the damsel, "that were ye, and yet are, of any sinful man of the world. King Nacien the Hermit sends ye greeting that to thee shall befall the greatest worship that ever befell king in Britain, for this day the Sangreal appeared in this thy house, and fed thee and thy fellowship of the Round Table." Then the damsel departed in the way she came.

Then the King and all went home to Camelot, and after evensong they went to supper, whereat every knight sat as he did beforehand. Anon they heard thunder, so that they thought the palace would be riven. But in the midst of the tumult entered a sunbeam more clear than ever they saw, and each knight regarded his fellow fairer than ever they seemed before. Yet no knight could speak for a little time, and all were dumb.

Then there entered into the hall the Holy Grail covered with white samite, but none could see who bare it. The hall was filled with good odours, and every knight had such meat and drink as he loved best. When the Holy Vessel had been borne through the hall, it suddenly departed, and they wist not what became of it. Then had they breath to speak, and the King yielded thanks to God for His good grace that He had sent them, saying, "Certes, we ought to thank our Lord greatly for that He hath showed us this Day of Pentecost."

"Now," said Sir Gawaine, "one thing hath beguiled us. We might not see the Holy Grail, because it was so preciously covered. Wherefore I make a vow, that to-morrow, without longer abiding, I will make the quest of the Sangreal, that shall continue a twelvemonth and a day, and more if need be; and never will I return again to this Court till I have seen it more openly. But if I may not speed I will return again, as he that may not be against the will of our Lord Jesus Christ."

And the most part of those at the Table Round made like avow with Sir Gawaine.

But King Arthur was wroth, for he wist well they might not gainsay their vows. "Alas!" said he unto Gawaine, "ye have nigh slain me with the vows and promise ye have made. For ye have bereft me of the fairest fellowship and the truest knighthood in the world. When they depart hence I am sure we shall never all meet again, for many shall die in the quest. Wherefore it grieveth me right sore the departition of the fellowship."

Therewith the tears filled his eyes, and the King said mournfully, "Gawaine, Gawaine! ye have set me in great sorrow, for I have great doubt whether my true fellowship shall ever meet in this world again."

HOW THE KNIGHTS DEPARTED ON THEIR QUEST FOR THE HOLY
GRAIL

WHEN the Queen and her gentlewomen heard the tidings, they had such sorrow and heaviness that they scarce could tell it. But of all, the Queen made the greatest dole, saying, "I marvel my lord would suffer them to depart from him." Thus all the Court was troubled for the departure of the knights. Many of the ladies whose lords were going would have accompanied them, but were forbidden to do so by Nacien the Hermit.

Meantime the Queen sent for Sir Galahad, and spoke with him, and said, "Truly your father need not shame you, for he is the goodliest knight, and of the best in the world."

Then they went to rest, and Galahad lay in the King's own chamber. As soon as it was day, the King arose, and went unto Sir Gawaine and Sir Launcelot, who were going to hear mass. Then he said again,—

"Ah, Gawaine! Gawaine! ye have betrayed me. Never shall my Court be amended by you, but ye will never sorrow for me as I sorrow for you." And the tears ran down the King's cheeks. "Ah! knight Sir Launcelot," he continued, "I pray ye counsel me. Would that this quest were undone, if it might be."

"Sir," said Sir Launcelot, "ye saw yesterday so many worthy knights that then were sworn that they may not leave it."

"That wot I well," replied the King; "but it shall so heavy me at their departing, no manner of joy can remedy me."

Then the King and the Queen went into the minster, and anon Sir Launcelot and Sir Gawaine were armed, with their fellowship, and all went unto the service.

After it was over the King desired to know how many had taken the Quest of the Holy Grail, and he found there were a hundred and fifty, and all knights of the Table Round. So they put on their helms and departed, while there was weeping and great dole. But the Queen departed to her chamber, where she remained in great sorrow.

When Sir Launcelot missed her, he went to bid her farewell, and she said,—

"O Sir Launcelot, ye have betrayed me thus to leave my lord."

"Ah! madam," said he, "be not displeased, for I shall come again as soon as I may with worship."

"Alas!" said she. "But He that suffered death upon the cross for all mankind be to you good conduct and safety, and all the whole fellowship."

Right so departed Sir Launcelot, and found his fellowship that abode his coming. So they all mounted their horses and rode through the streets of Camelot, amid the crying of the rich and poor, and the King turned away, for he could not speak for weeping. So within a while they came to a city, and a castle called Vagon, and they entered it. The owner of the castle, whose name was also Vagon, made them welcome and gave them all the cheer he might.

On the morrow they made up their minds to depart every one from the other, so they did. Amid much weeping and mourning then they departed from each other, and every knight betook him his way.

CHAPTER IV

HOW GALAHAD GOT A SHIELD, AND HOW THEY SPED WHO PRESUMED TO TAKE IT DOWN. THE WHITE KNIGHT AND THE TALE OF JOSEPH'S SHIELD

FOR four days Sir Galahad rode without any shield and without adventure; but on the fourth evening he came to a white abbey, where he was with great reverence received and conducted to a chamber. In this abbey he met the knights of the Table Round, King Bagdemagus and Sir Uwaine.

"Sirs," said Galahad, "what adventure brought you hither?"

"Sir," they replied, "it was told us that here we should find a shield that no man may bear around his neck without he be mischieved, or maimed for ever, or dead within three days."

"I shall bear it to-morrow," said King Bagdemagus, "and if I may not undertake it, ye shall take it upon you, for I am sure you will not fail."

"Sir," replied Galahad, "I will agree thereto, for I have no shield."

So in the morning they arose and heard mass, and then King Bagdemagus inquired where the shield was. Anon a monk led them behind an altar, where hung the shield as white as snow, and in the midst was a red cross.

"Sir," said the monk, "this shield should not be hanged about any one's neck, except he be the most worthy knight of the world, therefore I counsel you knights to be well advised."

"Well," said King Bagdemagus, "I wot well I am not the worthiest knight of the world, but I will assay to bear it."

So he bare it out of the monastery, and requested Sir Galahad to remain where he was until his return. Then he called to his squire and rode away. But ere he had ridden two miles, there came a white knight to encounter with him, and King Bagdemagus broke his spear fairly upon the knight's shield. Yet the knight's spear broke through the King's mail, and wounded him deep in the shoulder.

Then the white knight alighted, and taking the white shield from the King, said, "Thou hast done thyself great folly, for this shield should have been borne out by him that hath no peer living." Calling to the squire, he said, "Bear this shield unto Sir Galahad that thou left in the abbey, and greet him well from me."

"Sir," said the squire, "what is thy name?"

"Take thou no heed of my name," replied the white knight; "it is not for thee to know, nor for any earthly man. This shield belongs to no one but Sir Galahad."

Then the squire went to King Bagdemagus and inquired whether he were wounded sore.

"Yea, forsooth," said he; "I shall escape hard from my death."

So the squire fetched his horse, and brought Bagdemagus with great pain to the abbey, where he was cared for gently, but he lay there long time and barely escaped with his life.

Sir Galahad received the message from the white knight, and said, "Blessed be God and fortune." Then he rode away, hung the shield about his neck, and commended himself to God. Sir Uwaine desired to bear him company, but Sir Galahad refused, saying he must go alone with only his squire. So they came to the hermitage where was the white knight, and they saluted courteously.

"Sir," said Galahad, "by this shield have many marvels fallen, I ween."

"Sir," said the knight, "it befell after the Passion of our Lord thirty-two years, that Joseph of Arimathæa departed from Jerusalem and came to a city named Sarras, where was there a King named Evelake, who had been warring with the Saracens, and specially against one whose name was Tolleme. They two met to do battle. Then Joseph the son of Joseph of Arimathæa went to Evelake, and told him he would

be slain unless he left the old and believed in the new law.
So he did, and this shield was made for Evelake in the name
of Him who died upon the Cross. Then through his good belief he vanquished the Saracen, and while he was fighting
men beheld the figure of a man upon the cross upon the
shield.

"Soon after the cross vanished away from the shield, and
no man knew whither it went. Then King Evelake was baptized and most of his people; so Joseph departed and came
into this country, with the King, which then was called Great
Britain, but there a Paynim who ruled put Joseph into prison.
By fortune tidings of this came unto Mendrames, a worthy
man, who assembled an army, and smiting the Paynim, delivered Joseph. Thus all the people turned to the Christian
faith.

"Not long after, Joseph was dying, and lay in his deathly
bed. King Evelake was very sorry, and then desired some
token by which he might remember him, and Joseph gladly
agreed. He gave him the shield which he wore when he went
into battle with the Paynim. Then Joseph bled sore at the
nose, and it could not be staunched, and with the blood he
made a cross upon the shield. Then he said, 'Now you may
see a remembrance that I love you, for when ye see the shield
ye shall think of me, and it will be always as fresh as it is
now. No man shall bear this shield about his neck but he shall
repent it, until the time that Galahad the Good shall bear
it, and the last of my lineage shall have it about his neck that
shall do many marvellous deeds.'

"Then he told him that the shield should be left with
Nacien the Hermit in the abbey, whither Galahad shall come
within fifteen days of his being made knight, and take it in
the same abbey with Nacien."

When the white knight had told Sir Galahad all this concerning the shield, he suddenly vanished away. Anon when
the squire heard the words, he kneeled and prayed to Galahad
to let him go with him till he was made knight. This Sir
Galahad granted him, and they returned to the abbey whence

they had come. These men made great joy of Sir Galahad, and when he had come to the abbey a monk brought him unto a tomb in the churchyard where there was such a noise that they deemed therein was a fiend.

So they led Galahad to the tomb, and thereout leaped a fiend, which cried out, "Galahad, I see so many angels about thee, I may not dare thee." Then the tomb was explained to him.

Next morning the squire Melias was made a knight, and Galahad granted him permission to ride with him to the recovery of the Holy Grail. So they rode together until they came to two ways, by which was written:—

"Now, ye knights-errant, see here two ways: the one way defendeth thee that thou go not that way, for he shall not go out of it again but if he be true man and worthy knight. If thou go on the left hand, thou shalt not lightly there win prowess, for thou shalt in this way be soon assayed."

"Sir," said Melias, "let me take the left-hand way, and have that adventure."

"Take it in God's name," replied Sir Galahad, but reluctantly. So they parted.

CHAPTER V

THE ADVENTURE MELIAS HAD; HOW GALAHAD REVENGED HIM, AND WAS CARRIED TO AN ABBEY; THE WICKED CUSTOM OF MAIDENS' CASTLE

SIR MELIAS accordingly rode on into an ancient forest, and continued therein for more than two days. At length he came to a meadow and a fair lodge of boughs, and espied there a chair whereon was a crown of gold subtilely wrought. Also there were clothes and meats delicious set upon the ground.

Sir Melias was not hungry; but he took the crown, and rode away with it. Anon he perceived a knight riding after him, who said, "Knight, set down that crown, which is not yours, and defend you."

Then they encountered; but Melias was conquered, and left for dead. So the stranger took the crown, and went on his way, leaving Sir Melias unable to rise. By fortune Sir Galahad came by that way, and found him in peril of death. Then said he, "Melias, who hath wounded you?"

Before he could answer came a voice from the leaves, "Sir Knight, keep yourself." And the knight who had wounded Melias came upon Sir Galahad. But he wounded him, and also defeated another knight who came to the battle. Thus Sir Galahad tended Melias his sometime squire.

Afterwards he carried him to the abbey, where he swooned by reason of his pains; but the monks said the new knight would be healed in seven weeks. Sir Galahad was then right glad, and after seeing him well bestowed and recovering, he departed, saying to the monk who tended Melias, that he and his friend were engaged in the Quest of the Holy Grail.

"Sir," said the good man, "for his sins he was wounded. I wonder how ye dare to take on you the order of knighthood without clean confession: that was the cause of the wound. The way of the right hand betokeneth the highway of Jesus Christ; the other way, that of sinners and unbelievers; and when the Evil One saw you take the way in your pride, and in search of the Holy Grail, he made you to be overthrown, for it may only be achieved by virtuous living. Also the writing on the cross-posts was a signification of heavenly deeds, and of no knightly deeds in worldly works; and pride, the head of all deadly sins, caused this knight to part from Sir Galahad. When thou tookest the crown of gold thou didst sin in theft and covetousness. This was no knightly deed. The two knights with which Sir Galahad fought signify the two deadly sins, which were wholly in you, Sir Melias, for Sir Galahad is without deadly sin."

Then departed Sir Galahad at length, and rode many journeys forward and backward as adventures led him. And at length he came to a mountain where was an old chapel, but nobody was there, for all was desolate; so he kneeled before the altar and besought of God counsel. While he prayed he heard a voice say unto him, "Go thou now, thou adventurous knight, to the Castle of Maidens, and there do away with the wicked custom."

CHAPTER VI

HOW GALAHAD FOUGHT WITH THE KNIGHTS AND DESTROYED THE WICKED CUSTOM

WHEN Sir Galahad heard this, he took his horse and had not ridden far before he came in sight of a strong castle with deep moats. There also ran before it a fair river called Severn. Then he met with a man of great age, and Galahad inquired the name of the castle.

"Fair sir," replied the man, "it is the Castle of Maidens."

"It is a cursed castle," said Sir Galahad, "and all therein."

"Therefore I counsel you, Sir Knight, to turn again," said the old man.

"Sir," replied Galahad, "wit ye well I will not turn again."

Then the knight examined his arms and put on his shield, and anon there met him seven fair maidens, who said to him, "Sir Knight, ye ride here in great folly, for there is water to pass over."

"Why should not I pass the water?" he said, and rode along. Then met he with a squire, who told him that the knights in the castle defied him, and forbade him to advance till he had said what he wanted.

"I am to destroy the wicked custom of the castle," replied Sir Galahad.

"An ye will abide by that, ye shall have enough to do," said the squire.

"Go you now," said Galahad, "and haste my needs."

Then the messenger returned to the castle, and therefrom came out seven knights who were brethren. When they saw Galahad they cried, "Knight, keep thee—we assure ye of nothing but death."

"Why," said Galahad, "will ye all have ado with me at once?"

"Yea," they replied, "in that mayest thou trust."

Then Sir Galahad put forth his spear and smote one assailant in the neck, and the others smote Sir Galahad and brake their spears upon his shield. Then he drew his sword and so set upon them that they fled from the field, and Galahad chased them until they entered a castle, and passed through it at another gate. Here Galahad met an old man in religious dress, who offered him the keys of the place.

Sir Galahad opened the gates, and saw a quantity of people in the streets, who welcomed him as their deliverer. Then came to him a gentlewoman, and said, "These knights be fled, but they will come again, to use the evil custom there was aforetime."

"What will ye that I should do?" asked Sir Galahad.

"Sir, that ye send after all the knights who hold their land from the castle, and tell them to do as in the olden time."

"I will well," replied Sir Galahad.

Then she brought him a horn of ivory tipped with gold, and said, "Blow this horn, which will be heard at two miles around."

So Sir Galahad blew the horn, and meantime came a priest and told him concerning the custom of the castle.

He said, "Sir, it is past seven years that these seven brethren came to this castle and lived with Duke Lianor, who is the lord of the country; he had a son and a daughter. And they conspired and killed the duke and his son, while they imprisoned the lady and kept the treasure. Then by force they held it, and put all under tribute, pillaging the people. One day the lady complained of the treatment she underwent, and prophesied that by one knight they should all seven be overcome. 'Well,' said they, 'since ye say so, never shall knight or lady pass this castle; they shall abide, maugre their heads, or die, until the knight you tell of arrive, and we lose this castle.' Therefore it is called the Maidens' Castle, for they have thus destroyed many maidens."

Then Sir Galahad inquired whether the duke's daughter was still alive.

"Nay," replied the priest, "she died three days after that her father and brother had been slain; but they have retained her younger sister with many more."

By this time were the knights of the country come, and they did homage to the duke's young daughter by Galahad's intercession and command. On the morrow there came a messenger to him to say that Sir Gawaine, Gareth, and Uwaine had killed the seven knights. Then Sir Galahad rejoiced, and, commending the people of the Castle to God, he took his armour and his horse, and rode on his way.

CHAPTER VII

HOW SIR GALAHAD MET SIR LAUNCELOT AND SIR PERCIVALE. HOW SIR LAUNCELOT WAS SHRIVEN, AND OF THE GOOD EXAMPLES SHOWED HIM

WHEN Sir Galahad had departed from the Castle of Maidens he rode on into a waste forest, and therein met Sir Launcelot du Lake and Sir Percivale, but as he was disguised they did not recognize him. So Galahad made him ready, and encountered with Sir Launcelot and smote him down; then turning to Sir Percivale, he nearly slew him with one stroke.

Close by there was a hermitage, and in it there dwelt a recluse, who perceiving the jousting, cried out, "If yonder two knights had known thee as well as I do, they would not have encountered with thee."

But when Sir Galahad heard her say this he feared to be known, and so he spurred his horse forward, and quick the others perceived who he was. Then they followed after him, but he escaped; and they turned back with heavy hearts to the hermitage, and then forward into the forest, which was trackless.

In search of adventure they thus continued their way, and came at length to a stone cross where two paths met; and by the cross was a stone, but the day was so dark that Sir Launcelot could not quite perceive what it was. But looking around he saw a chapel; so tying up his horse and hanging his shield upon a tree, he went up to the chapel, the door of which was broken. Looking within, he found an altar richly arrayed with silk, and a candlestick with six candles. When Sir Launcelot saw the light he had great desire to enter, but he could find no place to go in, whereat he was heavy and dismayed.

So he returned to his horse and took off the bridle and
saddle, and let it have pasture; then unlacing his helm and
ungirding his sword, he lay down to sleep upon his shield
before the cross. While he lay there, half waking and half
sleeping, there came by him two palfreys which bare a litter,
upon which was laid a sick knight, and till Launcelot heard
him speak he fancied he was himself dreaming.

"Oh, sweet Lord," said the sick knight, "when shall this
sorrow leave me, and the Holy Vessel come by, through
which I shall be blessed, for I have endured long for little
trespass?"

When the knight spake thus, Sir Launcelot, looking
through the broken door of the chapel, perceived the candlestick moving before the cross, but could see no one who bore
it. Also there came a table of silver, and the Holy Vessel of
the Sangreal. Therewith the knight held up his hands and
prayed; then he kneeled and kissed the vessel. Anon he was
made whole, and gave thanks.

Then the knight armed him, and talked with his squire
concerning the healing, and of the sleeping Sir Launcelot,
who had not awaked when the Holy Vessel came; so when
the knight was ready, seeing Launcelot's horse was better than
his own, he took it, and went on his way. As soon as he had
gone Sir Launcelot waked, and, sitting up, wondered whether
he had dreamed or not.

Then came a voice to him, and said, "Sir Launcelot—
harder than is the stone, more bitter than is the wood, more
naked and barer than is the fig-tree—go thou therefore hence,
and withdraw thee from this holy place."

When Launcelot heard this he was passing heavy, and, not
knowing what to do, he departed, weeping sorely. But when
he would have mounted he saw his steed had been taken away;
and he said, "My sin and wickedness have brought me to this
dishonour, for when I sought worldly adventures for worldly
ends I ever achieved them; but now, when I take upon me
holy things, I can see and understand that my old sin

hindereth me, so that I had no power to speak when the Holy Blood appeared."

So he sorrowed till it was day; then, when he missed his horse and harness, he wist God was displeased at him, and he departed on foot. After a while he came to a hermitage, where he heard mass and was confessed. Then the hermit showed Launcelot his wickedness and sins, and counselled him to look into his doings in future, else he could not prosper. "The Lord hath called thee," said the hermit, "and, as He found no fruit upon the fig-tree as He was entering Jerusalem, so when thou wert brought before Him He found in thee no fruit, nor good thought, nor good will."

Then Launcelot repented him of his wickedness, and was enjoined to do penance as he might. So the holy man assoiled him, and begged Sir Launcelot to abide with him all day.

"I will well," replied the knight, "for I have neither helm. horse, nor sword."

"As for that," replied the hermit, "I will help you tomorrow of a horse and all that belongeth to you."

So Sir Launcelot repented him greatly, and remained with the hermit three days, after which the good man gat him a horse, a helm, and a sword. Then Sir Launcelot departed, and after little adventure he rode into a deep valley, where he could perceive a river and a high mountain. Through this river he must pass, though it was hideous, but in the name of God he took it with a good heart.

When he came over he saw an armed knight, horse and man as black as any bear, who without a word smote Sir Launcelot's horse to the earth, and so he passed on. Then Sir Launcelot took his helm and shield, and thanked God for his adventure.

BOOK THE ELEVENTH: SIR PERCIVALE DE GALIS AND SIR GALAHAD

CHAPTER I

HOW SIR PERCIVALE ASKED COUNSEL OF THE RECLUSE, WHO WAS HIS AUNT; HOW HE CAME TO KING EVELAKE, AND WAS AFTERWARDS RESCUED BY SIR GALAHAD

WHEN Sir Launcelot had ridden after Sir Galahad, Sir Percivale turned again to the recluse, and told her who he was and whence he came. When she heard this she had great joy of him, for she loved him as she ought to do, being his aunt. Then she commanded the gates to be opened, and made him as good cheer as was in her power.

On the morn Sir Percivale asked concerning the knight with the white shield, with whom he wished to encounter. But the recluse said,—

"Ah, Percivale! I see well ye have great will to be slain, as your father was, through outrageousness."

"Madame," said Percivale, "it seemeth by your words you know me."

"Yea," said she, "I well ought to know you, for I am your aunt, sometime called the Queen of the Waste Lands, and had most riches in the world; but my riches never pleased me so much as doth my poverty."

Then Sir Percivale wept for very pity; after that they had other conversation, and then Sir Percivale departed in search of Sir Galahad, for he had great wish to find him. So the recluse directed him to go by the castle of Carbonek, where lay his cousin-german, and there would tidings of Sir Galahad be heard.

He rode on till evensong, and at length became aware of a house, well enclosed with walls and deep ditches. He went up and was admitted. Next morning he went to hear mass, and became aware of a very old man with a crown on his head;

and Sir Percivale perceived he had great wounds upon his shoulders, arms, and visage.

Sir Percivale inquired who this was, and was told it was King Evelake, who had been converted by Joseph of Arimathæa; and the King was always busy in his quest of the Sangreal, and one time was so nigh it that our Lord was displeased with him, and as he ever followed it more and more he was stricken blind.

At this the King prayed for mercy, and said, "Fair Lord, let me never die till the Good Knight of the Ninth Degree be come, that I may see him openly that he may achieve the Sangreal."

Then a voice answered him that his prayer was heard, and so King Evelake lived on for three hundred years; and when that knight came he knew the clearness of his eyes would return to him. When Sir Percivale had heard this he departed, and rode on till noon; but in a valley he met twenty men-at-arms bearing a knight, who was dead. And when they came to Sir Percivale, they inquired who he was and whence he came.

He replied, "From King Arthur's Court."

And then all the men cried out, "Slay him!" So at once seven knights set upon him, and others slew his horse; and they had slain or taken him had not the good knight Sir Galahad, with the red arms, come by adventure to that place. As soon as he perceived that the men were all about to attack the knight, he came to his assistance and smote many. At every stroke he killed a man, put them to such shame, that the remnant fled, and Sir Galahad pursued them; but when Sir Percivale perceived them depart, and the knight after them, he was grieved, because he wist well it was Sir Galahad who had fought for him.

Sir Galahad, however, rode on, and came not back, so he departed out of sight, while Sir Percivale was following him on foot. He soon met a yeoman riding upon a fine black horse, and prayed the man to lend him the steed; but the yeoman excused himself, saying that, did he lend it, the owner thereof would slay him.

So the squire departed, and Sir Percivale seated himself under a tree and made great sorrow. But it came to pass that soon after, when night came, that he was awakened out of sleep as he lay under the tree, and a damsel gat him a black steed, on condition that he would assist her, which he did. Then Sir Percivale had many adventures, as had also Sir Launcelot; but at the present we will follow the fortunes of Sir Galahad, who had ridden away after rescuing Sir Percivale.

CHAPTER II

WHEN Sir Galahad had achieved the rescue of Sir
Percivale from the twenty men-at-arms, he rode into a
vast forest, wherein he remained for many days journeying,
and met with adventures of which the chronicle makes no
mention.

He continued his way towards the sea, and it happened he
came to a place where was a tournament; but those within
the castle had been worsted by those without. When Galahad
perceived this, and that the men were even then being slain, he
dressed him and put his spear in rest; at once advancing, he
smote one man to the earth, but his spear broke to pieces in
his grasp. Then Sir Galahad drew his sword, and rushing into
the thickest of the affray, performed wonderful deeds of arms,
so that all marvelled greatly.

But it happened that Sir Gawaine and Sir Ector de Maris
were at this tournament, and when they espied the white
shield with the red cross thereon, they said to each other,
"Yonder is Sir Galahad the Haut Prince, and any would be
foolish to knowingly encounter with him."

It adventured, however, that Galahad came near by Sir
Gawaine and smote him a terrible stroke, so that he clave
his helm unto his head, and Sir Gawaine fell to the earth;
but the stroke was so mighty that it slanted down still, and
cut the shoulder of the knight's horse in two. Afterwards Sir
Ector de Maris retreated, and so it happened that Sir Galahad, having no men to fight against, drew quickly away, and
no one knew what had become of him.

"By my head," said Gawaine to Sir Ector de Maris, "now

is it true that the sword in the stone should give me such a buffet, that I would not have for the best castle of the world. Now is that proved true, for I never before had stroke of man's hand as I have had this day."

"Sir," said Ector, "it seemeth that your quest is over."

"Yours is not done," said Sir Gawaine, "but mine is finished, and I shall seek no farther."

So Gawaine was carried back to the castle and was unarmed, nor was he whole within a month; so Sir Gawaine and Sir Ector de Maris abode together until the former was whole.

Meanwhile Sir Galahad rode on to come to the castle of Carbonek, but he was benighted at a hermitage, where he was summoned to adventure by a gentlewoman who would lead him to the highest doings that ever knight saw. So Galahad armed him, and told the gentlewoman he was ready to follow her whithersoever she listed.

She accordingly rode on until she came to the sea called Callibe, and there they found a vessel in which were Sir Bors and Sir Percivale, who welcomed Galahad warmly. Soon the vessel set sail, and by adventure it stuck between two great rocks, so that they could not land, and there was great danger. But there was another ship, and upon it they might go.

"Go we thither," said the gentlewoman, "for it is the Lord's will that we see adventures."

And when they came thither they found in this ship two letters written, which said dreadful and marvellous words, but of people found they none whatever. The words were these:

"Thou man which shall enter into this ship, beware thou be in steadfast belief, for I am Faith, for an thou fail I cannot help thee."

Then said the lady unto Sir Percivale, "Wot ye what I am?"

"Certes," he replied, "not of my witting."

"Wit ye well then," said she, "that I am thy sister, the daughter of King Pellinore, and I love thee most of any in the world. Now, therefore, go not in unless ye be in perfect faith, for there shall ye perish in the ship, which will suffer no sin, it being so perfect."

Sir Percivale was very glad when he heard that the gentlewoman was his sister, and he said, "Fair sister, I shall enter therein, for if I be an untrue knight or evil disposed creature, there I shall perish."

HOW SIR GALAHAD ENTERED THE SHIP, AND OF THE MARVELS
THEREOF, AND OF A SWORD; HOW KING PELLES WAS SMITTEN
BECAUSE HE DREW THE SWORD; AND OTHER MARVELLOUS
HISTORIES

THEN Sir Galahad blessed himself, and he entered into
the ship. After him came the gentlewoman, then Sir Bors
and Sir Percivale. When they were therein, they marvelled at
the richness of the ship, in which was a fair bed, where was
a crown of silk; and at the feet was a sword rich and fair, and
it was drawn out of the scabbard half a foot or more. This
sword was of divers patterns. The pommel was of stone, with
all manner of colours, and every colour had divers virtues,
and the scales of the haft were of two ribs of divers beasts.
The one beast is called the Serpent of the Fiend, and the other
is a fish which haunted the flood of Euphrates. That fish is
called Ertanax, and his bones be of such kind that whoso
handleth them shall have so much will that he will never be
weary, and he shall not think of joy nor sorrow that he hath
had, but only that thing which he holdeth before him. As for
the sword, there shall no man grip it but one, and he shall be
beyond all others.

"In the name of God," said Sir Percivale, "I shall essay to
handle it."

So he tried to grip the sword, but he might not grip it.

"By my faith," he said, "now have I failed."

Then Galahad beheld the sword, and saw letters like blood,
which said, "Let see who shall essay to draw me out of my
sheath, but if he be more hardier than other; and whoso
draweth me, wit ye well that he shall never fail of shame of
his body, or to be wounded to the death."

"By my faith," said Galahad, "I would draw the sword;

but the offending is so great that I shall not set my hand thereto."

"Wit ye well," said the gentlewoman, "that the drawing of this sword is forbidden to all men save only you. This ship," she continued, "arrived in the realm of Logris, and at that time there was deadly war between King Labor and King Hurlame, who was a Saracen. Then he was newly christened, and it fell upon a day that these two Kings assembled their people upon the sea when this ship had arrived. Then King Hurlame was defeated, and fearing to be slain, he retreated to his ship, where he found this sword, and drew it. Then coming out, he found King Labor, the man in whom was the greatest faith in all Christendom.

"When King Hurlame saw him he clave him through the helm, and felled the horse he rode. Upon that stroke great pestilence and famine fell upon both Kings' realms, and there was no corn nor grass, nor fish in the waters. Then, when King Hurlame found the sword so very keen, he came into this ship and put it in the scabbard; and when he had done so he fell down dead. Thus was the sword proved: that none handled it but he died or was maimed. And there the King lay, until a damsel was so hardy as to come and cast him out, for no man would enter into the ship."

Then the knights inspected the scabbard, which was of serpent's skin, on which were golden and silvern letters, which said, "He which shall wield me ought to be more hardier than any other, if he bear me as truly as I ought to be borne; for the body of him I ought to hang by, he shall not be ashamed in no place while he is girt with this girdle, for it ought not to be done away but by a maiden, a king's daughter."

"Sir," said Percivale, "let us look what is on the other side."

It was red as blood, with black letters as any coal, which said, "He that shall praise me most, most he shall find me to blame at great need; and to whom I shall be most debonnaire I shall be most felon, and that shall be at one time."

Then the gentlewoman told her brother and the other

knights concerning the marvels of the sword. How Nacien, brother-in-law of King Mordrains, handled the sword to fight an immense giant, and how it brake in his hand, because he was not worthy to handle it; and also how he was smitten down and wounded, because he had thus presumed to draw the sword, being unworthy.

"Ye are right wise of these works," said Sir Galahad to the lady.

"Sir," she continued, "there was a King named Pelles—the Maimed King—and it happened one day he was hunting in a wood of great extent unto the sea, and left all his knights, save one, till they came toward Ireland and found the ship. But when he saw the writing he understood it, so he entered, for he was of perfect life, and drew the sword as much as ye may see. Thereupon entered a spear, wherewith he was smitten through both thighs, and never could he be healed, nor shall he before we come to him. Thus was your grandsire maimed for his hardiness."

"In the name of God, damsel," said Sir Galahad.

Then went they toward the bed, and beheld above it two swords; also two spindles as white as snow, and others as red as blood, and others as green as emeralds.

"These spindles," said the damsel, "were when sinful Eve came to gather fruit. She took with her the bough on which the apple hung, and she wished to keep the bough, so she put it in the earth, where, by the will of the Lord, it grew first quite white, but after it all became green as any grass, and all that came out of it. So it befell after that, under the same tree, Cain killed Abel; whereon came great marvel, for, after he was killed, the tree became red as blood. Anon all the plants died thereof; but the tree grew, and was the fairest tree that any man might behold.

"The tree endured till Solomon, David's son, reigned, who was very wise; and the Spirit of God told him of the coming of the Virgin Mary. And his wife made a ship of the finest and best wood, and King David's sword was brought and hilted with precious stones. When the ship was ready for sea,

the lady caused a great bed to be made and put the sword at
the foot, and brought a carpenter to make the spindles out of
the wood of the tree which was red. And while he worked
there came blood out of the wood, but she made him per-
severe, and three spindles were made of the red, white, and
green woods. Solomon and his wife then entered into the ship,
and he sprinkled it and wrote the letters on the sword. While
the King was resting the vessel was suddenly drawn away
from land, and a voice came to him, saying, 'The last of thy
lineage shall rest in this bed.' "

After considering these things the knights said to Galahad,
"In the name of Jesus Christ we pray you gird on this sword,
which has been so much desired in the land of Logris."

"Let me begin," said Galahad.

And then the lady girt him about the middle with the
sword, much of the girdle being of her own hair, which she
had made for it.

"Damsel," said Sir Galahad, "ye have done so much that
I shall be your knight all the days of my life."

Then they left the ship and gained the other one, but a
tempest arose and drove them towards the castle of Carteloise
in Scotland.

CHAPTER IV

HOW THE CASTLE WAS TAKEN, AND HOW PERCIVALE'S SISTER BLED TO DEATH FOR THE HEALING OF A LADY

AS THEY were conversing, a squire came unto them and inquired whence they had come. They told him from King Arthur's Court, and then the squire departed. Anon a gentlewoman came to them and besought them to retire, as else they would meet their deaths.

Meantime, as they talked, came three knights in armour, who rushed upon them, the travellers being on foot, for they had left their horses in the ship. But Sir Percivale smote the foremost assailant and took his horse; likewise did Sir Galahad and Sir Bors to others. Then they pursued the knights and people into the castle, and slew many in the hall. They were greatly abashed when they perceived how many they had slain, and when an old man came out with the Holy Cup, they kneeled down before him, who told them of the castle, and that they had slain cruel and heathen men. "The Earl Hernox, whom they have here wrongfully imprisoned, told me by revelation that ye would come and deliver him."

So they delivered the earl, who was weak and feeble, and soon after he died, and was buried by Sir Galahad in honour. The three knights then departed, and Percivale's sister with them. In time they came to a castle where a lady lay sick, and it was the custom for every maiden who passed by to be bled a dishful, to heal the malady of the gentlewoman of the castle.

So Percivale's sister was required to conform to this custom, and she consented. But she bled so much that she swooned and might not live.

"Fair brother Percivale," said she, "I die for the healing of this lady. So I require that ye bury me not in this country, but as soon as I am dead put me in a boat at the next haven, and let me go as adventure will lead me; and as soon as ye come to the town of Sarras, to achieve the Holy Grail, ye shall find me under a tower there arrived. Bury me in the spiritual place, for there shall ye also be buried, and Sir Galahad."

Then her soul departed and she died. So Sir Percivale wrote out the story of her life and put it in her right hand; he then laid her in a barge and covered it with silk. When the wind arose it carried the barge from land, and all the knights stood watching it until it was out of sight; then they returned to the castle.

Forthwith there fell a terrible tempest of thunder, lightning, and rain, and a great part of the castle was destroyed. Then there came a voice to the three knights, which said, "Depart ye now asunder until ye meet again where the Maimed King is lying." So they all departed, and went into a forest.

"Now," said Sir Percivale unto Galahad, "we must depart. So pray we to our Lord that we may meet together in a short time."

Then took they off their helms, kissed together, and wept at their departing.

CHAPTER V

HOW SIR LAUNCELOT FOUND SIR PERCIVALE'S SISTER IN THE SHIP; HOW HE MET WITH SIR GALAHAD, HIS SON, AND ESSAYED THE HOLY GRAIL

WHEN Sir Launcelot left the Hermit, as already related, he lay down beside the water of Mortoise to sleep; and as he slept, there came to him a voice saying, "Launcelot, arise, take thine armour, and enter into the first ship that thou shalt find."

When he heard these words, he obeyed the vision, and made ready. He then rode on till he came to the sea-shore, and by adventure he found there a ship without sail or oar. Entering in, he perceived the greatest sweetness he had ever felt, and the sweetest savour, and seemed filled with all the good things he could desire.

So in this way he laid him down in the ship, and slept until day. When he woke, he perceived a bed, and thereupon was laid a gentlewoman who was Sir Percivale's sister. In her hand was the writing which Sir Launcelot read, telling of her lineage and all her adventures. More than a month abode he in that ship, and if ye would ask how he lived, we can say that He who fed the children of Israel with manna sustained him.

One evening it came to pass that Sir Launcelot, being somewhat weary of the ship, went ashore, and as he was there he heard a horse approaching, which carried a knight. So he let him go by unto the ship, which the knight entered; which when Launcelot saw, he dressed him to him, and said, "Ye be welcome."

The knight saluted him again, and inquired of Sir Launcelot what his name was, for he said, "My heart goeth unto you."

"Truly," replied the other, "my name is Launcelot du Lake."

"Fair sir," replied the knight, "then be ye welcome, for I am Galahad, thy son, and long time have I sought for thee."

"Ah!" exclaimed Sir Launcelot, "are ye Galahad?"

"Yes, forsooth," replied the knight.

Then he kneeled down and asked his father's blessing; then took he off his helm and kissed him. There was great joy between them, and no one can tell the joy they made of each other. They told each other of the adventures which had befallen them both since they had departed from Arthur's Court. Galahad told his father concerning the gentlewoman who lay dead in the ship, and showed him the marvellous sword.

"Truly," said Sir Launcelot, "I never heard of such adventures done, so marvellous and strange."

So for half a year they abode in the ship, and served God day and night with all their power. Often they arrived in islands far from any people, amid wild beasts, where they found many adventures and perilous; but as these were not gained in the Quest of the Sangreal, this history taketh no notice of them, which they thus brought to an end.

After a time they came to the edge of a forest, where before a cross they saw a knight armed all in white, richly horsed. He came leading a horse down to the shore, and saluted the knights in the ship on the High Lord's behalf, and said,—

"Sir Galahad, ye have been long enough time with your father. Come away from the ship, and ride this horse till ye achieve the Holy Grail."

So Galahad went to his father, and said, "Fair sweet father, I wot not when I shall see thee more till I see the body of Jesus Christ."

"I pray ye," said Sir Launcelot, "that ye pray to the High Father to hold me in His service."

Then there came a voice, which said, "Think for to do well, for the one shall never see the other before the dreadful day of doom."

"Now, son Galahad," said Sir Launcelot, "since we must never see each other more in this life, I pray the High Father to preserve both you and me."

"Sir," said Galahad, "no prayer availeth so much as yours."

Then Sir Galahad landed, and went through the forest; but Sir Launcelot remained in the ship and was driven about for more than a month through the sea, when he prayed to see something of the Sangreal.

Thus it fell upon a night that he reached the back of a castle, rich and fair. There was a postern opening towards the sea, and no one kept it, save two lions. The moon shone clear. Anon Launcelot heard a voice saying, "Launcelot, arise; go out of the ship and enter the castle, when thou shalt see a great part of thy desire."

Then he ran for his arms, and went up to the gate where he saw the lions. He then drew his sword, but there came a dwarf on him suddenly, who struck him on the arm, and the sword fell from his hand, while a voice cried, "O man of evil faith! why trustest thou thy arms above thy Maker?"

Thereupon Sir Launcelot sheathed his sword, and making a cross upon his forehead, came to the lions, which made as if to harm him; but he passed them by without hurt, and entered the castle, where all were at rest. All the doors were open but one, which he found tight closed; and he set his hand to open this one, but he could not do so.

While he endeavoured to unfasten this door he heard a voice singing sweetly, like no earthly thing, "Joy and honour be to the Father of Heaven!" Then Sir Launcelot kneeled down, for he knew that the Sangreal was within, and prayed that he might be permitted to see what he had so long sought. With that the door of the chamber opened of its own accord, and there came out a brightness as if all the torches of the world were alight together. Sir Launcelot would have entered, but he heard a warning voice, "Flee, Launcelot, and enter not." Then he withdrew and felt heavy.

But he looked into the chamber and saw a table of silver, and the Holy Vessel, covered with red samite, and many angels about it holding burning candles, and a cross with ornaments of the altar. There was also a man dressed as a priest, who seemed to sink under the vessel as he held it.

Then, with a prayer, Sir Launcelot came into the chamber to help him, and when he came nigh he felt a breath, and thought he had been surrounded with fire, which smote him so hard that he fell to the ground, and he could not arise. Many hands then came to help him up, and bore him away in his swoon. They laid him outside the room, where he remained until day, when the people came and found him dead, to all seeming. But they looked at him, and, finding life in him, took him and put him upon a bed, where he remained four and twenty days and nights.

On the twenty-fifth day he awoke, and inquired where he was. The attendants told him at the castle of Carbonek.

"Tell your lord, King Pelles," said he, "that I am Sir Launcelot du Lake."

At that they marvelled greatly, but went; and Sir Pelles requested Launcelot to tarry with him.

But Launcelot said, "Nay; I know well that I have now seen as much as mine eyes may now behold of the Holy Grail, and therefore I will return unto mine own country."

So he returned towards Logris and met with many adventures on the way, passing through many realms. He passed the abbey where Galahad won the white shield, and thence to Camelot, where he found King Arthur and the Queen. But many knights of the Round Table were slain, more than half.

All the Court was passing glad of the return of Sir Launcelot, and inquired if he had seen Sir Galahad. Then Launcelot told the King of his adventures, and concerning Galahad, Percivale, and Bors, which he had read about in the letter the dead damsel carried in her hand.

"Would they were all here," said the King.

"That may never be," replied Launcelot. "Two of them shall ye never see; but one of them shall come again."

CHAPTER VI

HOW SIR GALAHAD FOUND THE HOLY GRAIL, AND HOW HE DIED

AFTER Sir Galahad had quitted the ship he rode in vain for many days; but after that time he came to the monastery where the blind King Evelake lay. The King welcomed him gladly, and took him in his arms, saying, "Welcome, Sir Galahad, servant of the Lord! Long have I abided thy coming; take me now in thine arms and I shall die in peace."

Then Sir Galahad embraced him, and when he had done so the King's eyes were opened, and he said, "Fair Lord Jesus, suffer me to come to Thee." Anon his soul departed. Then they buried him royally, as a king ought to be buried, and Sir Galahad went on his way.

After this he rode many days, and at length encountered Sir Percivale, and a little farther on Sir Bors. When they had each related to the other his adventures, they all rode on together to the castle of Carbonek, where King Pelles gave them a hearty welcome, for he knew that they should achieve the Holy Grail.

And anon came a voice which said, "Let them who ought not now to sit at the table of the Lord arise, and depart hence."

So all but the three knights rose up and departed, except King Pelles and his son, and a maiden, his niece. Anon they saw knights all armed come to the door, who did put off their helms and armour, saying to Galahad, "Sir, we have tried sore to be with you at this table, where the holy meat shall be parted."

"Ye be welcome," said Sir Galahad. "But whence be ye?"

Three of them said they were of Gaul, and other three of

Ireland, and three other of Denmark. But as they sat and ate thus, a voice came and cried, saying, "There be two here not in the Quest of the Sangreal." At that the King and his son departed.

Then came there in a man in the likeness of a bishop, with four angels from heaven. A table of silver was before them, whereon was set the Sangreal; the angels bare the bishop in a chair, and set him down before it. Then came other angels, two bearing candles burning, the other a towel, and another a spear, which bled marvellously, and three drops fell within a box he held in his hand. Anon the bishop took up the sacred elements, and there came up the likeness of a child, whose face was as bright as fire, which soon vanished into the wafer.

Thereat the bishop went to Galahad and kissed him, and bade him go and kiss his fellows, saying, "Now, servant of the Lord, prepare ye for food as none ever yet were fed with since the world began."

With that the likeness of the bishop vanished, and the knights were filled with a great dread, praying devoutly. Then they saw a bleeding figure, as in the semblance of a man, come out of the Holy Vessel, and holding it, He said to Galahad,—

"Son, now hast thou seen what thou most desiredst to see, but as yet not so openly as thou shalt see it in the city of Sarras in the spiritual place; therefore thou must go hence and bear with thee this Holy Vessel, for this night it shall depart from the realm of Logris. Go ye three to-morrow unto the sea, where ye shall find your ship ready; and take the sword with the strange girdles, and no other but Sir Percivale and Sir Bors. Also take this spear and anoint the Maimed King, and he shall have his health."

Then He gave them His blessing and vanished away. So Galahad took the spear, touched the blood on it, and came to the Maimed King. Therewith he anointed his legs, and the King started up a whole man, and thanked our Lord that He had healed him.

Then Sir Galahad, Sir Bors, and Sir Percivale departed as

THEREWITH SIR GALAHAD KNEELED DOWN AND
PRAYED. THERE CAME A HAND FROM HEAVEN AND
TOOK UP THE SPEAR AND THE VESSEL. SINCE THEN
NO MAN HAS SEEN THE HOLY GRAIL

they had been commanded, and after three days came to the sea, where they found the ship and entered therein. In it was the silver table and the Vessel of the Sangreal, covered with red samite. Then were they glad and made reverence.

Sir Galahad prayed that he might depart out of the world, and a voice told him his prayer was heard, and "When he asked the death of his body he should have it, and find the life of his soul."

Meanwhile, as they prayed the ship sailed on, and when they looked they saw the city of Sarras and likewise the ship in which Sir Percivale's sister lay. Then the three knights, bearing the Sangreal, took up the body of Sir Percivale's sister and buried her solemnly.

At the gate of the city they perceived a cripple, and healed him by means of the Sangreal, which was noised abroad; but the tyrant of that country, named Estorause, took Galahad and his fellows, and put them in prison in a deep hole. Here they abode for a long time; but the Sangreal fed them, and they had much joy and comfort.

At the end of the year the King fell sick, and the people took counsel to choose a King; but a voice in their midst called out, "Take the youngest of the three knights in the prison for your King." So they sought Sir Galahad, and made him King against his will, else had they slain him.

On the day twelvemonth after they had crowned Sir Galahad, as he was praying, there came before him a man in the likeness of a bishop, with a great company of angels, and he cried to Galahad,—

"Come forth, good servant of the Lord, for the time has come which thou hast desired so long."

Then Sir Galahad lifted his hands and prayed, "Now, blessed Lord, would I no longer live an it please Thee."

Anon the bishop gave him the blessed food, and said he was Joseph of Arimathæa, come to bear him fellowship.

When he heard this, Sir Galahad went to Sir Bors and Sir Percivale, and kissed them, commending them to God, say-

ing, "Salute for me my lord Sir Launcelot, and bid him remember of this unstable world."

Therewith he kneeled down and prayed, and suddenly his
soul departed, a multitude of angels bearing it up to heaven.
Then came a hand from heaven, and took up the spear and
the Vessel. Since then has no man been so hardy as to say that
he has seen the Holy Grail.

Great sorrow was made for Sir Galahad, and after he was
buried, Sir Percivale betook him to a hermitage wherein he
also died after a year and two months. And Sir Bors caused
him to be buried near his sister and Sir Galahad. Then Bors
departed from Sarras, and entered into a ship. After a while
he came into the realm of Logris, and rode to Camelot, where
the King was.

There was great joy made for him, for they all thought he
had been dead. Then Bors told of his adventures, which were
all written down, and Launcelot told of his adventures also.
Afterwards Sir Bors told Sir Launcelot of his son Galahad's
last message, and he said.—

"I trust his prayer will avail me."

Then Launcelot took Sir Bors in his arms, and said,
"Gentle cousin, ye are right welcome to me, and all I may do
for you and for yours ye will find my poor body ready to perform while the spirit is in it, and never to fail. And wit ye
well, gentle cousin, that ye and I will never depart in sunder
while our lives may last."

"Sir," said Bors, "I will as ye will."

BOOK THE TWELFTH: THE LILY MAID OF ASTOLAT

CHAPTER I

HOW THE QUEEN WAS ARRAIGNED OF TREASON

AFTER the Quest of the Sangreal had been fulfilled, and all of the knights who remained of the Round Table had come to Camelot, there was great joy made concerning them. Sir Launcelot had won great fame, and so many ladies desired him to joust for them; whereat Guenever grew angry, because she had nominated Sir Launcelot her own champion. She was therefore wroth at him and bade him leave the Court, for she would never more trust him. So Launcelot departed, and calling his friends Sir Bors, Sir Ector, and Sir Lionel, told them how he had been upbraided by the Queen.

But Sir Bors advised him not to be over-hasty, but to remain at the hermitage near Windsor until news came. To this Sir Launcelot consented; but the Queen was also sorrowful at his departure, yet she would not show it, but made a private feast to all the other knights who remained. Amongst those at the dinner were Sir Mador de le Porte, Sir Patrice, an Irish knight, Sir Pinell le Savage, Sir Gawaine and his brothers, with many more. Sir Pinell hated Sir Gawaine, because he had slain one of his kinsmen.

Now, Sir Gawaine was exceedingly fond of all manner of fruit, which Sir Pinell knew. He therefore poisoned some apples at the table, with intent to slay Sir Gawaine. Thus it happened that while they feasted, Sir Patrice, who was seated by Sir Gawaine, took a poisoned apple, and, having eaten it, fell dead, swelled with the poison.

When the other knights beheld this they were very wroth and ashamed. They all leaped up from the banquet, and because the Queen had privately bidden them to the feast, they had suspicion of her.

"My lady the Queen," said Sir Gawaine, "I wit well this fruit was meant for me, for all know I love well fruit. Now, I see I have nigh been slain; wherefore, madam, I dread ye will be ashamed."

Then the Queen stood still, feeling greatly abashed, and not knowing what to say to him.

"This cannot so end," said Sir Mador de la Porte. "I have lost a noble knight of my own blood. For this despite I will be revenged to the uttermost."

Then openly he appelled the Queen of having murdered Sir Patrice his cousin; and all there spake nothing, for they had suspicion of the Queen, who could not speak, but wept and fell swooning. At the noise and crying came King Arthur, and, when he learnt of the trouble, he was passing heavy, standing still, while Sir Mador addressed him and again impeached the Queen of treason—for all manner of shameful death was then called treason.

"Fair lords," said Arthur, "ye trouble me sorely. I must be rightful judge, and so I cannot do battle for my wife, for as I deem this deed was none of hers. I suppose she will not be disdained nor lack a champion, and some good knight will surely put his body in jeopardy, that she be not burnt in a wrong quarrel. Therefore, Sir Mador, be not so hasty; desire thou thy day of battle, and she shall purvey her of some good knight who shall answer you, else it were great shame to me and all my Court."

"My gracious lord, be not displeased," said Sir Mador; "but all the four and twenty knights who were bidden to this banquet have great suspicion of the Queen. What say ye, my lords?"

Then they answered that they could not excuse the Queen, for, as she had made the dinner, the poison must have come by her or the servants.

"Alas!" cried the Queen, "I made this dinner for good intent and no evil; so God help me in my need."

"My lord," said Sir Mador to Arthur, "I require you as a righteous judge to give me a day when I may have justice."

"Well," said the King, "I give ye fifteen days hence, when ye be armed and ready in the meadow beside Westminster. If there be a knight to meet you, God speed the right; if not, my Queen must be burnt."

"I am answered," said Sir Mador. And then every knight went where he pleased.

Then, when Arthur and his Queen were alone, he asked her how the matter had occurred. But the Queen could not tell him. Then he inquired for Sir Launcelot; but he was told he was not within the realm.

"These be evil tidings," said Arthur. "I pray you send for Sir Bors, and ask him to do battle for you for Launcelot's sake."

So the Queen sent for Sir Bors, who at first would not consent; but when the Queen kneeled down to him, and besought him to have mercy on her, he consented on his faith.

Then the King and Queen thanked him heartily, and departed. But Sir Bors rode to the hermitage, and told Sir Launcelot all that had happened, and he said, "Do so, but tarry till I come."

Yet many knights were displeased that Sir Bors would do battle for the Queen. But Sir Bors said to them, "Wit ye well, fair lords, that it were shame to us to see the most noble Queen dishonoured for lack of a champion. She hath ever proved herself a lover of good knights, and I doubt not she is guiltless of the treason."

Some of the knights then believed what Sir Bors said, and were pleased; but others were not, and were passing wroth.

Thus the time passed on until the day came when the battle was to be; and all the knights, with the King and Queen, went down to Westminster to the meadow. The Queen was then put in ward, and a great fire was made about an iron stake, for if Sir Mador had the better, the Queen would be burned.

When the heralds blew, in came Sir Mador, and took oath

before the King that the Queen was guilty of Sir Patrice's death; and his oath he would sustain with his body, hand to hand, let any say the contrary.

Then came Sir Bors, and maintained that the Queen was innocent of the treason. So Sir Mador called upon Sir Bors to dress him and prove him in the right.

"Sir Mador," said Bors, "wit ye well I know ye for a good knight, and I trust in God to withstand you; but I promised my lord King Arthur, and my lady the Queen, to do battle for her to the uttermost, unless a better knight can be found."

"Is that all?" said Sir Mador. "Either come thou and do battle or else say nay."

"Take your horse," said Sir Bors; "ye shall not have to tarry long."

So each departed to their tents and made ready. Sir Mador came quickly into the field with his shield upon his shoulder, and Sir Bors took his own place and waited. Presently came there a knight armed, carrying a white shield, and, riding to Sir Bors, said, "Be not offended, fair knight; here cometh a better knight than ye are to have this battle. Therefore I pray withdraw you."

Then Sir Bors rode unto King Arthur, and told him that a knight had come to fight for the Queen.

"What knight is he?" asked the King.

"I wot not," replied Sir Bors; "but such covenant he made with me to be here this day. So now, my lord, I am discharged."

CHAPTER II

THE QUEEN'S CHAMPION, AND HOW THE TRUTH WAS KNOWN.
THE MAID OF ASTOLAT

THEN the King called the knight and questioned him, but he was in a great hurry to depart. All the knights wondered who he was, for he openly rebuked them for permitting the Queen to remain under suspicion.

Then said Sir Mador to the King, "Let me know, I pray thee, with whom I shall have to do."

So when all was ready the knights rode to the ends of the lists, couched their spears, and ran together with all their might. Sir Mador's spear brake all to pieces, but the stranger knight's held and bare Sir Mador's horse and all backwards in a great fall. Then suddenly he avoided his horse, and battled on foot with the other knight. So they fought for an hour.

At length, however, the strange knight smote Sir Mador upon the helm, and laid him flat upon the ground; but he, recovering, smote the other through the thighs. Then the stranger, waxing wroth, rose up and dealt Sir Mador terrible strokes, so that he fell to the earth, and the knight pulled off Sir Mador's helm to kill him.

"Spare me, I pray thee," cried Sir Mador.

And he yielded to the knight, who only granted him mercy when he openly released the Queen of all treason for ever. To this Sir Mador agreed, and then the knight-parters of the lists came up and took Sir Mador to his tent. The other knight went to the stair-foot, where sat the King; and the Queen also thanked him heartily. So they presented him with a cup of wine, and when he took off his helm to drink all saw the champion was Launcelot du Lake. The Queen when she beheld him sank down weeping, both for sorrow and for joy:

for sorrow at her unkindness, and for joy at his defence of her.

Then the knights of his blood drew to him and made great joy also, and all the knights of the Table Round welcomed him. Soon Sir Mador was attended by leeches, and Sir Launcelot was healed of his wound; thus there was great rejoicing and mirth in the Court.

But it so befell that the damsel of the lake, who was called Nimue, who had wedded Pelleas the good knight, came to the Court; and being greatly angered at the accusation made against the Queen, she said by whom the murder had been done, naming Sir Pinell, and for what cause he had done it. Then the Queen was excused, and Sir Pinell fled away to his own country.

Sir Patrice was buried in Westminster, and upon the tomb was written, "Here lieth Sir Patrice of Ireland, slain by Sir Pinell le Savage, that empoisoned apples to have slain Sir Gawaine, and by misfortune Sir Patrice ate one of the apples and suddenly died." There was also written upon the tomb that Queen Guenever was appelled of treason of the death of Patrice by Sir Mador de la Porte, and how Launcelot fought for the Queen and overcome him.

Sir Mador sued long and daily to stand again in the Queen's grace, and afterwards was forgiven.

Within fifteen days came the Feast of the Assumption, and the King let cry a great tournament at Camelot. Arthur gave out that he and the King of Scots would joust against all comers; and many knights came thither. But the Queen excused herself from going, wherefore the King was heavy and passing wroth; but he departed with his following towards Winchester, which is Camelot.

By the way he lodged at Astolat, which is Gilford in English, and there he stayed in a castle. And Sir Launcelot also rode thither, and at evening-time he found himself near a castle held by Sir Bernard of Astolat. King Arthur espied Launcelot as he was walking in the garden beside his lodging, and told his knights that he had seen one who would play his part in the jousts. but he mentioned not his name.

When Sir Launcelot had come into his lodging, the baron welcomed him in his best manner; and the knight begged him to lend him a shield that was not so well known as his own. The old man consented, saying he had two sons: one Sir Torre, who was unable to joust, being hurt, and the other Sir Lavaine, who was desirous to go to the tournament. Then he promised to lend Launcelot, whose name he did not know, the elder son's shield when the younger son would accompany Sir Launcelot. So it was settled.

This old baron had a daughter, who was called the Fair Maid of Astolat, and she wondered at Sir Launcelot, and fell in love with him exceedingly, whereof she died. Her name was Elaine la Blanche. She besought Sir Launcelot to wear a token of hers at the jousts.

"Fair damsel," said he, "if I do so, it will be more than I have ever done for lady living." Then, remembering that he intended to enter the lists disguised, he consented to wear a token, and, as he had never before done so, it would tend to his concealment.

"Fair damsel," he said, "I will wear your token upon my helmet,—show it to me."

"Sir," she said, "it is a red sleeve of mine, embroidered with great pearls."

When she brought it, he said, "Never did I so much for any damsel." Then he gave her his shield, and besought her to keep it until he came again. But all the time the maiden kept about Sir Launcelot, for she was in love with him, though all the while she suffered.

CHAPTER III

OF THE TOURNAMENT AT CAMELOT; HOW LAUNCELOT AND
LAVAINE OPPOSED KING ARTHUR, AND IN WHAT JEOPARDY
THEY WERE

THE King tarried at Astolat three days, and then departed. When he had gone Sir Launcelot and Sir Lavaine also made ready, and bore white shields; and Sir Launcelot carried the sleeve of the damsel in his helm as a token.

At Camelot was a great throng of kings and knights, but Sir Launcelot lodged in private, by Sir Lavaine's means, with a rich burgess, and remained quiet until the day appointed for the tournament. King Arthur was seated high to behold the best, and every man made him ready and joined Arthur's party, or the side of the King of North Galis, as suited him best.

Sir Launcelot and Sir Lavaine departed privily from Camelot, and came to a little wood behind the army which was opposing King Arthur; there they remained until the attack began. The King of Scots and the King of Ireland were of King Arthur's party. Against them was the King of Northumberland. Sir Palamides was with Arthur, and he smote down Sir Galahault, and both fell. Then came Sir Sagramore the Desirous, Sir Brandiles, Sir Dodinas le Savage, Sir Kay, and other knights—fifteen in all of the Table Round. They, with others, beat back the Kings of Northumberland and North Wales.

When Sir Launcelot heard this he said to Sir Lavaine, "An ye will help me a little we will see yonder fellowship go back as fast as they have come forward."

"Sir, spare not," said Lavaine; "for I shall do what I may."

Then Sir Launcelot and Sir Lavaine came on into the thickest of the fight, and Sir Launcelot smote down Sir Brandiles, Sir Sagramore, Sir Kay, Sir Griflet, and others, while Sir Lavaine smote Sir Lucan le Buttelere and Sir Bedivere. After that they gat new spears and overturned more knights, so that the knights of the Table Round drew back, and gat their horses as well as they might.

"Oh, mercy!" said Sir Gawaine unto King Arthur; "what knight is yonder that doeth such marvellous deeds?"

"I wot who he is," replied the King; "but I will not name him."

"I would say he were Sir Launcelot by his riding," remarked Gawaine; "but for the token in his helmet I wist it cannot be he, for he never weareth token."

"Let him be," said Arthur; "he will be better known and do more ere he depart."

Meantime the knights gathered together against Launcelot and Lavaine, and they smote down many knights of the Kings of Northumberland and North Galis. Then Sir Launcelot gat a spear in his hand, and encountered Sir Bors, Sir Ector, and Sir Lionel all at once. But by mischance Sir Bors smote Sir Launcelot through the shield to his side, and the spear brake, leaving the head in the wound.

When Sir Lavaine saw his companion fall, he rushed at the King of Scots, and smote him to the earth. He then took the King's horse, and brought it to Launcelot, and made him mount, notwithstanding them all. Sir Launcelot being mounted, then set to again, and smote down Sir Bors, horse and man, to the earth, as well as Sir Ector and Sir Lionel. But when he drew his sword he felt like to die. Yet he fought; but spared Sir Lionel and his fellows when he found who they were. So he rode, furiously smiting right and left, until he laid low thirty knights, most part being of the Table Round. Sir Lavaine also did full well that day, for he smote down ten knights of the Round Table.

So the prize was given to the knights with the red sleeve and the white shield. Then came the Kings of Northumberland and North Galis, and thanked the knights for all they had done for their party.

"Fair lords," said Sir Launcelot, "wit ye well if I have deserved thanks, I have sore bought them, for I am like to die. Therefore, I beseech you, suffer me to depart, for I am greatly hurt. I had liever repose me than be lord of all the world."

Therewith he groaned piteously, and rode away from them, until he came to a field, and then he prayed Sir Lavaine to help him with the truncheon of the spear from out his side. But Sir Lavaine hesitated, for he was afraid that if he did so Sir Launcelot would die.

"I charge ye draw it out," said Sir Launcelot, "an ye love me."

Then Sir Lavaine did so, and Sir Launcelot gave a loud shriek and a grisly groan, while the blood burst out, near a pint at once; so he swooned, and lay half an hour as if dead.

At length he revived, and begged Sir Lavaine to help him on his horse to the hermitage hard by, where a noble knight had become a hermit, and was an excellent surgeon. Then, with great pain, Sir Lavaine helped him upon his horse and they rode away, while Sir Launcelot's blood ran down to the earth.

They quickly came to the hermitage, and entreated to be let in. Then came a child and asked what they would.

"Fair son," said Sir Lavaine, "go and pray the hermit to let in here a knight that is full sore wounded."

So the child departed and brought the hermit, who inquired who the wounded man was, and which side he had taken in the tournament. Sir Lavaine could not tell the name, but he told him they had opposed King Arthur, and the hermit agreed, though he had himself been one of the Table Round. Then he questioned Sir Launcelot, who was leaning over his horse and bleeding continually, who he was.

"I am a stranger, and a knight adventurous," replied Launcelot.

But the hermit observed him closely, and by a wound upon the cheek he recognized Sir Launcelot.

"Alas!" he said, "my own lord, why hide ye your name from me? Forsooth I ought to know ye of right as the noblest knight of the world; I know ye are Sir Launcelot."

"Sir," said he, "since ye know me, help me an ye may, for God's sake, for I would be out of this pain either for death or life."

"Have ye no fear," said the hermit, "ye shall live and fare right well."

Then he called two of his servants, who bore him into the hermitage and laid him on a bed, where his blood was staunched, and himself well refreshed.

In those days it was not the guise of hermits as is now: then there were none hermits but what had been men of worship and prowess, and they held great household to refresh people that were in distress.

CHAPTER IV

HOW SIR LAUNCELOT WAS DISCOVERED BY ELAINE; HOW SHE TENDED HIM, AND PROFFERED HIM HER HAND

WE WILL now leave Sir Launcelot, and return to King Arthur.

When all the kings were come together to the great feast, King Arthur asked the King of North Galis where was that knight that bare the red sleeve, so that he might receive the prize.

Then Sir Galahad said, "We suppose the knight is hurt; he is never like to see you or any of us, which is the greatest pity that ever we wist of any knight."

King Arthur then inquired his name; but they could not tell him anything concerning the Knight of the Red Sleeve.

"Alas!" said the King, "I would not for all the lands I hold that the noble knight were slain; I would we had good tidings of him."

"By my head," said Sir Gawaine, "it is great damage and pity to all this land if the knight be so sore hurt; but if he may be found, I shall find him, for he cannot be far from this town."

So Sir Gawaine took a squire with him, and rode all about Camelot within six or seven miles; but he came again without hearing word of him.

Within two days Arthur and his fellowship returned to London, and as they rode, it happened that Sir Gawaine lodged at Astolat with Sir Bernard, where Sir Launcelot had stayed. The old baron and his daughter Elaine came to hear the tidings and who had done best at the tournament at Winchester.

"Truly," said Sir Gawaine, "there were two knights that bare white shields; but one of them bare a red sleeve upon his helm, and he was one of the best knights I ever saw joust. I daresay that one knight smote down forty valiant men of the Table Round, and his fellow did right well and worshipfully."

"Blessed be God," said the fair maid of Astolat, "that the knight sped so well, for he is the man in the world I first loved, and truly he shall be the last."

"Then know ye his name?" said Sir Gawaine.

"Nay, truly," said the damsel, "I know not his name, nor whence he cometh; but I say that I love him."

Then she told him how her father had lent the knight her elder brother's shield when he left his own, because it was so well known amongst knights.

Then Sir Gawaine asked to see the shield, and when it was brought he knew it was Sir Launcelot's.

"Ah, mercy!" he said; "now is my heart heavier than before. Is the knight that owneth this shield your love?"

"Yea, truly," she replied; "I would I were his love."

"Fair damsel," said Sir Gawaine, "an he be your lover ye love the most honourable knight of the world, and the man of most worship; but I have known him this four and twenty year, and yet never saw till that day that he bore token or sign for lady or maiden at joust or tournament. But I dread me ye will never see him again in this world."

"Alas!" said she; "is he slain?"

"I say not so," said Sir Gawaine; "but he is grievously wounded, and more likely to be dead than alive. Wit ye well that he is the noble knight Sir Launcelot, for I know him by this shield."

"Fair father," said Elaine, "I require you give me leave to ride and to seek him, or else I shall go out of my mind, for I cannot stop till I find him and my brother Sir Lavaine."

"Do as it liketh you," said her father.

So the maiden made ready, and was sore grieved before Sir Gawaine. On the morn he returned to King Arthur, and told him of the shield he had found.

"That I knew beforehand," said King Arthur, "for I espied Sir Launcelot in his lodgings at Astolat."

Afterwards the King and all came to London, and then Sir Gawaine told the Court that it was Sir Launcelot who had jousted best at the tournaments at Winchester.

The fair Elaine meantime had made ready, and came to Winchester and sought all about for Sir Launcelot, but in vain, till she met by adventure her brother Lavaine, who accompanied her to the hermitage. When she beheld Sir Launcelot so ill and pale, she swooned away. Then he bade her brother lift her up, and, kissing her, he said,—

"Fair maiden, why act ye thus? Ye put me to pain instead of cheer, for if ye be come to comfort me ye are right welcome, and I shall be quickly whole, by the grace of God."

Then the maiden told him how she had discovered his name by Sir Gawaine recognizing the shield. She never left him, but watched him day and night, and never did woman kindlier than she; but Sir Launcelot prayed Lavaine to send espies for Sir Bors, who he knew would come to seek him, and he desired to see him.

Anon Sir Lavaine came to Winchester and found Sir Bors, who told him the Queen was wroth because he had worn a token in his helm, being her own champion, as it became known through Sir Gawaine. "Is this she," continued Sir Bors, "that men call the Fair Maid of Astolat?"

"She it is," replied Launcelot; "and I cannot put her from me."

"Why should ye?" said Sir Bors; "she is a passing fair damsel and well beseen, and God would ye might wed her; but as to that I cannot counsel. I see well she loveth you."

"That me repenteth," replied Sir Launcelot.

Then they talked of many more things, and it happened that within three or four days Sir Launcelot was well and strong again. So they all departed from the hermitage, and took their horses and fair Elaine with them, and when they came to Astolat they were well lodged, and had great cheer of Sir Bernard the old baron, and of Sir Torre his son.

Upon the morn, when Sir Launcelot would depart, fair Elaine came with her father and brother to see him, and said, "My lord Sir Launcelot, I see ye are about to depart; fair and courteous knight, I pray ye have mercy upon me, and suffer me not to die for thy love."

"What would ye that I did?" asked Sir Launcelot.

"I would have you to my husband," said Elaine.

"Fair damsel, I thank you," replied Sir Launcelot; "but truly I cast me never to be wedded man."

"Alas!" cried she, "then must I die for your love!"

"Ye shall not so," replied Launcelot. "But because ye love me so well, I will for your goodwill and kindness give you, whenever you shall set your heart upon some good knight that will wed you, a thousand pounds yearly to you and to your heirs. This much I will give you, fair maiden, for your kindness, and always while I live to be your own true knight."

"Of all this," said the damsel, "I will none; if ye will not wed me, all my good days are done."

Then she shrieked shrilly and fell down in a swoon. The women bare her to her chamber, where she made overmuch sorrow. Then came Sir Bernard, and said to Launcelot,—

"I cannot but see that my daughter will die for your sake."

"I may not do as ye would," said Sir Launcelot, "but it me sore repenteth, for I never was the causer of it as I report me to your son: nor early nor late proffered I her bounty or fair behests. I do all that a good knight dare. She is a true maiden, and I am right heavy for her distress, as she is gentle, good, and well taught."

"Father," said Lavaine, "she is good, as my lord Launcelot hath said; but she doth as I do, for since I first saw my lord Launcelot I could never depart from him, and I must follow him."

Then Sir Launcelot took his leave, and he with Sir Lavaine came to Winchester, where King Arthur welcomed him, and all the knights beside save Sir Agravaine and Sir Mordred; but the Queen was wroth, and estranged herself from him.

CHAPTER V

HOW THE MAID OF ASTOLAT DIED FOR LOVE OF LAUNCELOT; AND
HOW THE BODY ARRIVED BEFORE KING ARTHUR, AND LAUNCELOT
OFFERED THE MASS-PENNY

AFTER the departure of Sir Launcelot the Fair Maid of
Astolat never slept, nor ate nor drank, and ever complained of her love. So when she had endured a ten-days'
fast, she was so feebled that she must needs pass out of this
world. Then she shrived her clean, and received the Sacrament, yet ever she complained of Sir Launcelot. Then her
ghostly father bade her leave such thoughts.

"Why should I?" she replied. "Am I not an earthly woman?
My belief is, I do none offence for loving an earthly man, and
I take God to witness, I never loved other than Sir Launcelot,
and never shall. And since it is the sufferance of God that I
die for love of so noble a knight, I beseech Him to have
mercy on my soul."

Then she called her father, and her brother Sir Torre, and
begged her father to write a letter as she might indite it. So
it was done; and when it was written, she said, "Let me be
watched until I am dead, and while my body is hot let this
letter be put into my right hand, and my hand bound fast
till I be cold. Let all my richest clothes that I have about me
and my bed be laid with me in a chariot to the next place
where Thames is, and there let me be put in a barget, and
but one man with me such as ye may trust to steer thither, and
that my barget be covered with black samite. Thus, father, I
beseech you let it be done."

So her father granted it her faithfully that all things should
be done as she had devised. Then her father and her brother
made great dole, for when this was done she died.

When she was dead, the corpse and the bed and all was led

the next way unto the Thames, and there a man and the corpse and all were put into Thames. So the man steered the barget unto Westminster, and there he rowed a great while to and fro before any one espied it.

But by fortune King Arthur and the Queen Guenever were speaking together at a window, and looking unto the Thames, they perceived the black barget, and had marvel what it meant. Then the King called Sir Kay, and told him to go and bring him word what it meant. So he, with Sir Brandiles and Sir Agravaine, went into the barget, and found the fairest corpse lying on a bed, and a poor man sitting on the barget's end, but not a word would he speak.

So they returned unto the King and told him what they had found. Then the King took the Queen by the hand and went to see the body, and she espied the letter in her right hand, and told the King, who took it, and said,—

"This letter will tell us who she was, and why she is come hither."

Then the King and the Queen went out of the barget and commanded a certain man to wait upon the vessel. When the King had reached his chamber, he called his knights about him, and said that he would make known openly what was within the letter. Then the King brake it, and made a clerk to read it, as follows:

"Most noble knight, Sir Launcelot, now hath death made us two at debate for your love. I was your lover that men called the Fair Maiden of Astolat, therefore unto all ladies I make my moan; yet pray for me at least, and offer ye my mass-penny. This is my last request; pray for my soul, Sir Launcelot, as thou art peerless."

This was the substance of the letter, and when it was read the Queen and King, and all the knights, wept for pity. Then was Sir Launcelot sent for, and when he was come, King Arthur made the letter to be read to him, and when he had heard it, he said,—

"My lord, wit ye well I am right heavy at the death of this damsel. God knoweth I was never the causer of her death by my willing, and that I will refer to her own brother, Sir Lavaine. Here he is. She was fair and good, but she loved me out of measure."

"Ye might have showed her some bounty and gentleness," said the Queen, "and preserved her life."

"Madam," replied Launcelot, "she would in no other way be answered but for my love. I did offer her a thousand pounds yearly, when she wed any knight, to her and her heirs; but I love not to be constrained to love, which must arise out of the heart."

"It will be to your worship," said the King then unto Sir Launcelot, "that ye oversee that she be interred worshipfully."

"Sir," said Launcelot, "that shall be done as I can best devise."

Then many knights went thither to behold that fair maiden, and in the morn she was interred richly. Sir Launcelot offered the mass-penny, and all the knights present did so likewise. Then the poor man went again with the barget.

After that all the winter passed in hunting and hawking, jousts and tourneys. Even Sir Lavaine got great worship, so that he became renowned amongst the knights of the Table Round.

BOOK THE THIRTEENTH: THE DEATH OF KING ARTHUR

CHAPTER I

HOW QUEEN GUENEVER WENT MAYING, AND WAS TAKEN PRISONER; HOW SIR LAUNCELOT RESCUED HER; AND OF OTHER MATTERS

THUS it passed from Candlemas unto Easter, until the month of May had come, when all nature begins to blossom, and giveth fruit and trees to flourish. And it befell in that month of May that Queen Guenever called her knights, and gave them warning that early in the morning she would ride a-maying into the woods and fields beside Westminster.

She desired them all to be clad in green, and she would bring ten ladies, every knight to have a lady behind him, and every knight a squire and two yeomen, all well horsed. So they made them ready in the freshest manner ten knights to wait upon the Queen.

They took their horses, and rode out, all clad in green, and the Queen had determined to be back with Arthur at ten of the clock. But there was a knight named Meliagrance, who had for a long season loved the Queen, and would ere this time have carried her away to his castle, within seven miles of Westminster, had he dared. But he always feared Sir Launcelot, who, with other valiant men, attended on the Queen, who were therefore called the Queen's knights. When any were slain, then the best were chosen to fill their places, and they carried white shields, but were all men renowned, like Launcelot and others.

At this time the knight Meliagrance perceived that Sir Launcelot was not with the Queen, only a posse of knights in green clothing. So he prepared twenty men-of-arms, and a hundred archers, for to destroy the Queen and her ten knights, thinking that was a good opportunity.

So when the maying was done, and all was freshly bedecked with flowers, there came Sir Meliagrance, and bade the Queen and her knights abide.

"Traitor knight," exclaimed the Queen, "what seek ye? Wilt thou dishonour the noble King, and shame thy knighthood?" And the ten knights likewise upbraided him.

But he only answered by bidding them leave or defend the Queen; and then they all charged upon the knights who were armed only with their swords. But these ten defended the Queen manfully, and slew or maimed full forty men-at-arms, until the Queen for pity, seeing she must be taken, and they all slain at the last, cried out to Sir Meliagrance,—

"Slay not my noble knights," she said, "and I will go with thee upon this covenant: that thou save them, and let them suffer no more hurt, and that also they be led with me wheresoever I go, for I would rather slay myself else."

"Madam," said Meliagrance, "for your sake they shall be led with you unto mine own castle; with that ye will be ruled, and ride with me."

Then the Queen prayed the remaining four knights to leave their fighting, and she and they would not part.

"Madam," said Sir Pelleas, "we will do as you do; as for me, I take no heed of life or death."

But Sir Brandiles, Sir Persant, Sir Ironside, and Sir Pelleas were the only knights not *hors de combat* in that encounter, and Sir Pelleas gave such buffets none could hold him.

So by the Queen's command the battle was stayed, and the wounded knights were carried away on horseback as they might; but the Queen secretly called a page of her chamber unto her, and gave him a ring to bear unto Sir Launcelot, and tell him to come unto her rescue.

So the page rode away quickly, but Sir Meliagrance espied him, and feared for Sir Launcelot. Then he sent after the page to kill him, but the child escaped all pursuers. And Meliagrance said to the Queen, "Ye are about to betray me, but I shall ordain for Sir Launcelot that he shall not easily approach you."

Sir Meliagrance then commanded an ambush of archers, who, when they should perceive Sir Launcelot, were ordered to kill his horse, but to avoid the knight, who was over hard to be overcome. Then the Queen came to the castle, but would not permit any of her wounded knights to leave her, for she would attend to them herself. But Sir Meliagrance shut them all up, men and ladies, in the tower, and the gates were closed and barred, for the knight dreaded that Sir Launcelot had had warning.

Meantime the page came and told Sir Launcelot of the capture of the Queen. He at once made ready, and, sending the boy to inform Sir Lavaine to follow him, he heard the account of the battle, and swam the Thames to Lambeth, where he came upon the field of the encounter. Passing thence, he was met by the ambushment of the archers, who desired him to stand; but he refused, so they smote his steed with many arrows. And Sir Launcelot dismounted, but could not reach the archers, who were behind the hedges and ditches, and escaped.

Sir Launcelot, in his heavy armour, could scarcely proceed, but he met a cart and two carters, who refused him conveyance, being servants of Sir Meliagrance; but Sir Launcelot, being wroth, struck one such a buffet with his hand, that the man fell dead, and the other, in fear, let the knight ride in the cart to the castle.

Queen Guenever perceived him from the window, leading the horse, which had forty arrows, broad and rough, in him; and her waiting-women said the knight looked like a man going to the gallows in a cart, but were rebuked when the Queen found it was Sir Launcelot who had come to her rescue.

She was in her chamber, but the gates of the castle were closed. So Launcelot descended from the cart and knocked at the gate long time, crying out against Sir Meliagrance. The porter opened the postern a little way, but Sir Launcelot pushed it in, and gave the man such a buffet with his mailed hand, that he fell back with his neck broken. Then Sir

Launcelot sought admittance to the Queen, and at length, at eveningtide, spying a ladder, he mounted to the window of the chamber, and, setting his hands upon the bars of iron, he pulled them out, and entered to the Queen, and the ten wounded knights who lay in the adjoining chambers.

Meantime Sir Meliagrance had been advised of Sir Launcelot's entry into the court of the castle, and sought the Queen. "Mercy, madam," he said; "I put myself wholly under your grace. All that is amiss on my part shall be wholly amended as you yourself would desire, and ye can take all into your hands; rule Sir Launcelot, and such cheer will be made as this poor castle can afford. In the morn ye can return unto Westminster, and my body and all mine shall be at your rule."

"Ye say well," replied the Queen: "better is peace than war; the less noise the more to my worship."

Then the Queen and her ladies waited Sir Launcelot, and told him he must come in peaceably, for all things had been put into the Queen's hand, "and the knight had sore repented him of the adventure."

Then Sir Launcelot was appeased, but said he, "There is none but my lord Arthur or you who would have let me, so that I should not make Sir Meliagrance's heart cold for ever."

Then the Queen took Sir Launcelot by the hand, and led him into her own chamber, where she caused him to be unarmed. And then she showed him the ten knights who had been wounded; and they all made joy of Sir Launcelot, but complained bitterly of their hurts, and would have avenged themselves but for the command of the Queen.

Still Sir Meliagrance was a deep traitor, and sent a writing, sealing it with his seal, and gaging his glove that the Queen had been treasonable to the King. This defiance took up Sir Launcelot, and when Sir Meliagrance asked him to visit the parts of the castle, the traitor showed him from chamber to chamber, Sir Launcelot fearing no perils. But as he went along he trod upon a trap that had been prepared, and the board let him down into a cave full of straw, full ten fathom deep. Then Sir Meliagrance departed, and made believe he knew not where Sir Launcelot was.

After dinner the Queen and her ladies, with the wounded knights and Sir Lavaine, returned to Westminster, and told the King how Meliagrance had accused the Queen of unfaithful conduct and high treason, and how Sir Launcelot had taken up the challenge for eight days hence.

But still no one knew what had become of Sir Launcelot at that time, and they fancied he had gone away upon some adventure, as he was ofttimes wont to do, for it was supposed he had Lavaine's horse, which Sir Meliagrance had hidden.

CHAPTER II

HOW LAUNCELOT ESCAPED, AND SLEW SIR MELIAGRANCE WITH
ONE HAND TIED BEHIND HIM; THE QUEEN IS AGAIN ACCUSED
BY THE KING'S KNIGHTS

KING ARTHUR, however, was assured that Sir Launcelot would come, unless he were trapped with some treason. But meanwhile the time passed, and he did not appear.
All these days the knight was lying in the cave, bruised by
his fall, and attended by a damsel who brought him meat and
drink.

This fair damsel fell in love with Sir Launcelot, and had
pity upon him when she heard how he had to defend the
Queen. Then, after some parley, she agreed to let him go
free, but not until the very day on which the tournament was
to be. So she brought unto him his armour, and let him choose
the best courser in the stable. Then Sir Launcelot looked upon
a white courser, and had him saddled; then he gat his spear
and his sword, and commending the damsel unto God, said,—

"Lady, for this good deed I shall do you service if ever
it be in my power."

In the meanwhile Queen Guenever had been appelled of
treason, and was in danger of being burned, for Sir Meliagrance had so arranged his perfidy that Sir Launcelot could
not appear, as he deemed; and in the absence of her champion, Guenever would be destroyed. This was his revenge;
but the King and all the Court were exceeding sorry that the
Queen should suffer by default of Sir Launcelot.

Then Sir Lavaine begged to do the battle for the Queen,
in case Sir Launcelot did not arrive in time; and the King,
feeling assured of the Queen, and all the wounded knights,
asserting her innocence, would have done battle for her if
they might.

When the time came Sir Meliagrance was ready, and Sir Lavaine also gat him to horse at the end of the lists; but just as the heralds were about to cry "Laissez aller!" Sir Launcelot appeared, spurring, and arrived in the lists. So the King commanded him to come and explain all, which he did, telling of Sir Meliagrance's treason and evil intents, so that they were all ashamed for him. So no more could be said, and the knights made ready to battle. They met like thunder, and Sir Launcelot bare Sir Meliagrance over his horse's croup. They both then dismounted and fought on foot, until Sir Meliagrance, having received a great stroke upon the helm, begged for mercy, and yielded him.

Then Sir Launcelot knew not what to do, and looked to the Queen, who shook her head, as much as to say, "Slay him." So he commanded Sir Meliagrance to arise and fight to the utterance; but he would not. Then said Sir Launcelot, "I will give you advantage. I will unarm my head and my left side, and let bind my left hand behind me, and then I will do battle with you."

This set Sir Meliagrance upon his legs, and cried out, "My lord Arthur, take heed of this proffer, for I will take it. Let him be disarmed and bounden as he said."

Sir Launcelot consenting, the squires unarmed him and bound him with his left arm behind his back, without shield but only his sword. Many a one marvelled that Sir Launcelot would adventure himself in such wise. Then came Sir Meliagrance with his sword on high, and Sir Launcelot showed him his left side all unarmed; and when Meliagrance thought to have smitten him upon the bare head, Sir Launcelot skilfully avoided the stroke and parried it. Then with sleight and great force he struck Sir Meliagrance such a buffet that the stroke carved the head into two parts, and Sir Meliagrance was drawn out of the field. The King suffered him to be buried, and made mention of the reason why he was slain.

But again, after this deliverance, a plot was laid against the Queen by Sir Mordred and Sir Agravaine to implicate her of treason, as also concerning Launcelot du Lake. These plots and plans caused much evil and dissensions, whereby King Arthur was no more at peace, and which led him to his death; wherefore this Book is called "Morte d'Arthur."

Sir Launcelot's enemies soon beset him, but he rushed out of the chamber in which they thought to kill him, and first slaying Sir Colgrevance at the door, he armed him in his armour. Then he rushed out upon the remainder of his assailants, and slew twelve of his fellows; Sir Mordred only fled, being wounded; the others were all dead.

So the knight called his friends, and said, "Wit ye well, my lords, that ever since I came into this country I have well willed unto my lord King Arthur and unto lady Queen Guenever, and this day, because my lady the Queen sent to speak with me (I suppose it was made by treason), I was by a forecast near slain; but, as God provided me, I was enabled to escape all their malice and treason. And because I have slain these knights, I am now sure of mortal war, for they were, I believe, sent and ordained by King Arthur to betray me. Therefore the King will in his heat and malice judge Queen Guenever to the fire; but that I may not suffer, for I will fight for the Queen, as she is a true lady unto her lord."

Then said Sir Bors, "My lord Sir Launcelot, by mine advice ye will take the weal with the woe, and in patience. If the Queen be in danger, it is my advice that ye knightly rescue her; if ye did otherwise all the world will say ye wrong. It is to your part to rescue the Queen, and if she be put to the fire it is your worship to rescue her from the peril; and in Joyous Gard ye may retain her until the heat of the King be past. Then shall ye bring her home with great worship, and shall have thanks of the King."

After discussion they all agreed to rescue the Queen if the King brought her to the fire, and they put themselves in an ambushment near Carlisle as nigh as they might, and there abode to see what the King would do.

CHAPTER III

HOW SIR LAUNCELOT RESCUED THE QUEEN, AND CARRIED HER TO JOYOUS GARD; OF THE RECONCILIATION BY THE POPE BETWEEN THE KING AND QUEEN

WHEN Sir Mordred, being only wounded, hurried away, he came to King Arthur, and told him what Sir Launcelot had done, and how he had slain twelve knights.

"It me repenteth," said the King, "that Sir Launcelot should be against me. Now am I sure that the noble fellowship of the Table Round is broken for ever, for with him will many a knight hold. But as it has fallen so, the Queen must suffer the death."

But Sir Gawaine endeavoured to persuade the King, and declared that there was none harm done, and "your lady is both good and true. I will avenge me not of my brother's death, or of my son's, for I gave them warning aforehand what would fall in the end; and as they would not abide by my counsel, I will not meddle me thereof."

"Make you ready," said the King, "for the Queen shall have her judgment anon."

"Alas!" said Sir Gawaine, "that ever I should live to see this day." And he turned into his chamber and wept heartily.

Then the Queen was led forth without Carlisle, and despoiled unto her smock. Her ghostly father was brought to her to be shriven of her misdeeds. There was weeping and wailing and wringing of hands, but there were few lords who would bear any armour for the death of the Queen.

Sir Launcelot had meanwhile sent one to spy for him, and when he saw the Queen despoiled unto her smock, he came and told Sir Launcelot. Then was there a spurring and plucking up of horses. So came they to the fire, and any that stood against them, there were they slain, full many a noble knight, and amongst them Sir Gaheris and Sir Gareth, who were unarmed and unaware.

When Sir Launcelot had put all to flight, he rode straight unto Dame Guenever, and causing a kirtle and a gown to be cast upon her, bade her mount behind him and to be of good cheer. Wit you well the Queen was glad to be rescued from death, and thanked God and Sir Launcelot. So he rode away unto Joyous Gard, and there he kept her as a noble knight should do, while many knights and kings drew unto him. When it was known that Sir Launcelot and the King were at debate, many were full heavy because of the strife between them.

King Arthur was at once informed how Sir Launcelot had rescued the Queen, and of the death of many noble knights, in particular of Sir Gaheris and Sir Gareth. When he heard this the King swooned away for pure sorrow, and when he awoke he said,—

"Alas! that ever I bare crown upon my head, for now have I lost the fairest fellowship of knights that ever held Christian king together. Mercy!" cried the King, "why slew he Sir Gareth and Sir Gaheris? As for Sir Gaheris, he loved Sir Launcelot above all men earthly."

"They were slain in the hurtling," said the knights, "as Sir Launcelot rushed in the thick of the press; he wist them not when he smote, and so unhappily they were slain."

"The death of them," said Arthur, "will cause the greatest mortal war that ever was. Ah, Agravaine! Agravaine! Jesu forgive it thy soul, for thine evil will that thou and thy brother Sir Mordred haddest unto Sir Launcelot hath caused all this sorrow."

When Sir Gawaine heard that his brothers were slain by Sir Launcelot by misadventure, he would not at first believe it; and when he found it was true, he wept and swooned, and lay as if he had been dead. Then when he had recovered he hied him to the King, and they both wept sore together.

"My King, my lord, and mine uncle," said Sir Gawaine, "wit you well now I shall make you a promise, which I shall make by my knighthood, that from this day I will never fail Sir Launcelot until one have slain the other. Therefore I require you, my lord and King, dress you for the war, for I promise unto God, for the death of my brother Sir Gareth, I shall seek Sir Launcelot throughout seven kings' realms but I shall slay him, or else he shall slay me."

"Ye need not seek so far," said the King, "for I hear say Sir Launcelot will abide me at Joyous Gard, and much people draweth unto him."

So the King sent letters throughout all England to summon all his knights, and when they were assembled the King informed them how Sir Launcelot had bereft him of the Queen; and they made ready to besiege Sir Launcelot in the castle of Joyous Gard. There came King Arthur with Sir Gawaine and a huge host, and laid siege to the castle; but in nowise would Sir Launcelot ride out, nor permit any of his knights to do so, until fifteen weeks were passed.

Much recrimination passed between Sir Launcelot and Sir Gawaine, and also King Arthur accused Launcelot of his perfidy. But he showed how it had happened, and declared on his truth and knighthood, being willing to make good his words, that the Queen had behaved well.

"Sithen I have done battles for your Queen, my lord Arthur," he said, "in other quarrels, meseemeth I had more right to do battle for her in right quarrel. Therefore take your Queen unto your good grace, for she is both fair and true and good."

But they would not listen to Launcelot, and war ensued, in which Launcelot saved King Arthur's life; and the tears burst from the King's eyes, thinking on the great courtesy that was in Sir Launcelot more than in any other man. This war was at last noised abroad, and reached the Pope. He considering the goodness of Arthur and Sir Launcelot, called unto him a noble clerk—the Bishop of Rochester—and the Pope gave him bulls to King Arthur, charging him, upon the interdicting of all England, that he take his Queen Guenever unto him again, and accord with Sir Launcelot.

When the Bishop came unto Carlisle he showed the King the bulls, and Arthur would fain have been accorded with Sir Launcelot. But Sir Gawaine would not suffer him to do so; he was quite willing that the Queen should be received, but he would not accord with Sir Launcelot.

The Bishop then had of the King his great seal and assurance that Sir Launcelot should come safe and go safe, and that no reference should be made as to the past. Then the prelate departed unto Joyous Gard, and showed Sir Launcelot the letters of the Pope.

"Now, I thank God!" said the knight, "that the Pope hath made her peace, for God knoweth I will be a thousandfold more gladder to bring her again than ever I was to take her away; with this I may be sure to come safe and go safe. She never from this day stands in no peril, for I dare adventure me to keep her from a harder attack than ever I kept her."

So the bishop departed, and came unto the King at Carlisle; and afterward Sir Launcelot purveyed him a hundred knights, all clothed in green velvet, each carrying a branch of olive in his hand as token of peace. The Queen had four and twenty gentlewomen following her in the same wise; and Sir Launcelot had twelve coursers following him, and on every courser sat a young gentleman. And all they were arrayed in green velvet. The Queen and Sir Launcelot were clothed in white cloth of gold tissue; and they rode from Joyous Gard to Carlisle.

Then Sir Launcelot himself alighted and took the Queen, and led her to where King Arthur was in his seat; and Sir Gawaine sat before him, and many great lords. So when Sir Launcelot saw the King he led the Queen by the arm, and then he kneeled down and the Queen both. Wit you well there were many bold knights there with King Arthur that wept tenderly.

CHAPTER IV

HOW SIR LAUNCELOT DEFENDED HIMSELF, AND HOW HE WAS
BANISHED FROM KING ARTHUR'S COURT

THEN Sir Launcelot saw the King's countenance; he arose, and said, "My most redoubted King, ye shall understand, by the Pope's commandment and yours, I have brought to you my lady the Queen, as right requireth; and if there be any knight except your person who shall say but that she is true to you, I here myself, Launcelot du Lake, will make it good upon his body that she is a true lady unto you. But to liars ye have listened, and that has caused debate betwixt you and me; for time hath been when ye were greatly pleased with me, my lord Arthur, when I did battle for my lady your Queen. And full well ye know, my most noble King, that she has been put to great wrong at this time; and sith it pleased you many times that I should fight for her, meseemeth, my good lord, I had more cause to rescue her from the fire. For they that told you those tales were liars, and so it fell upon them; for had not the grace of God been with me, I never could have withstood fourteen knights: they armed and afore-purposed, I unarmed and not purposed. Sir Agravaine, when I was sent for by the Queen, called me traitor and recreant knight——"

"They called thee right," said Sir Gawaine, interrupting.

"My lord Sir Gawaine," said Sir Launcelot, "in their quarrel they proved themselves not in the right."

"Well, well, Sir Launcelot," said the King, "I have given thee no cause to do unto me as thou hast done, for I have worshipped thee more than all my knights."

"My good lord," said Sir Launcelot, "so ye be not displeased, ye will understand, I and mine have oft done you better service than any other knights. I have myself rescued you from many dangers. I have matched Sir Tristram and Sir Lamorak; Sir Caradock of the Dolorous Tower was a full noble knight and a passing strong man, and that wit ye, my lord Gawaine, as he by force pulled you out of your saddle and bound you to his saddle-bow, when I rescued you and slew him. Also I rescued your brother Sir Gaheris likewise from Sir Turquine; therefore, Sir Gawaine, ye ought to remember this, for an I might have your good will, I would trust to God to have my lord King Arthur's."

"The King may do as he will," said Sir Gawaine; "but wit thou well, Sir Launcelot, thou and I shall never be accorded while we live, for thou hast slain three of my brethren, and twain of them ye slew traitorly and piteously, for they bare none harness against you, and none would bear."

"God would they had borne arms, for now would they have been alive. I slew never Sir Gareth or Sir Gaheris by my will. But this much I will offer, if it please you. I will begin at Sandwich, and there I will go in my shirt, barefoot, and at every ten miles I will found an house of religion with an whole convent, to sing and read day and night for Sir Gareth's sake and Sir Gaheris'. This I will perform from Sandwich to Carlisle, and every house shall have sufficient livelihood. This I promise you faithfully."

Then all the ladies wept, and tears fell on King Arthur's cheeks.

Then said Gawaine, "Sir Launcelot, I have heard thy proffer, but let the King do as he pleases, I will never forgive my brothers' deaths, and in especial Sir Gareth's. If mine uncle will accord with you, he shall lose my service, for thou art false both to the King and me. The Pope hath charged mine uncle the King to take his Queen, and to accord with thee, therefore thou art safe as thou camest; but in this land thou shalt not abide past fifteen days—such summons I give you. Were it not for the Pope's command I would do battle with mine own body; and that shall I prove upon thy body when thou art departed from hence, wherever I find thee."

Then Sir Launcelot sighed, and the tears fell on his cheeks.

"Alas! most noble Christian realm," he said, "I have loved thee above all other realms, and in thee have I gotten a great part of my worship, and now I must depart in this wise. Truly it me repenteth that I ever came into this realm, that I should thus be shamefully banished, undeserved and causeless. I may live upon my lands, Sir Gawaine, as well as any knight here; and if ye, most redoubted King, will come upon my lands with Sir Gawaine to war upon me, I must endure as well as I may. But as to you, Sir Gawaine, I pray ye not to come and charge me with treason, else I must answer you."

"Do thy best," said Sir Gawaine. "Therefore hie thee fast that thou were gone; and wit thou well we shall soon come after, and break the strongest castle that thou hast, upon thy head."

"That shall not need," replied Launcelot, "for were I as proud as ye are I would meet with thee in the midst of the field."

"Make thou no more language," said Sir Gawaine, "but deliver the Queen from thee, and pike thee out of this Court lightly."

Then said Launcelot unto Guenever, in hearing of them all, "Madam, now I must depart from you and this noble fellowship for ever; and sith it is so, pray for me and say me well, I beseech you. And if ye be hard bested by any false tongues, let send me word, and I will deliver you."

Therewithal Sir Launcelot kissed the Queen, and said openly, "Now let us see who he be in this place that dare speak against the Queen."

Therewith he brought the Queen to the King, and departed. Then there were neither King, duke, ne earl, ne baron, ne knight, lady, nor gentlewoman but all wept, as people out of their minds, except Sir Gawaine; and when the noble knight Sir Launcelot took his horse to ride out of Carlisle, there was sobbing and weeping for pure dole of his departing.

So he took his way to Joyous Gard, and there ever after he called it the Dolorous Gard. Thus departed Sir Launcelot from the Court for ever.

CHAPTER V

WHEN they came to Joyous Gard Sir Launcelot called his fellows unto him, and told them how he had been banished.

"And that," he added, "is my heaviness, for I fear ever after that they shall chronicle upon me that I was banished out of the land with no worship."

Then spake many noble knights, as Sir Palamides, Sir Safir his brother, and Sir Bellangere le Beuse, and Sir Urre, with Sir Lavaine and many others.

"Sir," said they, "an ye be so disposed as to abide in this country, we will never fail you; and if ye list not to abide in this land, there is none of the good knights that here be that will fail you for many causes."

"My fair lords," said Sir Launcelot, "I well understand you; and as I can I thank you. But unto such livelihood as I was born I will depart with you; that is to say, I shall divide all my livelihood and lands freely amongst you, and I myself will have as little as any of you, for I have sufficient that may long to my person. I will ask no other array, and I trust in God to maintain you on my lands as well as ever were maintained any knights."

Then said all the knights at once, "He have shame that will leave you."

So they accorded to go with Sir Launcelot unto his lands. Wholly a hundred knights departed, and vowed they would never leave him for weal or woe. So they shipped at Cardiff and sailed to Benwick, or as some call it Bayonne, some

"Beaume"—where the wine of "Beaume" is. But to say sooth, Sir Launcelot and his nephews were lords of all France.

Then all the people came unto them on foot and hands, and he called a Parliament, where he made Sir Lionel King of France, and Sir Bors King of all Claudas' Lands, and Sir Ector de Maris (Sir Launcelot's younger brother) he crowned King of Benwick, with many other rewards to Sir Blamor, Sir Galahad, and many others that were too long to rehearse.

Meanwhile King Arthur and Sir Gawaine made a great host ready, and when all were prepared, they went to Cardiff to pass over the sea. King Arthur made Sir Mordred King of all England, and put Queen Guenever under his government, because Sir Mordred was Arthur's son. Then King Arthur and his hosts passed over the sea, and landed upon Sir Launcelot's lands, burning and wasting, for the vengeance of Sir Gawaine, wherever they went.

When these tidings came to Sir Launcelot, Lionel counselled to keep within their strong walls; but others were of opinion that they should sally forth and slay the invaders. But Sir Launcelot having heard their counsels, and feeling loth to engage King Arthur, sent out a maiden and a dwarf with a treaty of peace to the King to leave his warring on his lands.

So the maiden came, and was courteously received. "Fair damsel, came ye from Sir Launcelot du Lake?" they said.

"Yea," she replied. "I came to speak with the King."

"Alas!" said Sir Lucan, "my lord Arthur would love Sir Launcelot, but Sir Gawaine will not suffer him. I pray God, damsel, ye may speed well, for all we that are about the King would that Sir Launcelot did best."

So Lucan led the maiden unto the King, who sat with Sir Gawaine to hear her; and when she told her tale, the tears ran from the King's eyes, and all the lords were full glad to advise the King to be accorded with Sir Launcelot, save only Sir Gawaine, who advised Sir Arthur, and then said,—

"Damsel, say ye to Sir Launcelot that it is waste labour now to sue mine uncle. For, tell him, an he would have made

any labour for peace, he should have made it ere this time,—
now it is too late. And say that I, Sir Gawaine, so send him
word that I promise him by the faith I owe to God and to
knighthood, I shall never leave him till he have slain me or
I him."

So the damsel departed, and came to Sir Launcelot, who,
when he heard the answer, wept.

Nevertheless, they prepared for the siege which Arthur
would make. They defied him from the tower, and beat them
from the walls mightily. Then came forth Sir Gawaine and
cried before the chief gate for Sir Launcelot, and daring the
knights to break a spear with him. Then Sir Bors made ready
and encountered, and Sir Lionel his brother after him, but
both were smitten down and sore wounded. Sir Gawaine came
every day, and failed not to strike down some knight or
other.

This endured for half a year, until the knights called upon
Sir Launcelot to undertake Sir Gawaine, who addressed to
him many insults, daring him to the encounter. So Sir Launcelot dressed him, and got his best courser at the gate: then encountered he Sir Gawaine. This knight had a gift that every
day from nine o'clock until noon his strength increased to that
of three men, and caused him to win great honour. So King
Arthur, who, with few beside, knew the secret, made all
tournaments begin at nine.

Thus Sir Launcelot fought with Sir Gawaine, and when
the knight felt Sir Gawaine's strength increase he wondered,
and had sore dread to be shamed. Therefore he traversed and
traced, covering himself with his shield, deeming Sir Gawaine a fiend and no earthly man, keeping his might for
three hours, while Sir Gawaine gave him many sad strokes.
The knights all marvelled that Sir Launcelot endured, but
few guessed how great travail he had to endure.

When it was past noon Sir Gawaine had no more but his
own might, and when Sir Launcelot felt him so come down
he stretched up, and standing near him, said, "Sir Gawaine,
now I find ye have done, and now I will do my part, for many

grievous strokes have I endured with great pain from you this day."

Then Sir Launcelot gave him such a buffet on the helm that he fell down on his side, and Sir Launcelot withdrew from him.

"Why withdrawest thou?" cried Sir Gawaine; "now turn again, false traitor knight, and slay me, for an thou leave me thus when I am whole I will do battle with thee again."

"I shall endure you, sir, by God's grace; but wit thee well, Sir Gawaine, I will never smite a fallen knight."

Then Sir Launcelot went into the city, and Sir Gawaine was born into one of King Arthur's pavilions.

"Have ye good day, my lord the King," said Launcelot by message, "for wit ye well ye have no worship at these walls, and would I my knights outbring there would many a man die; therefore, my lord Arthur, remember you of old kindness, and however I fare, Jesu be your guide in all places."

"Alas," said the King, "that ever this war were made!" And he fell sick because of Sir Gawaine, who was sore hurt, and of the war betwixt him and Sir Launcelot.

But the siege continued, though with little fighting, for long time, and Sir Gawaine was not whole of his wounds for three weeks. As soon as he was able he again defied Sir Launcelot, calling him traitor, and Sir Launcelot again went out to encounter him.

Both hosts were assembled, and had engaged to hold them still, and then the combatants met like thunder. This time also Sir Gawaine had his might increased until noon, and Sir Launcelot as before had much ado to defend himself. They at length fought on foot, and all parties had great wonder at Launcelot, who, when he felt Sir Gawaine so marvellously increase, got under covert of his shield, and traced and traversed to break Sir Gawaine's strokes.

But when the three hours were passed, and Sir Gawaine had come to his proper strength, then Sir Launcelot said, "Now have I proved you twice to be a full dangerous knight, and a wonderful man of your might. By your might increasing ye have deceived many a noble knight; but now ye have done your mighty deeds, and I must do my deeds."

Then he stood near Sir Gawaine and doubled his strokes. Sir Gawaine defended himself mightily, nevertheless Sir Launcelot smote him terribly on the helm near the old wound, so that Sir Gawaine sank down in a swoon; but when he awaked he again defied Launcelot, and declared he would yet prove him to the uttermost.

"I will," said Sir Launcelot, "when you can stand upon your feet. When thou art whole I will do battle with thee again, till one of us be slain."

Thus as the siege endured Sir Gawaine lay sick for near a month, but when he was well recovered, and ready within three days to do battle again with Sir Launcelot, there came tidings from England that made King Arthur and all his host remove.

CHAPTER VI

HOW KING ARTHUR RETURNED TO ENGLAND; OF THE DEATH
OF SIR GAWAINE; AND OF THE GREAT BATTLE WITH SIR
MORDRED

WHILE Arthur was fighting against Sir Launcelot, Mordred was in possession of the English crown as ruler during the King's absence, and he pretended to receive letters from France saying that Arthur was dead. So he called a Parliament, and made the lords choose him as King. He was crowned at Canterbury, and even desired to detain Queen Guenever; but she escaped to the Tower of London, which she fortified and kept.

After this, and while Mordred sought Guenever, came message from King Arthur's army, that it had quitted Sir Launcelot and was coming to England. So Mordred advanced to Dover to meet Arthur, but was beaten in the engagement which ensued; and in that battle was Sir Gawaine slain—he was found in a boat more than half dead, and King Arthur wept sore.

When Sir Gawaine had recovered from his swoon, he said, "Mine uncle King, wit you well my day has come, and all is through mine own hastiness and folly, for I am smitten upon the old wound that Sir Launcelot gave me. Had he been with you as he was, this unhappy war had never begun, and of all this am I causer. But, alas! I would not accord with him, and therefore I pray you, mine uncle, that I may have paper, pens and ink, to write to Sir Launcelot a schedule."

When the paper was brought to him he wrote unto Sir Launcelot thus: "Unto Sir Launcelot, flower of all noble knights that ever I heard of, I, Sir Gawaine, King Lot's son, sister's son unto noble King Arthur, send thee greeting, and let thee have knowledge that the tenth day of May I was smitten upon the old wound that thou gavest me at the city of Benwick, and through the same wound am I come to my death this day. And I will all the world wit that I, Sir Gawaine, knight of the Table Round, sought mine own death, and not through thy desiring, but it was mine own seeking. Wherefore I beseech thee, Sir Launcelot, to return again unto this realm, and see my tomb, and pray some prayer more or less for my soul. Also, Sir Launcelot, for all the love that was ever betwixt us, make no tarrying, but come over the sea in all haste that thou mayest with all thy noble knights rescue the noble King that made thee knight—my lord Arthur—for he is straitly bested with a false traitor, Sir Mordred, whom he put to flight at Dover. Then it misfortuned me to be stricken upon thy stroke, and at the date of this letter was written but two hours and a half afore my death, written with mine own hand, and so subscribed with part of my heart's blood."

Then Sir Gawaine wept, and King Arthur with him. At the hour of noon Sir Gawaine yielded his spirit, and he was interred in a chapel within Dover Castle, where all men may yet see the skull of him.

Afterward it was told King Arthur that Sir Mordred had pitched a new field upon Barham Down. Upon the morn the King rode thither to him, and there was a great battle betwixt them; but at the last King Arthur's party stood best, and Sir Mordred fled unto Canterbury. Then much people drew unto King Arthur, who came down near Salisbury.

Sir Mordred also raised many people about London, for they of Kent, Southsex, and Surrey, Eastsex, Southfolk, and Northfolk, held mostly with Sir Mordred. Upon that Trinity Sunday at night Arthur dreamed a wonderful dream, and he saw Sir Gawaine come unto him with a number of fair ladies. Then Sir Gawaine said that his companions were ladies for whom he had fought while living, and they had been permitted to appear with him to warn the King of his death.

"For," said Gawaine, "an ye fight as to-morn with Sir Mordred, as ye have both assigned, doubt ye not ye must be slain, and the most part of your people on both parties. God hath sent me to give you warning that in no wise ye do battle as to-morn, but that ye take a treaty for a month, for within that time shall come Sir Launcelot and his noble knights, and rescue you worshipfully."

Then Sir Gawaine and all the ladies vanished. Anon the King called his knights and squires to fetch his noble lords and his bishops unto him. Then he told them of his vision, and commanded Sir Lucan and Sir Bedivere to arrange a treaty for a month with Sir Mordred, "And spare not: proffer lands and goods as ye think best." At the last Sir Mordred was agreed to have Cornwall and Kent, and all England after the death of Arthur.

CHAPTER VII

HOW, BY AN ADDER, THE BATTLE WAS CAUSED; HOW MORDRED WAS SLAIN, AND ARTHUR HURT TO THE DEATH

IT WAS arranged that King Arthur and the traitor Mordred should meet between the hosts, and each one bring fourteen persons. So thus word came to King Arthur, who said, "I am glad this is done"; and he went not into the field.

But when he was departing, he said unto his men, and warned all his host, that if they saw any sword drawn, they should at once come on fiercely, and slay the traitor Sir Mordred. And in like manner did Mordred advise his host, for he did not trust the King, who wished to be avenged upon him.

So they met at their appointment, and agreed thoroughly. Wine was fetched, and they drank; and as they were pledging each other, right so there came an adder out of a bush, and stung a knight upon the foot.

When the knight felt himself wounded he looked down, and seeing the adder, he drew his sword to slay it, thinking of none other harm. But when the parties perceived the sword drawn they blew trumpets and horns and shouted, all ready to rush upon each other. King Arthur seeing this rode to his men, crying, "O this unhappy day!" And Sir Mordred went likewise to his army.

Never was seen a more dolorous battle in any Christian land. For there was riding and rushing, foining and striking, and many a grim word spoken, with many a deadly stroke given. All the day King Arthur rode through the battle, and did full nobly, fainting never. Sir Mordred that day put him in great peril, and did his devoir. So they fought all day, and never stinted till the noble knights were lain to the cold ground by nightfall, when there were near one hundred thousand lay dead upon the plain.

King Arthur was wroth without measure when he perceived the people lying all dead around him. He looked around him and was aware of his host; and of all his good knights only two were left on live—Sir Lucan, and Sir Bedivere his brother, and they were sore wounded.

"Jesu mercy!" cried the King, "where are all my noble knights? Alas that ever I should see this doleful day! For now am I come to mine end. But would to God that I wist where was that traitor Sir Mordred, who hath caused all this mischief."

Then King Arthur was aware of Sir Mordred leaning upon his sword amid a great heap of dead men.

"Give me my spear," cried Arthur unto Sir Lucan de Butlere, "for yonder do I espy the traitor that all this woe hath wrought."

"Sir, let him be," said Sir Lucan, "for he is unhappy, and if ye pass this day ye shall be revenged upon him. Remember ye of last night's dream, and what the spirit of Sir Gawaine said unto you? Yet God of His great goodness hath preserved you hitherto. Leave off this, for, blessed be God, ye have won the field. Here be we three on live, and with Sir Mordred there be none alive. If ye leave off now, the day of destiny is past."

"Tide me life or tide me death," said King Arthur, "he shall never escape my hands. I see him yonder alone, and at a better avail shall I never have him."

"God speed you well," said Sir Bedivere.

Then the King gat his spear in both his hands, and ran to Sir Mordred, crying, "Traitor! now is thy death come."

When Sir Mordred heard King Arthur he ran unto him with his sword drawn in his hand, and the King smote him with a foin of his spear and through his body more than a fathom. And when Sir Mordred felt he had his death-wound, he thrust himself up with all the might he had up to the burr of King Arthur's spear, and right so he smote the King, with his sword holden in both his hands, on the side of the head, so that the sword pierced the brain-pan. Therewithal Sir Mordred fell dead to the earth.

King Arthur fell down in a swoon upon the ground, and oftentime he swooned after. Then Sir Lucan le Butlere and Sir Bedivere ofttimes heaved him up, and he was so weakly they led him to a little chapel not far from the seaside, and when the King was there he felt better and more eased.

But they could hear the people crying in the field, and King Arthur said, "Go thou, Sir Lucan, and do me wit what is that noise in the field."

So Sir Lucan departed, though he was grievously wounded in many places. As he went, he saw and hearkened in the moonlight how pillagers and robbers had come into the field to rob many a noble knight of brooches and beads, and many a good ring and rich jewel. Those who were not dead they slew for their harness and riches.

When Sir Lucan understood this, he came to the King and told him all he had heard and seen.

CHAPTER VIII

HOW SIR LUCAN DIED; HOW SIR BEDIVERE THREW THE SWORD EXCALIBUR INTO THE WATER; AND HOW KING ARTHUR WAS CARRIED AWAY IN A BARGE

B Y MY advice," said Sir Lucan, "it is best we bring you to some town."

"I would it were so," said the King; "but I cannot stand, my head works so. Ah, Sir Launcelot! this day have I sore missed thee!" continued Arthur. "Alas, that ever I was against thee! for now have I my death, whereof Sir Gawaine warned me in my dream."

Then Sir Lucan took up the King on one part, and Sir Bedivere on the other part; but in the lifting the King swooned, and Sir Lucan also swooned in the lifting, and therewith, and his wounds, the noble knight's heart burst. When King Arthur came to himself he found Sir Lucan dead at his feet.

"Alas!" said the King, "this is to me a full heavy sight, to see this noble duke so die for my sake, for he would have holpen me who had more need of help than I. Now Jesu have mercy on his soul!"

Then Sir Bedivere wept for the death of his brother.

"Leave this mourning and weeping," said the King, "for all this will not avail me, for wit thou well an I could live myself, the death of Sir Lucan would grieve me evermore; but my time hieth fast. Therefore take thou Excalibur, my good sword, and go with it yonder to the water's edge, and when thou comest thither, I charge thee throw my sword into the water, and come again and tell me what thou seest."

"My lord," said Bedivere, "your commandments shall be done, and lightly bring you word again."

So Sir Bedivere departed, and by the way he beheld that

noble sword, and the pommel with all its precious stones, and then to himself he said, "If I cast this rich sword into the water, thereof shall never come good but harm and loss." So he hid Excalibur under a tree, and returned to the King.

"What sawest thou?" asked Arthur.

"Sir," replied Sir Bedivere, "I saw nothing but waves and winds."

"That is untruly said of thee," replied the King. "Go thou therefore and do my command. Throw it in—spare not."

Then Sir Bedivere turned again, and took the sword in his hand; but he thought it great sin to throw away that noble sword, so he hid it, and told the King he had done his command.

"What sawest thou there?" asked Arthur.

"Sir," he replied, "I saw nothing but the waves wap, and the waters wan."[1]

"Ah, traitor and untrue!" exclaimed the King, "now hast thou betrayed me twice. Who would have thought thou, a noble knight, wouldst have betrayed me for the riches of the sword? But now go again lightly, for thy long tarrying putteth me in great jeopardy of my life, as I have taken cold."

Then Sir Bedivere departed, and went to the sword, and took it up. At the waterside he bound the girdle about the hilt, and then he threw the sword as far into the water as he might. Then there came an arm and a hand above the water, and met it, and caught it, so shook it thrice, and brandished it; then vanished away the hand, with the sword, into the water.

So Sir Bedivere came unto the King, and told him what he saw.

"Alas!" said the King, "help me hence, for I dread me I have tarried too long."

Then Sir Bedivere took the King upon his back, and so went with him to the waterside. When they got there, hoved a little barge with many fair ladies in it, and among them all

---

[1]"Lapping on the crag."—TENNYSON.

was a Queen. They all had black hoods, and all wept and shrieked when they saw King Arthur.

"Now put me into the barge," said the King. And so Sir Bedivere did, softly.

So the ladies received him with great mourning, and they set him down, and in one of their laps he set his head; and then that Queen said,—

"Alas! dear brother, why have ye tarried so long from me?"

Then they rowed from the land, and Sir Bedivere beheld the ladies go from him, and he cried,—

"Oh, my lord Arthur, what shall become of me now ye go from me, and leave me here alone among mine enemies?"

"Comfort thyself," said the King, "and do as well as thou mayest; for in me is no trust to trust in. I will go into the Vale of Avilion to heal me of my grievous wound, and if thou never hear any more of me, pray for my soul."

Ever the Queens and ladies shrieked so that it was piteous to hear; and as soon as Sir Bedivere had lost sight of the barge, he wept and wailed, and took to the forest. He went all that night, and in the morning he was aware of a chapel and a hermitage, and found a hermit grovelling on all fours fast by a new tomb.

CHAPTER IX

HOW SIR BEDIVERE MET THE HERMIT AND ABODE WITH HIM; OF THE DEATH OF ARTHUR, AND HOW GUENEVER BECAME A NUN; OF LAUNCELOT; AND THE END OF THE BOOK

SIR BEDIVERE was passing glad to see the hermit, who knew him well, for he had formerly been Archbishop of Canterbury that Mordred had banished.

"Sir," said Sir Bedivere, "what man is there interred that ye pray so for?"

"Fair son," replied the hermit, "I wot not verily but by deeming. This night came a number of ladies, and brought hither a corpse, which they prayed me to bury, and here they offered me a hundred bezants."

"Alas!" cried Sir Bedivere, "that was my lord King Arthur." Then he swooned, and when he awoke he prayed the hermit that he might abide with him, and live in prayer and fasting. "From hence never will I go," said he, "by my will; but all the days of my life will pray for my lord King Arthur."

So there abode Sir Bedivere with the hermit, and served him full lowly, in fasting and prayer.

Thus of King Arthur. Never more is written in books that be authorized, nor more of the certainty of his death; but thus was he led away in a ship with three Queens. One was his sister Morgan le Fay, the other the Queen of North Galis, the third the Queen of the Waste Lands. Also there was Nimue the Lady of the Lake, who had wedded Pelleas, and done much for King Arthur.

More of the death of King Arthur could never be found. Yet some say that he is laid in another place; and men say he shall come again and win the Holy Cross, and that on his tomb is written:

Hic Jacet Arthurus Rex Quondam Rex Que Futurus

Thus we leave Sir Bedivere with the hermit, who dwelled in a chapel beside Glastonbury. And when Queen Guenever understood that Arthur was dead, she stole away, and five ladies with her. Then she went to Almesbury, and there made herself a nun, wearing white clothes and black, and never creature could make her merry, but she lived in fasting and prayers.

When Sir Launcelot heard of the war of Mordred against Arthur he was wroth, and said it were shame that Mordred had escaped his hand, and he felt by the letter Sir Gawaine sent him that all was unhappy.

"Leave your complaint," said Sir Bors. "First avenge you of the death of Sir Gawaine, and secondly ye may avenge my lord Arthur."

Then they made ready to return to England, and Sir Launcelot passed over and came to Dover, where he landed with seven kings, and inquired concerning Arthur. The people told him how the King had been slain, and of the great battle as already related.

"Now, fair sirs," said Launcelot, "show me the tomb of Sir Gawaine."

So he kneeled down when they brought him to the tomb in the castle of Dover, and prayed for Gawaine's soul. In the morn, after offering money and incense, and then lying for two nights upon the tomb, Sir Launcelot called his nobles and people, and said, "Fair lords, we come too late into this country, and that shall repent me while I live. But sith it is so, I will myself ride and seek my Lady Guenever, for as I hear say she hath great pain and much disease, and has fled into the west country. Wherefore abide me here for fifteen days, and then, if I come not, depart into your country, for I will do as I say."

Sir Bors tried to dissuade him, but he rode on westerly for seven or eight days, and came at last unto a nunnery. Then was Queen Guenever aware of Sir Launcelot as he walked in the cloister, and when she saw him then she swooned thrice, and commanded Sir Launcelot never to seek her more.

"Go to thy realm," she said, "and take thee a wife, and live with her in joy and bliss."

But Sir Launcelot determined to live in a hermitage and pray while his life lasted, "If that I may find any hermit, either white or grey, that will receive me," he said.

Thus they departed, and Sir Launcelot spent all the night in weeping. In the morning he rode on, and was at length aware of the hermitage where was Sir Bedivere and the Bishop of Canterbury. After the mass Sir Bedivere told Sir Launcelot all that had happened, and he was in great woe. Then he besought the bishop to assoil him, and he did so, putting a habit on Launcelot, who there served God day and night.

Meantime the army abode in Dover; while Sir Lionel took fifteen knights to seek Sir Launcelot, but Sir Lionel was slain in London, and many of his lords. Then Sir Bors de Ganis made the host go home again, while he, with Sir Ector, Sir Blamor, and Sir Bleoberis, with others of Launcelot's kin, undertook to ride through England and to seek Sir Launcelot.

Sir Bors, as it happed, came to the hermitage where Sir Launcelot was, and when he saw him, he prayed the bishop to do the same for him. So he had a habit put on him, and remained with other knights that came after, viz., Sir Galahad, Sir Galahadin, Sir Blamor, Sir Bleoberis, Sir Villiars, Sir Clarrus, and Sir Galahantine. So there those seven knights abode, and took the habit, remaining in fasting and prayer, and took no force what pain they endured.

But upon a night came a vision to Sir Launcelot, which charged him to arise, and go to Almesbury, where he would find Queen Guenever dead. Therefore he was commanded to take his fellows, and get them an horse bier, and fetch her body to lay it beside her husband, the noble King Arthur. This vision came to Sir Launcelot thrice in one night.

Then King Launcelot rose up, and told the hermit, who counselled him to go. So he called his followers, and proceeded to Almesbury, which is more than thirty miles from Glastonbury. Thither they came in two days, for they were weak and feeble, but found Queen Guenever had died half an hour before. The ladies told the hermit knights that the Queen had foretold their coming.

Then Sir Launcelot wept and sighed when he saw Guenever dead; and he did all the service himself, both the dirge and the mass, in the morning. He and his fellows went on foot from Almesbury unto Glastonbury, where, after the services, the corpse was wrapped in cloth of Raines, and put in a coffin of lead and one of marble. The body was then buried, and Sir Launcelot swooned away. The hermit came and rebuked him for this, saying, "Ye be to blame, for ye displease God by such sorrow making."

"Truly," replied Launcelot, "I trust I do not displease God, for He knoweth mine intent; my sorrow is not for any rejoicing of sin, but it may never have end. For when I saw her corpse and the King's, and when I remember all her beauty and his nobleness, truly mine heart would not serve to sustain my careful body. Also when I remember me how by my own pride and wickedness they were laid full low, this remembrance of their kindness and mine unkindness sank to my heart, and I could not contain myself."

After that Launcelot ate but little meat, nor drank, until he was dead; for he sickened and pined away, so that no one knew him. Evermore day and night he prayed, sometime he slumbered a broken sleep, and ever he was lying grovelling upon the tombs of the King and Queen. None of his fellows could comfort him, as he lay in his bed, and at last he sent for the bishop, and said in a dreary voice,—

"Sir Bishop, I pray you give me all my rites that belong to a Christian man. Wit you well, my fair lords, my careful body will into the earth. I have warning more than I will say; therefore give me my rites."

So when he had received absolution and all that a Christian man ought to have, he prayed the bishop that his fellows might bear the body to Joyous Gard, which some call Alnwick, and others Bamborough.

Then there was weeping and wringing of hands among his fellows. So at night they all went to their beds; but in the middle of the night the bishop awoke with great laughter, and therewith all came unto him and asked him what ailed. "Truly," replied the bishop, "never was I so merry and so well at ease, for I saw the angels heave Sir Launcelot into heaven."

"It is but the vexing of dreams," said Sir Bors. "I doubt not Launcelot aileth nothing."

"It may well be," replied the bishop; "but go ye to his bed, and ye shall prove the sooth."

So when Sir Bors went to the bed with his fellows, they found Sir Launcelot stark dead, and he lay as if he smiled, and the sweetest savour they had ever smelt was about him. Then was there wringing of hands and the greatest dole that was ever made amongst men.

On the morn the requiem was read, and they gat the same horse-litter which had carried Queen Guenever, and carried the body of Sir Launcelot to Joyous Gard, where they arrived in procession after fifteen days. Then they laid his corpse in the body of the choir, and read many prayers. His visage was uncovered that all men might see him; and as they were at service, there came Sir Ector de Maris, who had seven years sought England, Wales, and Scotland to find Sir Launcelot.

They all knew Sir Ector, but he knew not them, and when Sir Bors went unto him and told him Sir Launcelot his brother was lying dead, Sir Ector threw his shield from him and fell down in a swoon. When he awaked it was hard for any tongue to tell the lament he made for his brother. But after fifteen days Sir Launcelot was buried. Then at leisure went they all to the hermitage, where they abode a month and more.

Then Sir Constantine—Sir Cador's son of Cornwall—was

chosen King. He was a full noble knight, and worshipfully he ruled the realm. He sent for the Bishop of Canterbury, and restored him to his See. So he left the hermitage, which Sir Bedivere retained unto his life's end.

Sir Bors de Ganis, Sir Ector de Maris, Sir Galahantine, Sir Galahad, Sir Galahadin, Sir Blamor, Sir Bleoberis, Sir Villiars de Valiant, and Sir Clarrus de Cliremont, all drew themselves into other countries. King Constantine would have had them with him, but they would not abide, and they after lived as holy men.

It is said that some went and waged battles upon the Turks. Sir Bors, Sir Ector, Sir Blamor, and Sir Bleoberis were all four slain on a Good Friday for God's sake.

Here is an end of the whole Book of King Arthur, and of his noble knights of the Round Table, that, when they were whole together, there was ever an hundred and forty.

And here is the end of the "Death of King Arthur."

THE END

APPENDIX

PREFACE OF WILLIAM CAXTON

After that I had accomplished and finished divers histories, as well as contemplation as of other historical and worldly acts of great conquerors and princes, and also certain books of ensamples and doctrine, many noble and divers gentlemen of this realm of England came and demanded me many and ofttimes, wherefore that I have now made and imprint the noble history of the Saint Greal, and of the most renowned Christian king, first and chief of the three best Christian, and worthy, king Arthur, which ought most to be remembered amongst us Englishmen tofore all other Christian kings; for it is notoriously known through the universal world, that there be nine worthy and the best that ever were, that is to wit, three Paynims, three Jews, and three Christian men. As for the Paynims, they were tofore the Incarnation of Christ, which were named, the first Hector of Troy, of whom the history is comen both in ballad and in prose, the second Alexander the Great, and the third Julius Cæsar, Emperor of Rome, of whom the histories be well known and had. And as for the three Jews, which also were tofore the Incarnation of our Lord, of whom the first was duke Joshua which brought the children of Israel into the land of behest, the second David king of Jerusalem, and the third Judas Machabeus. Of these three the Bible rehearseth all their noble histories and acts. And since the said Incarnation have been three noble Christian men, stalled and admitted through the universal world into the number of the nine best and worthy. Of whom was first the noble Arthur, whose noble acts I purpose to write in this present book here following. The second was Charlemain, or Charles the Great, of whom the history is had in many places, both in French and in English. And the third and last was Godfrey of Boloine, of whose acts and life I made a book unto the excellent prince and king of noble memory, king Edward the Fourth. The said noble gentleman instantly required me to imprint the history of the said noble king and conqueror king Arthur, and of his knights, with the history of the Saint Greal, and of the death and ending of the said Arthur; affirming that I ought rather to imprint his acts and noble feats, than of Godfrey of Boloine, or any of the other eight, considering that he was a man born within this realm, and king and emperor of the same: and that there be in French divers and many noble volumes of his acts, and also of his knights. To whom I answered that divers men hold opinion that there was no such Arthur, and that all such books as been made of him be but feigned and fables, because that some chronicles make of him no mention, nor remember him nothing, nor of his knights. Whereto they answered, and one in special said, that in him that should say or think that there was never such a king called Arthur, might well be aretted great folly and blindness. For he said that there were many evidences of the contrary. First ye may see his sepulchre in the monastery of Glastingbury. And also in Policronicon, in the fifth book the sixth chapter, and in the seventh book the twenty-third chapter, where his body was buried, and after found, and translated into the said monastery. Ye shall see also in the history of Bochas in his book *De Casu Principum* part of his noble acts, and also of his fall. Also Galfridus in his British book recounteth his life: and in divers places of England many remembrances be yet of him, and shall remain perpetually, and also of his knights. First in the abbey of Westminster, at St. Edward's shrine, remaineth the print of his seal in red wax closed in beryl, in which is written, *Patricius Arthurus Britannie, Gallie, Germanie, Dacie, Imperator*. Item in the castle of Dover ye may see Gawaine's scull, and Cradock's mantle: at Winchester the Round Table: in other places Launcelot's sword and many other things. Then all these things considered, there can no man reasonably gainsay but that there was a king of this land named

Arthur. For in all places, Christian and heathen, he is reputed and taken for one of the nine worthy, and the first of the three Christian men. And also, he is more spoken of beyond the sea, more books made of his noble acts, than there be in England, as well as in Dutch, Italian, Spanish, and Greekish, as in French. And yet of record remain in witness of him in Wales, in the town of Camelot, the great stones and the marvellous works of iron lying under the ground, and royal vaults, which divers now living have seen. Wherefore it is a marvel why he is no more renowned in his own country, save only it accordeth to the Word of God, which saith that no man is accepted for a prophet in his own country. Then all these things aforesaid alleged, I could not well deny but that there was such a noble king named Arthur, and reputed one of the nine worthy, and first and chief of the Christian men. And many noble volumes be made of him and of his noble knights in French, which I have seen and read beyond the sea, which be not had in our maternal tongue. But in Welsh be many and also in French, and some in English but no where nigh all. Wherefore, such as have late been drawn out briefly into English I have after the simple coming that God hath sent to me, under the favour and correction of all noble lords and gentlemen, enprised to imprint a book of the noble histories of the said king Arthur, and of certain of his knights, after a copy unto me delivered, which copy Sir Thomas Malorye did take out of certain books in French, and reduced it into English. And I, according to my copy, have down set it in print, to the intent that noble men may see and learn the noble acts of chivalry, the gentle and virtuous deeds that some knights used in those days, by which they came to honour, and how they that were vicious were punished and oft put to shame and rebuke; humbly beseeching all noble lords and ladies, with all other estates of what estate or degree they been of, that shall see and read in this said book and work, that they take the good and honest acts in their remembrance, and to follow the same. Wherein they shall find many joyous and pleasant histories, and noble and renowned acts of humanity, gentleness, and chivalry. For herein may be seen noble chivalry, courtesy, humanity, friendliness, hardness, love, friendship, cowardice, murder, hate, virtue, and sin. Do after the good and leave the evil, and it shall bring you to good fame and renommee. And for to pass the time this book shall be pleasant to read in, but for to give faith and belief that all is true that is contained herein, ye be at your liberty; but all is written for our doctrine, and for to beware that we fall not to vice nor sin, but to exercise and follow virtue, by the which we may come and attain to good fame and renown in this life, and after this short and transitory life to come unto everlasting bliss in heaven; the which He grant us that reigneth in heaven, the blessed Trinity. Amen.

Then to proceed forth in this said book, the which I direct unto all noble princes, lords and ladies, gentlemen or gentle-women, that desire to read or hear read of the noble and joyous history of the great conqueror and excellent king, king Arthur, sometime king of this noble realm, then called Britain; I, William Caxton, simple person, present this book following, which I have emprised to imprint: and treateth of the noble acts, feats of arms of chivalry, prowess, hardiness, humanity, love, courtesy, and very gentleness, with many wonderful histories and adventures. And for to understand briefly the content of this volume, I have divided it into XXI Books, and every book chaptered, as hereafter shall by God's grace follow. The First Book shall treat how Uther Pen-dragon gat the noble conqueror king Arthur, and containeth xxviii chapters. The Second Book treateth of Balin the noble knight, and containeth xix chapters. The Third Book treateth of the marriage of king Arthur to queen Guenever, with other matters, and containeth xv chapters. The Fourth Book how Merlin was assotted, and of war made to king Arthur, and containeth xxix chapters. The Fifth Book treateth of the con-quest of Lucius the emperor, and containeth xii chapters. The Sixth Book treateth of Sir Launcelot and Sir Lionel, and mar-vellous adventures, and containeth xviii chapters. The Seventh Book treateth of a noble knight called Sir Gareth, and named by Sir Kay Beaumains, and containeth xxxvi chapters. The Eighth Book treateth of the birth of Sir Tristram the noble knight, and of his acts, and containeth xli chapters. The Ninth Book treateth of a knight named by Sir Kay Le Cote male taille, and also of Sir Tristram, and containeth xliv chapters. The Tenth Book treateth of Sir Tristram, and other marvellous adventures, and containeth lxxxviii chapters. The Eleventh Book treateth of Sir Launcelot and Sir Galahad, and containeth xiv chapters. The Twelfth Book treateth of Sir Launcelot and his madness, and containeth xiv chapters. The Thirteenth Book treateth how Galahad came first to king Arthur's court, and the quest how the Sangreal was begun, and containeth xx chapters. The Fourteenth Book treateth of the quest of the Sangreal, and containeth x chapters. The Fifteenth Book treateth of Sir Launcelot, and containeth vi chapters. The Sixteenth Book treateth of Sir Bors and Sir Lionel his brother, and containeth xvii chapters. The Seventeenth Book treateth of the Sangreal, and containeth xxiii chapters. The Eighteenth Book treateth of Sir Launcelot and the queen, and containeth xxv chapters. The Nineteenth Book treateth of queen Guenever and Launcelot, and containeth xiii chapters. The Twentieth Book treateth of the piteous death of Arthur, and containeth xxii chapters. The Twenty-first Book treateth of his last departing, and how Sir Launcelot came to revenge his death, and containeth xiii chapters. The sum is twenty-one books, which contain the sum of five hundred and seven chapters, as more plainly shall follow hereafter.

Finis